D1290206

UNDER THE EDITORSHIP OF

H. Bentley Glass

THE JOHNS HOPKINS UNIVERSITY

A HISTORY

ELMER VERNER McCOLLUM

Professor Emeritus of Bio-chemistry

The Johns Hopkins University

OF NUTRITION

The sequence of ideas in nutrition investigations

HOUGHTON MIFFLIN COMPANY · BOSTON

The Riverside Press Cambridge

The Riverside Press
Cambridge, Massachusetts
Printed in the U.S.A.

PREFACE

"More than uncommonly incurious must he be who would not find delight in stemming the stream of the ages; returning to times long past, and beholding the state of things and men." [1]

The above quotation from the writings of the founder of the Smithsonian Institution in Washington expresses the author's motive in gathering information and in writing this volume. The objective was to trace the story of the observations and speculations of early clinicians by which they sought to discover the effects of foods on the sick and the well; that of the physiologists, who sought to understand by what processes of change foods so unlike each other and unlike the body constituents could be so altered by digestion as to be prepared for absorption from the alimentary tract and conversion into blood, and then into body tissues; and finally, that of the reasoning and experimenting by which chemists sought to learn the nature of foods and their transformations, or "metamorphoses," as they served as nutrients for the body.

It was proposed to write a history of the beginnings of new trends in thought and experimental inquiry — a history of fertile ideas which opened new vistas of speculation and discovery. An attempt was made to include only those thoughts and experiments which contributed to delineation of new types of problems, so that the task of detailed experimental inquiry could be left to reflective and enthusiastic men who were inspired to accumulate data and extend knowledge as followers rather than as creators of new viewpoints. Those who have read widely in the source materials from

[1] James Smithson: An Examination of Egyptian Colors. Annals of Philosophy 7, 115 (1824).

which this history is written will realize that it was often difficult to decide whether to include or exclude a meritorious contribution to knowledge. The author is well aware that differences of opinion as to the choices made may prevail among those best able to judge.

The period covered by this study is approximately the two hundred years between mid-eighteenth century and 1940. The magnitude of the undertaking to follow in chronological order the succession of discoveries which were believed to have had the greatest influence on later investigators will be appreciated when it is realized that during the two centuries approximately two hundred thousand papers were published which in some way had to do with inquiry about foods, their properties, their utilization, and their effects on animals. These papers include the efforts of the apothecary type of chemists to learn about the constituents of plant materials; of physiologists who made the early digestion studies; of the occasional penetrating studies of chemists which brought order out of chaos in comprehending the chemical phenomena of the organic kingdom of nature; and also of the feeding studies of the animal husbandry type of investigator, and of the progressively well-controlled studies on men and animals, which made the science of nutrition. Out of this great repository of published records the author has selected approximately one-half of one per cent from which to relate the story of progress in discovering human error in this segment of science. Error resulted from over-simplification of the subject, and progress consisted of successive discoveries which revealed greater complexity than had been suspected in the chemistry of foods and the processes of their utilization.

This history of ideas in nutritional investigations represents a ten-year adventure into times past; an adventure which involved leafing the pages of hundreds of dusty and often disintegrating volumes, most of which had not previously been seen by anyone now living. It was an interesting and instructive experience, and afforded opportunity of beholding the state of things and of men's thoughts in twenty decades during which a new segment of science came into being and yielded results of incalculable benefit to mankind. It is hoped that an account of the more important incidents in the adventure will entertain and instruct those interested in the science of nutrition who, by reason of preoccupation with the here and now, and the where do we go from here?, have not the opportunity to return to times past.

Critical and informed readers may well be justified in taking issue with the author concerning the wisdom of his selections and omissions. When it was believed that an investigation was based upon an idea which had become apparent to any well informed and reflective person, and use was made only of established chemical, histological, physiological and anatomical technics, it was rejected, however important were the results obtained.

It was not possible to give due credit to those analytical chemists who, by discovery of the individual, naturally occurring compounds, and by devising accurate methods for their detection and estimation, made possible the investigations discussed in this volume. Limitations of space, and the impossibility of making laboratory procedures interesting reading, made it necessary to omit merited recognition of some important contributors to knowledge of experimental technics.

It is quite unlikely that in an undertaking of this kind a history free from serious omissions and errors of judgment should be produced. Communications from any readers who can offer suggestions for improvement of the accuracy and fairness of the interpretations will be appreciated.

The author and publishers are indebted to The Nutrition Foundation, Inc. for a grant provided to meet a portion of the cost of publication of this book.

The author wishes to express appreciation to Mr. J. Louis Kuethe, of the Johns Hopkins University Library, for his interest in securing books and journals difficult of access, without which it would have been impossible to examine data of historical importance. His knowledge of reference library procedures often illuminated perplexing problems.

Grateful appreciation is due Dr. Elsa Orent Keiles and Dr. Maurice Shils for reading the manuscript and making suggestions. Criticism and suggestions for improvement of the chapter on experimental rickets by Dr. Edwards A. Park were especially valuable.

To the author's wife, Ernestine Becker McCollum, is due credit for sustained enthusiasm in making helpful suggestions in every stage of manuscript production.

E. V. McCollum

Baltimore, July 1956

CONTENTS

1

Some Pre-Scientific Ideas About Foods

THROUGHOUT THE GREATER part of human history, in most parts of the habitable regions of the earth, the most pressing problem of mankind was securing food to satisfy hunger. Whatever was edible was eaten without any thought of nutritive values. What was available depended on geographic environment, climate, proximity to rivers or oceans, and the nature of vegetation, whether forest, grassland, or semi-desert. Thus the food of the colder regions of the earth was principally marine animals, and a few land animals; that of peoples living in temperate forested areas was derived from game animals, with some vegetable cultivation and gathering of wild fruits, vegetables, and nuts; that of people living in grassland, especially semi-arid lands where cultivation of plants was generally unsuccessful, was derived principally from milk of grazing animals and their flesh; in the hottest and wettest areas of the earth, rice culture predominated, and the diet was in general more than in other areas restricted to vegetable foods. The fact that the human population in contrasting parts of the world, while subsisting on diets of different kinds, experienced approximately the same health standards was largely responsible for the belief of physiologists as late as the year 1900 that it did not matter much what kind of food people ate so long as the diet supplied enough protein and available energy.

Far beyond the dawn of history people everywhere must have been conscious that certain foods were more desirable than others because of taste and odor and the sense of satisfaction which they gave when eaten. Odor must have been the quality which tempted people to taste unfamiliar foods, just as it is the basis for the acceptance or rejection of many weeds by grazing cattle and horses.

Taste is a more reliable test of palatability and wholesomeness, and the final proof of acceptability was the after-experience of eating unfamiliar foods; if discomfort followed, eating the food would be feared. Experience early taught people that certain parts of an animal are more palatable than others, and that the flesh of one species tasted better than that of others. Accordingly, both man and animals, whatever their standards of palatability, have always sought the more palatable foods of both animal and vegetable origin.

Food Tabus

It would appear that experience with the wholesomeness or unwholesomeness of foods must have had something to do with the origin of food tabus. But tabus were often based upon the opinion of persons in authority, and appear sometimes to have been based on unfounded fear or on the commands of a Deity. While there may be well-founded reasons for the proscription of certain foods as related in Leviticus XI, modern knowledge does not find a cause for condemning the hare because, although it cheweth the cud, the hoof is not cloven. Condemnation of pork may well have been based on swine being frequently infested with trichina; but distinguishing among fishes on the basis of their having scales and fins, rather than skins or lacking fins, finds no justification in modern science.

Since primitive man endowed animate and inanimate nature and the forces of nature with fears, hopes, and friendly and unfriendly feelings similar to his own, prejudices or proscriptions about foods developed in some instances without justification from the standpoint of health, and in other instances foods were esteemed on the basis of equally fallacious beliefs. Such was the primitive belief that eating the heart or flesh of strong or aggressive animals would confer courage and strength, whereas eating the flesh of timid and weak animals would undermine man's most valued attributes. Transference of the attributes of eaten to eater seems to have been the earliest concept of differences in quality in foods, other than choice based on palatability.

Food tabus were based on belief in magic influences. Frazer (1) mentions, among numerous instances, the tabus against the soldiers in Madagascar eating the flesh of hedgehog because this animal, when alarmed, coils up into a ball, and it was feared that even tasting its flesh would impart a shrinking disposition to the man. Frazer also mentions the belief of several primitive peoples that the blood contains the life and the spirit of the animal, and must not be eaten because of magical influences. In Roman antiquity the Flamen Dialis, a priest in the service of a special deity, was forbidden to eat or even name several plants and animals for fear of offending a higher power. In ancient Egypt kings were permitted, for religious reasons, to eat no flesh foods other than veal and goose. It is evident that food tabus were so often based on fear of magical influences that we are scarcely warranted in seeking wisdom from this source.

Foods Possessing Remedial Properties

Personal and family experiences with illness referable to many causes, all mysterious, led mothers and medicine men from very early times to seek remedies for relief and restoration of health. Chance experience with plants led to the discovery of both emetic and cathartic properties in certain herbs, roots, fruits, and leaves. Application of such knowledge based on experience or on advice of individuals of more than common intelligence who were repositories of accumulated wisdom of the tribe was the beginning of medical science. A case in point is the experience of Jacques Cartier in 1536 (2) of learning from an Indian in Canada a specific cure for scurvy. This incident is discussed in Chapter 17. The Greeks, long before the Christian era, discovered the value of the mucilage of psyllum seed for the relief of constipation. Its use has been revived in recent years. The virtue of cinchona bark as a specific antimalarial drug is the outstanding discovery of a therapeutic drug by a primitive people.

Certain food plants have been esteemed above others because they were assumed to possess special merits. An example is cabbage, to which Cato the Censor (234–149 B.C.) in his book on farm management (3) devoted nine pages to discourse on its value as a restorer and preserver of health. When we consider the great extent to which the Roman people in Cato's time, and throughout the period of conquest, subsisted, at least seasonally, on dried and cooked (or parched) cereals, we must, in the light of modern knowledge, honor the grim old statesman as perhaps the earliest effective teacher of sound dietetics.

Many plants have long been believed to have remedial properties.

These have been compiled and discussed in old herbals. Vernon Quinn (4) has brought together, in three volumes, much of the grandmother lore and legends of roots, leaves, and seeds which will entertain and instruct the reader. For many centuries it was a common belief among the Chinese people that the plant ginseng was a veritable panacea for practically all diseases. So great was the profit from exporting ginseng, that the wild plant, which grew in abundance in the virgin forests of New York State in the colonial era, was almost exterminated (5). Other plants which were for centuries used as household remedies, and which possessed sufficient merits to justify listing in the XIII Ed. of the U.S. Pharmacopoeia, are ginger, rhubarb, poppy, mustard, caraway, fennel, anise, peppermint, lavender, colchicum, and foxglove.

Minnie Watson Kamm (6) in her book, *Old-Time Herbs for Northern Gardens,* listed forty-seven herbs which were used as remedies. Only the eleven just named have survived in Pharmacopoeias of the present. Mandrake root seems to have owed its popular esteem to its shape, which is so unusual as to suggest magic powers, rather than to its cathartic property.

The emergence of antibiotics, which are isolated from molds, bacteria, and certain of the higher plants, suggests caution and conservatism when judgment is passed on beliefs of our grandmothers about the medicinal values of simples in treatment of the sick. The extent to which primitive peoples explored their environment in search of plants which were nutritious or medicinal is well illustrated by the fact that before the era of written history the indigenous people of the Americas had discovered the unique properties of the tobacco leaf for smoking, and of erythroxylin and truxillo coca, the leaves of which are still chewed by many Indians of South America for their narcotic effect. Oriental peoples discovered the solace derived from opium smoking, and chewing the betel-nut, the fantasies resulting from smoking Indian Hemp (marihuana), and the natives of Fiji, the stimulating properties of *Piper methisticum.* Tea, cacao, coffee, and maté were all known to prehistoric man. No others comparable to these drugs were discovered until the era of scientific discoveries in synthetic organic chemistry. As by-products of the observations by primitive peoples of the properties of plants came the discovery of the usefulness of curare and the plants which yield strychnine, both of which were useful as arrow poisons.

Fermented Beverages

The ancient Egyptians manufactured a fermented drink called *bouza* from a thin barley mush. According to Lucas (7) they practiced malting as well as brewing, but did not discover the art of distillation to make liquors of high alcohol content. Pliny mentions the preparation of sorts of beer from durra in the Sudan, and from barley in Gaul. Nature frequently forced upon the attention of the earliest agricultural peoples the astonishing phenomena of fermentation — a decoction of cereal allowed to stand unheated formed gas and became sour. Fresh, sweet fruit juices spontaneously began to foam, lost their sweet taste, and acquired new and astonishing properties which changed one's outlook on life. We may, with good reason, suspect that scientific inquiry began with curiosity in the minds of the rare individuals capable of constructive thought about the how and why of these spontaneous changes in vegetable substances, and speculation on the subtle effects of a piece of dough or leaven in causing dough to rise quickly. In contrast to the putrefaction of other animal products, the souring of milk, with curdling and preservation of the milk against putrefaction and unwholesomeness, is a striking phenomenon, as is also the spontaneous change of wine or cider into vinegar. Experience with such changes was the basis for thought about conservation of the food supplies through drying, heating, salting, and in the far North, chilling, but they added nothing to man's knowledge of the nutritive values of foods. They remained mysterious, and useful practices of everyday life came from them only after they were studied with acumen in the nineteenth century, especially with the rare insight of the great innovator, Louis Pasteur.

Personal Experience with Reaction to Eating

Individual experiences in eating early taught observant people the folly of over-eating. The notorious Roman banqueters were as uncomfortable as are the over-indulgent in food and drink of today. That this truth was revealed to many is attested by the number of proverbs in various languages which instruct in the wisdom of moderation or abstemiousness. Examples are Socrates' advice to his pupils to eat only when hungry and drink only when thirsty, and never to leave the table with a feeling of satiety; a Latin proverb: Over-feeding destroys more than hunger; and a Scotch proverb: Feed sparingly and defy the physician.

Before any knowledge of the causes of food spoilage was acquired it was inevitable that from time to time people were made ill by taking food which did not appear spoiled, but which had been contaminated by contact with an individual with typhoid or dysentery or paratyphoid. The agencies which were involved in food poisoning were understood only after the science of bacteriology was created. Illness following eating of spoiled food must have been frequent from the earliest times to have established the belief of the early Egyptians, as related by Herodotus (8), that all diseases to which mankind is subject proceed from food. He stated that for this reason they purged themselves every month for three days, and made frequent use of emetics.

Knowledge of Nutrition Derived from Experiences of Husbandry

Farmers of antiquity were aware, as are even uneducated farmers of today in many parts of the world, that animals like certain plants and refuse others; that grass deteriorates in feeding value during drought; that grass is superior to straw; that green herbage is superior to dried forage plants. Very old is the knowledge of the need to dry promptly, and keep dry, grass mown for hay, if its feeding value is to be preserved. Association of pleasing odor with nutritious qualities of hay and loss of feeding value with darkening and development of a musty odor is as old as the care of domestic animals. Observation of the quick recovery of good condition by animals in a state of starvation upon gaining access to good pasture resulted in perception that feeding stuffs differ in quality. Although such knowledge was possessed from antiquity by many intelligent men, no effort seems to have been made to study feeds and feeding practices by any method which advanced understanding of the comparative values of different feeds, and combinations of feeds, until well in the nineteenth century. From this source we gain nothing of much value about the nature of the processes of nutrition, although accumulated experience of farmers brought to light good and bad feeding practices without understanding of the principles involved.

The Views of Hippocrates about Foods

Medical historians have often stated that Hippocrates, the Father of Medicine, paid strict attention to the diet of his patients as a feature of his therapeutic regimens. With little more than this broad generalization, writers on nutrition have in general dismissed this authority and turned to other topics. In order that his views may be better known, the following digest of his teachings about the special properties and uses of foods is presented. (9)

His dietetic prescriptions reveal close observation of the effects of individual foods upon both the sick and the well. He said that garlic, pulses, and vetch caused flatulence. Pulses, he said, should be eaten along with cereal foods. Cheese produced flatulence and constipation, heated other foods, and gave rise to crudities and indigestion. For dropsy he recommended that the patient eat dry and sour or bitter foods because they were believed to bring about the elimination of more than normal amounts of water. The obese he advised to labor much, drink little, and subsist upon well-fed pork boiled with vinegar.

For those with hot intestines, who pass acrid and watery stools, he recommended emesis with hellebore, and in cases where there was no fever a diet of a cold decoction of wheat, lentils, and bread, together with boiled fish; but if fever was present the fish should be roasted. Remedial foods were myrtle, apples, dates, water from crab apples, and milk of asses, taken hot. Other foods used in treatment of dysentery were linseed, wheat flour, beans, millet, eggs, and milk. Barley mush was a favorite prescription.

Beef, Hippocrates said, causes exacerbation of melancholic disorders and is difficult of digestion, and goat's flesh is as bad as beef. He condemned the flesh of young pigs, but recommended pork from not too fat or too lean hogs, and that it should be eaten cold.

Extreme abstemiousness and likewise eating to repletion, he regarded as dangerous, and he spoke of the slender and restricted diet being more dangerous than one a little more generous. From these selections it is clear that Hippocrates had little understanding of the nature of nutrition and held some groundless opinions about quality in foods.

Knowledge of Nutrition among the Romans about 200 A.D.

Athenaeus, a Greek who was a native of Egypt, lived in Rome about the end of the second century A.D., where he wrote the oldest cookery-book and commentary on foods in relation to health that has been preserved to us. This is the *Deipnosophistae,* or *The Sophists at Dinner* (10). Here, in about 700 pages of lengthy discourse by a company of men at a banquet, one may learn about all that anyone had to say about Greek, Roman, Persian, Sicilian and other cooks and their curious dishes, the food of different countries, and opinions about wines, waters, etc. The work has but little value beyond revealing the state of ignorance and credulity of educated and prominent men of the time. A few examples of the absurdity which it contains will show the futility of seeking information from this source.

Cabbage was extolled as a remedy against the intoxicating effects of wine (Vol. 1, p. 151). Philinus never used any other drink or food but milk in all his life (1, p. 191). Anchimolus and Moschus, Sophists of Elis, drank water all their lives, and though they ate nothing but figs, enjoyed as robust physique as anyone else; but their sweat was so ill-smelling that everyone avoided them at the public baths. Mago of Carthage crossed the desert three times, eating dry meal, and having nothing to drink (1, p. 193). Lasyrtas the Larionian felt no need at all of drink with his food, as other men do, yet he urinated like anyone else (1, p. 194).

The Regimen of Luigi Cornaro

Cornaro (1467–1566) (11), thirteen hundred years after the Sophists' banquet, was as little inclined as his ancestors to permit truth to spoil a good story. He wrote an essay, "The Sure and Certain Method of Attaining a Long and Healthful Life," in which emphasis was laid on abstemiousness in eating. He restricted his daily allowance to twelve ounces of solid food and fourteen ounces of wine. Later he experimented with further reduction of his food intake and found that he could sustain himself on one egg a day. He lived to the age of ninety-three years.

The earliest record of a nutrition experiment with human subjects, in which two contrasting diets were compared and which suggest the type of study which was long afterward to yield valuable results, is recorded in the Book of Daniel. Daniel requested of the chief of the eunuchs that he and his Jewish youth associates who were being given training at the court of Nebuchadnezzar be excused from defiling themselves with the king's delicacies, and the wine that he drank, and be permitted to subsist on "pulses" and water. After ten days they were better in appearance, and fatter of flesh than all the youths who ate of the king's delicacies. In the King James version the translation is "pulses," but in the Smith-Goodspeed translation the term used is vegetables, which accords better with modern conclusions as to the full adequacy of a well-selected vegetarian diet.)

REFERENCES

1. Frazer, J. G.: The Golden Bough. One vol. ed., New York (1931). pp. 21, 238.
2. Cartier, Jacques: The Voyages of Jacques Cartier. Ed. by Biggar, H. P.: Publication of Pub. Archives of Canada No. 111 (1924).
3. Cato the Censor on Farming. Trans. by Ernest Brehaut. Columbia Univ. Press, New York (1933).
4. Quinn, Vernon: Roots, Their Place in Life and Legend. F. A. Stokes Co., New York (1938).
   Seeds, Their Place in Life and Legend. Same publisher.
   Leaves, Their Place in Life and Legend. Same publisher.
5. Hedrick, U. P.: History of Agriculture in the State of New York. Published by the state.
6. Kamm, M. W.: Old-Time Herbs for Northern Gardens. Little, Brown and Co., Boston (1938).
7. Lucas, A.: Ancient Egyptian Materials and Industries. Edw. Arnold & Co., London (1948).
8. Herodotus: History. Rawlinson, Geo. Translation, Ed. by Komroff, M., New York, 1936 edition, pp. 106–07.
9. Hippocrates, The Authentic Writings of: Trans. by F. Adams, 2 vols. Wm. Wood & Co., New York (1929); Vol. 1, pp. 272–277; Vol. 2, pp. 42, 193–98.
10. Athenaeus: *Deipnosophistae*. 3 vols. Trans. by C. B. Gulick (1927). G. P. Putnam's Sons, New York.
11. Cornaro, L.: The Sure and Certain Method of Attaining a Long and Healthful Life. Padua (1558).

2

Investigation of Carbohydrates

In this chapter an attempt is made to give an account of the chemical discoveries made by early investigators of sugars, starches, cellulose, and their related or derived products, in so far as they were given consideration by inquirers into the phenomena of animal nutrition. The more searching chemical studies by organic chemists into the molecular structures of the numerous substances which come within the classification of carbohydrates had no influence on constructive thought by students of nutrition, and therefore belong in an account of intermediary metabolism.

Starch

Pliny (1) (23–79 A.D.) states that the art of preparing starch from cereal flour was practiced by the people of the island of Chios, and that it was used as an adhesive. The technological uses of starch made it a familiar substance to the earliest chemists.

Leeuwenhoek (2) (1632–1723), who is distinguished for his pioneering studies with the microscope, described the appearance of starch granules under magnification. Raspail (3) (b. 1794), an outstanding investigator among the pioneers in the study of the chemistry and microscopy of vegetable substances, announced in 1826 his conclusion that starch particles were vesicles, enclosing a clear, transparent fluid. He was first to describe the swelling of starch granules when heated in water. Fritsche (4), in 1834, described correctly the structure of starch granules.

In 1836 Guerin-Varry (5) fractionated starch into an integumentary part and two soluble substances which he called *amidin* and *amylin*. He analyzed amylin and amidin prepared from wheat starch and discovered that the hydrogen and oxygen which they contained were present in the proportion to form water. The term carbohydrate was suggested in 1844 by C. Schmidt (6) to include sugars, starches, and other natural products which on hydrolysis yield sugars.

Sugar Obtained from Starch

In 1812 Kirchhoff, a Russian chemist, communicated to Berzelius that he had found that when starch was boiled with dilute sulfuric acid it was converted into a sugar identical with the sugar of grapes. This sugar had long been known, having been first prepared by the Duc de Bullion (7). The discovery was of great importance and was soon extended by others. De Saussure (8) demonstrated that by Kirchhoff's method 100 parts of starch yielded 110.14 parts of sugar, which he explained on the assumption that water was taken up by starch in the process. Hence he drew the conclusion that sugar was a compound of starch and water. Vogel (9) ascertained that in Kirchhoff's procedure the acid remains unchanged.

Sugar Obtained from Wood, Straw, Linen, etc.

In 1819, Braconnot (1781–1855) (10), professor of natural history and director of the botanical garden at Nancy, discovered that by applying the method of Kirchhoff to sawdust, straw, linen rags, and the bark of trees, these substances also yielded the sugar of grapes (dextrose).

The Reaction of Starch with Iodine

In 1815 Colin (1784–1865), professor in the Military Academy at St. Cyr and Gaulthier de Claubry (11), professor of chemistry in the school of pharmacy at Paris, discovered that iodine reacts with starch to form a blue color. In the same year Strohmeyer (12) professor of medicine at Göttingen, also described this reaction.

Caventou (1795–1877) (13), the French pharmacist who with his associates became famous for the discovery of the alkaloids quinine, cinchonine, strychnine, brucine, and veratrine, and who coined the name chlorophyll for the green pigment of leaves of plants, made some important studies with starch. He employed starch from potato, salep, sago, tapioca, and arrow-root. He boiled aqueous solutions of starch for a long time and noted that the iodine color reaction gradually changed from blue to purple, whereas this change (converson into dextrine) occurred after brief action of dilute sulfuric acid on boiled starch. Caventou called attention to Raspail's memoir on fecula (14) published in 1826, in which it was stated that Bouillon-Lagrange (1764–1844), professor of chemistry in the school of pharmacy at Paris and Dobereiner (1780–1849), apothecary and professor of chemistry at Jena, had described the effects of "torrification" on starch, among which was the change of the iodine reaction from blue to purple. Dobereiner was one of the most talented chemists of the first half of the 19th century. He first noted the relationship between the atomic weights of calcium, strontium, and barium, and later pointed out that other "traids" of the elements existed. He was first to recognize the catalytic property of platinum. Other achievements of this able investigator were the preparation of furfural, and aldehyde ammonia, and the invention of a quick vinegar process on the basis of his studies of the relation between alcohol and acetic acid.

The Discovery of Enzyme Digestion of Starch

In 1814 Kirchhoff (15), the discoverer of the conversion of starch to grape sugar, presented a paper before the Academy of Sciences of St. Petersburg in which he announced a new method for preparing a sugar from starch. He said that when gluten prepared from wheat meal was added to a solution of boiled starch the pasty stiffness soon disappeared and a sugar was formed. The syrup obtained by evaporation of the water when the conversion was complete had, he said, the sweetness of malt syrup, which he distinguished as a sugar different from that of grapes. His erroneous belief that gluten of wheat was a ferment appears to have been derived from French chemists.

It is of interest in this connection to record that certain early chemists devoted considerable exertions to ascertaining the nature of the substance in yeast which produces the striking effect upon the infusion made from sprouted grains, known as wort, in the brewing of beer. In 1785 Fabroni (16) published a treatise on wine-making for which he was given a prize by the Academy at Florence. He said that by heating the juice of grapes and passing it through a filter he separated an adhesive matter which possessed the properties of gluten. Gluten, the sticky, tough mass which remains after washing the starch out of a cereal meal (wheat, barley), had been observed from the earliest preparation of starch but was first described in 1745 by Beccari. Fabroni said that the heated juice, deprived of this substance, refused to ferment, but that it fermented as usual when the "glutenous" matter was added. Westhrumb (17) (1757–1819), a German apothecary, studied the fermentation of beer. He stated that if yeast is filtered a matter remains upon the filter which has the properties of gluten, and that when this substance is separated the yeast loses its property of exciting fermentation.

Thenard (1777–1857) (18), a peasant boy who studied pharmacy and chemistry under Berthollet, Fourcroy, and Vauquelin, became a notable investigator in several fields of chemistry and was raised to a peer of France. The chemistry of ferments was one of his interests. He was also the discoverer of hydrogen peroxide. In 1815 he published studies which confirmed the findings of Fabroni, thus supporting the erroneous view that gluten of cereal had the properties of what was later to be known, as an enzyme, amylase, or diastase. Probably Kirchhoff owed his thoughts on the ferment, or enzyme property, of gluten to the observations of Fabroni and Westhrumb, who were discussing fermentation, and not starch digestion. It is probable that his use of gluten to liquefy boiled starch succeeded because some diastase remained adsorbed upon it. At any rate, his experiment resulted in the conversion of boiled starch to maltose, and stimulated further study of the phenomenon by which starch may be degraded into simple products.

The Discovery of Diastase

In 1833 Payen and Persoz (19) made the highly important discovery of a method for preparing from malt extract a substance which possessed remarkable power to convert a solution of boiled starch to sugar. Anselm Payen was professor of industrial chemistry in Paris and J. F. Persoz was professor in the school of pharmacy at Strasbourg. These investigators added alcohol to malt extract and obtained a precipitate which, when added to a solution of boiled starch, caused separation of an insoluble flocculent substance. The remaining part, which they called amidin, stayed in solution and turned into sugar. It was because of this separation of the starch granules into two substances that they gave the material the name diastase. They found that a diastase preparation, purified by repeated solution in water and precipitation with alcohol, was so powerful in its action that one part could convert two thousand parts of starch into sugar. This power was destroyed by heating.

Origin of the Name Dextrine

Biot (1774–1862), a French physicist whose extensive study of polarized light gained for him the Rumford Medal of the Royal Society in 1840, laid the foundation for a polarimetric analysis of optically active substances. With Persoz, in 1833, he prepared what was called "sweet liquid of Biot" by partial hydrolysis of starch with mineral acids, and obtained a product which was dextrorotatory with polarized light. From its effect on light Payen and Persoz called the material *dextrine* (20). It was also produced by brief action of diastase on boiled starch, and was often referred to as gum or starch gum. They noted that they could stop the process of conversion at any point by heating the solution to boiling, and that a prolonged action of either acid or diastase led to formation of sugar, but different sugars were obtained by the two procedures. The sugar formed by the action of diastase on starch was described as a disaccharide (maltose) in 1847 by Dubrunfaut (21). Leuchs (22) in 1831 was first to note that saliva converts boiled starch into sugar, thus revealing the usefulness of saliva as a digestive agent. In 1845 Mialhe (23) prepared from saliva, by alcoholic precipitation, a preparation which behaved like diastase.

Inulin

In 1802 Valentin Rose (24) washed out the starch-like substance from macerated roots of *Inula helenium* (Elecampane). When dry it resembled starch in appearance, but unlike starch, which can absorb as much as 18 per cent moisture and still feel dry, the new substance was hygroscopic. It gave a yellow color with iodine, and with dilute acid solutions it was more easily converted into sugar than is starch. He was unable to crystallize the sugar formed on hydrolysis, and gave to this starch-like substance the name inulin. Braconnot (25) discovered that the tubers of Jerusalem artichoke and of dahlia likewise contain inulin and no starch. The "uncrystallizable sugar" was levulose. It was first crystallized in 1880 by Jungfleisch and Lefranc (26).

Sucrose

Pliny (27) and Dioscorides (28) used the term *saccharum* to denote a substance which they described as brittle and white, and which exudes from a kind of reed. Bechmann (29), after making an historical study, concluded that the Greeks and Romans were unacquainted with cane sugar (sucrose). Cane sugar is supposed to have been introduced into the Mediterranean region as the result of the conquests of Alexander. It was brought to Europe by the returning Crusaders, but for a long time was used only as a medicine. Only after the introduction of slave labor into the West Indies did sugar become a common article of diet in Europe. Sucrose was almost the only substance derived from vegetable sources which occurred in a pure form as crystals for study by the earliest chemists.

The Earliest Chemical Study of Cane Sugar

Cruickshanks (1745–1800) (30), who was chemist to the British Artillery, made the earliest attempt to study quantitatively the products which result from destruction of sucrose by destructive distillation. He placed 480 grains of pure sugar in a retort and heated it gradually to higher temperatures until the bottom of the retort was red hot. Then collecting the distillate and measuring its acidity by titrating it with a solution of potassium hydroxide, he calculated that the acidity was equivalent to 270 grains of pyromucic acid. He weighed the remaining charcoal, which he found to be 120 grains, and collected 90 grains of gaseous products, which he identified as carburetted hydrogen (methane) and carbonic acid gas. He noted that no ammonia was disengaged, and concluded that sugar is free from nitrogen, and that, accordingly, it consisted entirely of carbon, hydrogen, and oxygen. Lavoisier had previously attempted to analyze sugar, but at that time pneumatic chemistry had made too little progress to make possible a close approach to the truth. The first accurate analysis of sugar for determining its elementary composition was made in 1811 by Gay-Lussac and Thenard (31).

Grape Sugar (Dextrose)

Although grape sugar had long been known, the first chemist to prepare it in pure form and make a careful study of its properties was Proust (32) (1754–1826). J. L. Proust studied chemistry in his father's apothecary shop in Angiers and with Rouelle in Paris, and was Director of the Royal Laboratory at Madrid. He established, after long controversy, the law of definite composition, and the law of multiple proportions in chemical compounds. He prepared grape sugar by neutralizing the juice of ripe grapes with potash, after which he boiled it down one-half and left it to stand and deposit crystals of several salts, principally acid potassium tartrate. After filtering off these salts, he clarified the solution by adding a little blood and boiling to coagulate blood proteins, then skimmed, filtered, and boiled down to a syrup. It gradually became crystalline. He found that a solution of the crystals, treated with yeast, was fermented to wine. This solution was later given the name dextrose because of its rotatory power on polarized light. Kirchhoff's sugar of starch proved to be identical with the sugar of grapes.

The Sugar of the Blood and Urine

Thomas Sydenham (1624–89), the father of modern clinical medicine, described diabetes but did not mention the sweet taste of the urine in this disease. This had been noticed by the Hindus in the 6th century (33), who called it "honey urine." The disease was ascribed to over-indulgence in rice, flour, and sugar. Sugar in urine remained unknown in Europe until it was discovered by Thomas Willis (1621–75), the famous English anatomist and physician, who described the "circle of Willis" in the brain. After he called attention to the sweetness of diabetic urine, the presence of sugar was employed as a diagnostic sign. Cruickshanks (34) was first to prepare sugar from urine in pure form. He gave an account of this in a book on diabetes by Dr. John Rollo, in 1797. Rollo advocated a meat diet for the control of diabetes.

In 1815 M. E. Chevreul (1786–1889) (35), the famous investigator of the chemistry of fats and successor to Vauquelin, separated sugar from the urine of a diabetic and observed that its crystalline form and solubility in water and in alcohol, as well as its behavior on heating, corresponded in every way with those properties of grape sugar. Callaud (36) first observed the remarkable property of glucose of forming a double compound with sodium chloride, which forms large crystals in concentrated diabetic urine when common salt has been added in suitable concentration.

The presence of sugar in blood was first shown in 1844 by C. Schmidt (37), a student of Liebig and a pioneer in studies of animal metabolism. In 1846 he went to the German University at Dorpat, Estonia, where he taught and carried on researches for forty-five years. Much of his work was done in collaboration with Frederick Bidder (1810–94) at the same institution. Schmidt's procedure for detecting sugar in blood was based on precipitation of the proteins from defibrinated blood by addition of 10 volumes of alcohol. The filtrate from the protein precipitate was evaporated to dryness and the sugar was extracted by hot alcohol. From the alcoholic solution he separated the sugar as the double compound of glucose with KOH, which flocculates from alcohol under the conditions of his experiment. He had at that time three methods of identifying glucose. These were the formation of the large crystals of the compound of glucose with sodium chloride (Callaud's discovery), the fermentation test with yeast, and Trommer's test, described in 1841, which depended on reduction of alkaline copper sulfate solution by glucose. Schmidt never failed to detect sugar in the blood of various animals examined.

The Fermentation Test for Sugar

The use of yeast as a test reagent for the detection and estimation of fermentable sugars was the very first test proposed for that purpose. It was suggested by Dobereiner in 1818 (38). He said, "The smallest particles of sugar concealed in any liquid may be discovered, and their affinity determined, by adding to such liquid some grains of yeast and enclosing the mixture in a vessel sealed with mercury. The fermentation, at the temperature of 16–20 degrees Reaumur, begins to manifest itself, and continues as long as any sugar remains, occasioning the disengagement of a quantity of bubbles of carbonic acid gas, from which the quantity of sugar which the yeast has decomposed may be easily calculated." Dobereiner found that five grains of sugar, dissolved in half a cubic inch of water, and brought into contact with yeast, uniformly produced 4.7 cubic inches of carbonic acid gas and 2.57 grains of alcohol. He expressed the view that "alcohol consists of three portions of deutero-hydroid of carbon and a proportion of carbonic acid." Before the year 1850 chemists, using these technics, had discovered that glucose is present in practically all body tissues and fluids.

The Discovery of Glycogen

The year 1856 is notable in the history of physiology for the discovery by C. Bernard (1813–78) (39) of the formation and storage, in the liver of a well-fed animal, of a polysaccharide called *glycogen.* Bernard was first to discover that pancreatic juice has digestive powers. His method for preparing glycogen was to dissolve the liver substance in strong potassium hydroxide and precipitate it by addition of alcohol. He found glycogen to be converted into malt sugar by action of the ferment in saliva, also by a ferment in pancreatic juice, as well as by extract of malt, and by yeast cells. It was shown to be hydrolyzed to glucose by boiling with dilute mineral acids in a manner comparable with starch. The problem of the origin of glycogen stimulated a great deal of experimental work by others in the years following its discovery. Bernard observed that after the death of an animal the glycogen of the liver is soon decomposed and sugar accumulates as the decomposition product. He believed glycogen to be formed from protein of the food.

The study of the origin of glycogen in the liver was furthered by C. Voit (40) (1831–1908), a pupil of Liebig and the most outstanding of the early investigators of metabolism, whose laboratory in Munich was for a quarter of a century the Mecca of students of metabolism and nutrition. He compared the glycogen content of the livers of fasting hens with those of others which were fasted and then given glucose (dextrose), levulose, cane sugar or maltrose, and found that all of these sugars were readily converted into glycogen and deposited in the liver, whereas lactose and galactose were of doubtful value for this purpose.

Bernard (41) had found that when cane sugar is injected into a vein of an animal it is excreted into the urine, whereas fructose (levulose), when similarly injected, is retained in the body. He further discovered (1873) that intestinal secretion contains an enzyme, *invertase,* which converts cane sugar into dextrose and levulose. This enzyme had been discovered in 1871 in yeast extract by Felix Hoppe-Seyler (1825–95), professor of physiological chemistry at Strassburg, and one of the most successful investigators of the chemistry of milk, bile, and chlorophyll. The discovery of invertase served to explain the utilization of cane sugar after hydrolysis in the intestinal tract, whereas when directly introduced into the blood it was valueless.

Lactose

In 1615 Fabricius Bartholetti (42) first described sugar of milk. Von Haller (43) stated that it had been known long before that time in India. It was early manufactured in Switzerland from whey, and a considerable demand for it was created by Ludovico Testi, a physician in Venice. He claimed to be its discoverer, and sold it as a powerful remedy in gout and other diseases. Analyses of milk sugar for its content of carbon, hydrogen, and oxygen revealed that it possessed the same percentage composition as sucrose, or cane sugar. This puzzling fact was not explained for many years. In 1856 Pasteur prepared galactose from milk sugar.

Fermentation of Milk Sugar

Ordinarily milk on standing at room temperature undergoes spontaneous lactic acid fermentation, accompanied by curdling of the casein and separation of sour whey. From unrecorded times the Tartars made an intoxicating drink by fermenting milk which they called *koumiss.* All of the earlier attempts in Europe to cause milk to undergo alcoholic fermentation were unsuccessful. Grieve (44) gave the earliest published directions for preparing koumiss as practiced by the Tartars. This they accomplished by adding a little very sour milk to mare's milk and agitating the milk frequently. Schill (45) gave an elaborate history of koumiss in 1839. A similar fermented milk with intoxicating properties is reported by Thomas Thomson (46) to have been prepared from cow's milk in Shetland and Orkney by essentially the same procedure described by Grieve. Schill succeeded in producing alcoholic fermentation of milk sugar. From 100 parts of lactose he secured 36.1 parts of absolute alcohol. Eventually it emerged that alcoholic fermentation of lactose is brought about by a variety of yeast known as *Saccharomyces fragilis.* Ordinary yeasts cannot ferment lactose.

Discovery of an Unfermentable Sugar

By imitating the procedures which enabled chemists to isolate the sugars mentioned above, principally by extraction of natural products with hot alcohol and crystallization from the concentrated extract, in 1813 Braconnot (47) prepared from (*Agaricus*) mushrooms, a crystalline substance which had the composition of sugar, melted on heating, and gave the odor of caramel when strongly heated. It proved to be non-fermentable. This sugar was d-mannite, or manna sugar, and was later found to be widely distributed in fungi.

Cellulose

It has already been noted that Braconnot, in 1819, had produced sugar by boiling wood, linen, etc. with dilute mineral acid. The next advance in knowledge of the chemical nature of the supporting tissues of plants was made by J. F. Gmelin (48) (1748–1804), a German chemist who wrote chemical treatises and pharmaceutical works. In 1830 he observed that when paper was treated with mineral acids a gelatinous substance was formed which gave a blue color with iodine similar to that formed by starch with this reagent. He interpreted this change of cellulose by acids to signify that it was convertible into starch. In 1842 M. J. Schleiden (49) (1804–1881), author of one of the most famous text-books of botany (1842), concluded from his study of all the experimental evidence available that there existed a series of celluloses which differed in yielding in addition to glucose, other sugars when hydrolyzed. This conclusion was supported by later investigations by others.

Payen (50) in 1834 began a series of experimental studies of cell wall substances of plants. He studied materials from many plants by successive treatment with acids, alkalies, water, alcohol, and ether with the objective of securing the purest possible preparations for analysis. He came to the conclusion that such methods always ended by separation of chemically resistant substances which he believed to be identical, and which were without exception isomeric with starch, having the composition $(C_6H_{10}O_5)_n$. To this material he gave the name *cellulose.*

Discovery of Chemical Reagents for Carbohydrate Studies

In 1815 H. A. Vogel (51) (b.1778) observed that a solution of glucose reduces alkaline solutions of the heavy metals with deposition of the metal (e.g. silver) or, in the case of cupric salts, formation of red cuprous oxide. In this reaction the sugar was oxidized. Becquerel (52), in 1831, studied the product formed from glucose by the action of alkaline copper solution and found it to be an acid. This observation was interpreted by Kekule, in 1860, to mean that glucose has the structure of an aldehyde. Becquerel's observation set the pattern for many important later studies on the kinds of acids formed from different simple sugars, several kinds of which were found to be widely distributed in the plant world.

Trommer's Test for Reducing Sugars

In 1841 Trommer (53) introduced alkaline copper sulfate solution as a sensitive test for glucose. It was reported to detect one part of glucose in 500 parts of water.

Fehling's Solution

In 1849 Fehling (54) improved on the sensitiveness of Trommer's reagent by including in the solution Rochelle salt, and increased the sensitiveness of the reagent so as to detect one part of glucose in 5000 dilution.

Schweitzer's Reagent

In 1857 M. E. Schweitzer (55), professor at the University of Zurich, discovered that a solution of cupric oxide in ammonia dissolves cellulose without decomposing it, and the cellulose could be recovered by making the solution acid. This reagent served G. Lange (56) in 1889 in isolating from wood lignic acid, which does not dissolve in Schweitzer's reagent.

Schulze's Reagent

In 1887 E. Schulze (57) introduced a solution of zinc chloride-iodine-potassium iodide in water for testing for cellulose, which it colors blue.

Hemicelluloses and Pentosans

It was not until 1891 that E. Schulze (58) observed that there were present in the woody substances of plants polysaccharides which were much more readily hydrolyzed to sugars by very dilute mineral acids than is cellulose. Among the sugars formed in this manner from different vegetable sources, he detected galactose, mannose, and the pentose sugars, arabinose and xylose. This pattern of investigation soon yielded information that gum acacia, cherry gum, and some others yield on hydrolysis the five-carbon sugar arabinose, whereas pentosans from straw, bran, and especially corncobs, yield another five-carbon sugar xylose.

The foregoing survey lists the most important steps in progress taken by chemists in gaining knowledge of the kinds and properties of the carbohydrates which were of importance to investigators of foods and nutrition during the 19th century. The earliest students of animal nutrition gave consideration only to starch and the sugars glucose and sucrose. Woody plant tissues were believed to be inert and resistant to the agencies in the digestive tract which effected solution and preparation of nutrient substances for absorption into the blood stream, and so were considered of no consequence as sources of nourishment. But after 1830 efforts were initiated, especially by Liebig and his students, to determine by chemical analysis the food values of various foods and feeding-stuffs. It was then that the estimation of these supposedly inert substances in foods of vegetable origin assumed importance. Liebig's distinction between tissue-building (plastic) and fuel-foods (fats and carbohydrates) called for chemical methods for distinguishing between useful and useless carbohydrates. In a later chapter the dilemma of the agricultural chemists in trying to solve this problem will be further discussed.

REFERENCES

1. Pliny: Book xviii, Chapt. 7.
2. Leeuwenhoek, A. van: Cited by Mulder, Physiological Chemistry 1844, p. 215.
3. Raspail, F. V.: Annal. sci. nat. (1826).
4. Fritsche, J.: Pogg. Ann. 32, 129 (1834).
5. Guerin-Varry, R. T.: Compt. Rend. II, 116 (1836).
6. Schmidt, C.: Liebig's Ann. *51*, 30 (1844).
7. Duc de Bullion: Cited by Th. Thomson: Organic Chem. of Veg. Bodies, London (1838), p. 636.
8. De Saussure, N. T.: Chemical Researches on Plants, Paris (1804).
9. Vogel, H. A.: Schweigg. Journ. *13*, 162 (1815).
10. Braconnot, H.: Ann. de chim. et de phys. *12*, 181 (1819).
11. Colin, J. J., and Gaulthier de Claubry, H. F.: Schweigg. Journ. *13*, 453 (1815).
12. Strohmeyer, F.: Gilbert's Ann. *49*, 146 (1815).
13. Caventou, J. B.: Ann. de chim. et de phys. *31*, 337 (1826).
14. Raspail, F. V.: Annal. sci. nat. (1826). Memoir on Fecula.
15. Kirchhoff, G. S. C.: Roy. Acad. St. Petersburg (1814); Nasse, M.: Schweigg. Journ. *4*, 111 (1812).
16. Fabroni: Cited by Th. Thomson: Organic Chem. of Veg. Bodies, London (1838) p. 636.
17. Westhrumb, J. F.: Cited by Th. Thomson, Ref. 7, p. 1016.
18. Thenard, L. J.: Ann. de chim. *46*, 308 (1803).

19. Payen, A., and Persoz, J. F.: Ann. de chim. et de phys. (2) 53, 73 (1833).
20. Payen, A., and Persoz, J. F.: Pogg. Ann. 32, 174 (1834).
21. Dubrunfaut: Ann. de chim. et de phys. (3) *21* (1847).
22. Leuchs: Kastner's Arch. *10* (1831). Cited by Simon, J. F.: Animal Chemistry, with reference to the Physiology and Pathology of Man. Trans. by Geo. E. Day. Two Vols. London, (1845). Vol. II, p. 9.
23. Miahle: Lancette Française, April 1845. Cited by Simon, Ref. 22, Vol. II, p. 9.
24. Rose, Valentin: Gehlen's Journ. *iii,* 217 (1804).
25. Braconnot, H.: Ann. de chim. et de phys. 25, 358–73 (1824).
26. Jungfleisch and Lefranc: Bull. soc. chim. II, *34,* 675 (1880).
27. Pliny: Natural History, Book xxii, p. 9.
28. Dioscorides: *Materia Medica.* Book ii, p. 104.
29. Bechmann: *Historia Sacchari Commentationes.* Trans. Roy. Soc. Göttingen *5* (1782); also Philos. Mag. 2 (1801) pp. 1–17.
30. Cruickshanks, W.: Nicholson's Journ. *1* and 2 (1797).
31. Gay-Lussac, J. and Thenard, L. J.: Recherches Physico-Chemique, ii, 288 (1811).
32. Proust, J. L.: Journ. de phys. *29,* 5 (1817); Ann. de chim. 57, 131 (1804).
33. Cited from Lusk, G.: Nutrition. Clio Medica, Vol. *10,* (1933) p. 13.
34. Cruickshanks, W.: In Dr. John Rollo's *Diabetes,* London (1797).
35. Chevreul, M. E.: Ann. de chim. *95,* 319 (1815).
36. Callaud: Journ. de Pharmacie II, 562 (1818).
37. Schmidt, C.: Liebig's Ann. *51,* 30 (1844).
38. Dobereiner, J. W.: Philos. Mag. *51,* 147 (1818).
39. Bernard, C.: Leçons sur le diabètes (1877) p. 553.
40. Voit, C.: Zeitschr. f. Biol. *28,* 291 (1891).
41. Bernard, C.: Gazet. medic. de Paris (1873) p. 200.
42. Bartholetti, Fabricius: Cited from Th. Thomson, Animal Chemistry, Edinburgh (1843) p. 131.
43. Haller, A. von: Mentioned by Th. Thomson, Animal Chemistry (1843) p. 131.
44. Grieve: Trans. Roy Soc., Edinburgh, Vol. *1.*

45. Schill: Ann. der Pharmacie *31*, 152 (1839).
46. Thomson, Th.: Animal Chemistry (1843) p. 437.
47. Braconnot, H.: Ann. de chim. *79*, 278 (1811); 87, 237 (1813).
48. Gmelin, J. F.: Schweigg. Journ. *58*, 374, 377 (1830).
49. Schleiden, M. J.: Pogg. Ann. *43*, 391 (1838); Flora (1842) p. 237.
50. Payen, A.: Ann. sci. nat. (2) Tome II, p. 21 (1839).
51. Vogel, H. A.: Schweigg. Journ. *13*, 162 (1815).
52. Becquerel: Ann. de chim. et. de phys. (2) *47*, 13 (1831).
53. Trommer: Liebig's Ann. *39*, 360 (1841).
54. Fehling: Liebig's Ann. *72*, 106 (1849).
55. Schweitzer, M. E.: J. prakt. Chem. *76*, 109, 344 (1857).
56. Lange, G.: Zeitschr. f. physiol. Chem. *14*, pp. 15, 283 (1889).
57. Schulze, E.: Mitt. pharm. Institute, Erlangen *2*, 280 (1889).
58. Schulze, E.: Ber. d. d. chem. Ges. *24*, 2277 (1891).

3

Investigations of Fats and Fat-like Substances

THE PREPARATION AND USE of various fatty substances in foods, technology, and medicine is as old as history. Lucas (1), in his work on the materials and industries of ancient Egypt, mentions the preparation of oils of almond, balanos, ben, ricinus (castor), colocynth, lettuce seed, linseed, leaves of cinnamon, olive, radish seed, safflour seed, and sesame. Some of these were used as cosmetics, and others for their medicinal properties. Castor oil is mentioned as a medicine in the Papyrus Ebers (2). Breasted (3) stated that according to the Hearst Papyrus a preparation for growing hair was made of the mixed fats of the gazelle, serpent, crocodile, and hippopotamus. In the Papyrus Ebers, according to Bryan (2), an ointment for the same purpose was compounded of fats of the lion, hippopotamus, crocodile, cat, serpent, and goat.

The terms fat, tallow, suet, lard, butter, etc., are very old, and show clearly that man was from the earliest times familiar with certain peculiarities which these substances exhibited and by which they could be recognized. An interesting example of a very early discovery of properties of special value in a fat was neat's-foot oil, prepared as a floating layer by boiling the hoofs of cattle. Although the body fat is tallow, a solid fat at room temperature, the oil from the feet does not solidify even at the freezing-point of water, and was for that reason especially useful as a lubricant. In the melted state all fats looked much alike except for color, some being white, others yellow, but their odors differed widely.

The earliest observers in physiology, medicine, and pathology noted the sites where fat tends most to be deposited in the healthy individual, and were struck with the rapidity with which fat could disappear from a plump, or obese, body as a result of starvation or wasting diseases. They also noted that persons who habitually engage in hard muscular exercise do not accumulate fat as do sedentary people, and that domestic animals in prime condition contained much more fat than do wild game animals. Such common experience as that horses which are sleek and plump soon become thin when subjected to continuous labor even though they are well fed, provided food for thought by the earliest physiologists on the relation of fat to work output. The great physiologist A. von Haller (1708–1777) (4) discussed at length the significance of food on the deposition of body fat; and considered such factors as the temperature of the environment and the *conditions of the mind* as affecting the corpulency or meagerness of the human body. The pathological accumulation of fat in degenerative changes in liver, kidney, and heart, and in paralyzed muscles, was early observed.

Earliest Chemical Examination of Fats

In 1797 Jean Darcet (1725–1801) professor at the Collège de France, with Lefevre and Pelletier (5), published a memoir on the preparation of different kinds of soap which was at that time a complete treatise on the subject. Soap-making was an old art, generally practiced by boiling fats or oils with potash, the alkaline leachings of wood ashes. But Dioscorides (6), who lived in the first century A.D. and was the author of the first *Materia Medica*, described a method for preparing lead soap (lead plaster) and zinc plaster for medicinal purposes. These plasters were made by boiling fat with lead oxide or zinc oxide.

Fourcroy in 1800 stated (6a) that C. L. Berthollet, professor in the École Normale who first showed the presence of nitrogen in animal matter, introduced hypochlorite in bleaching, and was distinguished for other discoveries, was the first to learn of a simpler way of preparing heavy metal soaps. His procedure was to pour a sodium or potassium soap solution into a solution of a metallic salt, whereupon the metallic soap precipitated out. In this way he prepared a green soap with copper and a brown soap with iron, as well as lead and zinc soaps, or "plasters."

In 1805 Vogel, instructor in the School of Pharmacy at Paris, published (7) a memoir on animal fat. Vogel died at an early age and his results were published by Bouillon-Lagrange, professor of Chemistry and Director of that institution. His work is interesting because it shows the lack of understanding of how to study the chemical nature of fats, and because he introduced a number of new procedures into his investigation. Vogel stated that he wished to study fats of animals whose exercises are violent, such as the hare and wolf, and that of carnivorous birds. He had difficulty in securing enough of these fats for his experiments, which were never completed, but he did extensive work with hog's lard and some with human fat.

He stated that when human fat is destructively distilled it yields a liquid product which has all the properties of an acid, such as neutralizing alkali, and turning blue vegetable pigments red. Following Senebier (8), the great pioneer plant physiologist, Vogel confirmed the effect of air and light on accelerating the development of rancidity, but he went further and exposed lard without contact with air to the sun's rays for two months and noted that it became extremely rancid. It is doubtful whether he rigidly excluded air from his preparation.

Vogel also tested the action of phosphorus and of hydrochloric and sulfuric acids on fats and reported that no action was manifest. Apothecaries had long sold pomade, fat in which sulfur was incorporated, for anointing the hair, but it appears that Vogel was first to heat this mixture and observe a copious evolution of hydrogen sulfide. Apparently this was the first observation that sulfur could remove hydrogen from organic compounds. Otherwise than the tests mentioned, Vogel knew only of "analysis by fire," or destructive distillation, as a means of examining fats.

The great pioneer studies on separation and description of fatty acids were made by M. E. Chevreul (1786–1889), professor at the Lycée Charlemagne. In 1811, when he was working in the laboratory of Vauquelin, he was assigned the task of examining the chemical nature of a sample of soap. He dissolved it in water and added hydrochloric acid, and observed that insoluble organic acids separated and formed a floating layer. This was the beginning of a long and fruitful investigation of the chemistry of fats which was published in 1823. In 1814 (9) he showed that hog's lard consisted of two distinct oily bodies: one a solid at ordinary temperatures of summer, the other a liquid at the same temperature. The first he named *stearin,* and the second *elain.* He made soap from lard and potash, and from the aqueous solution he crystallized potassium stearate, which he called mother of pearl substance. When this was dissolved in water and acidified with hydrochloric acid, there was set free a water-insoluble organic material of acid reaction to litmus which was solid at room temperature. To this material he gave the name *margarine* (from the Greek for mother of pearl). Chevreul defined the term acid as a substance sour to the taste, capable of being attracted by positively electrified substances, capable of neutralizing basic substances, of reddening litmus and the color of violets, and of reddening hematine. But he noted that, although it possessed all the other properties of acids, his solid fatty acid did not taste sour. The oily fatty acid which was isolated by Chevreul came to be known as *oleic acid*.

From goat's fat Chevreul isolated what he called *hircin*, a fat from which he secured *hircic acid* (caproic acid). He distinguished this acid from stearic acid by their different melting points. Chevreul also employed alcohol to separate mixed soaps into fractions having different properties. He observed that when stearic acid is distilled destructively, liquid products of acid nature are formed, and an exceedingly irritating odor is developed. He did not identify the irritating odorous substance (acrolein). Chevreul's researches and the publication of his famous memoir on fats stimulated many investigations by other chemists.

The Discovery of Glycerol

In 1783 C. W. Scheele (1742–1786), the famous Swedish chemist and apothecary, after preparing lead plaster by the old method of boiling olive oil with lead oxide had the curiosity to examine the mother liquor from which the lead soap separated. He removed the residual lead from this by precipitating it as sulfide, and the aqueous solution he evaporated to a syrup, which had a sweet taste (10). This he called glycerine (*glykeros* : Greek = sweet). He found that it yielded oxalic acid on oxidation with nitric acid, as did sugar when similarly oxidized. Chevreul afterwards showed that this substance always separates when fats are converted into soaps. The early chemists were puzzled concerning the nature of glycerine. In 1843 Thomas Thomson (11) described stearin as a salt-like compound of stearic acid with glycerine. It was shown by Berzelius to combine on heating with sulfuric, phosphoric, or tartaric acids, to form "acid-salts," but no insight into its chemical nature was gained until Marcellin Berthelot, in 1854, showed that glycerol "gave rise to three distinct series of neutral combinations" with acids, e.g., acetic acid. He described glycerol as a "tribasic alcohol."

First Synthesis of Fats

Berthelot (12) at once proceeded to heat glycerol with stearic acid in a sealed tube at 200° C. for 20 hours, and produced monostearin. Continued heating with excess of stearic acid led to the formation of di- and tristearin, the latter identical with natural tristearin isolated from solid fats. The chemical nature of fats was thus established.

Acrolein

In 1843 J. Redtenbacher (13) distilled glycerol with a small addition of phosphorus pentoxide and obtained acrolein (acrylic aldehyde), which he identified with the highly irritating vapors which are formed when fats are heated to decomposition. This odor formation was subsequently employed as a qualitative test for fats.

Earliest Studies of Rancidity in Fats

In 1792 J. Senebier (1742–1809), a Swiss clergyman and scientist, stated his observation (8) that oils, when exposed to air, absorb "this substance," become white, lose their fluidity, and in time become rancid. These changes, he said, take place in the dark, but occur much sooner when the oils are exposed to light. Further investigation convinced him that rancidity involved oxidation since he found that when fats were kept in oxygen the characteristic changes took place faster than in air.

Fourcroy (14), in 1800, stated that Berthollet had discovered that when a fat was spread upon the surface of water and exposed to air it became thick and resembled wax. Fourcroy stated that it had been demonstrated that this change was due to the absorption of atmospheric oxygen.

Although it was common knowledge among chemists and all who were experienced in the preservation of foods that unpleasant odors and unpalatability developed as fatty foods became rancid, no attention seems to have been given to the possible detrimental effects of ingestion of fats in a state of rancidity until well after the close of the nineteenth century. The fact that rancidity in fats in the diet could cause profound malnutrition, and the ways in which this is brought about, will be discussed in Chapter 23.

The Transformation of Oleic to Elaidic Acid

In 1819 Poutet (15) made the discovery that when olive oil was shaken with a concentrated aqueous solution of mercurous nitrate it was changed to the consistency of pork fat. In 1832 Boudet (16) made the observation that a small amount of hyponitrous acid ($H_2N_2O_2$) when in contact with olive oil caused the same striking change in it that had been described by Poutet. Oleic acid is very difficult to prepare in a state of purity. Varrentrapp (17) in 1840 discovered that the lead salt of oleic acid is soluble in ether, and that it could be extracted from the lead salts of all saturated fatty acids by this solvent. Gottlieb (18) in 1846, working with nearly pure oleic acid, showed that when exposed to the atmosphere it takes up 20 times its volume of oxygen without forming any carbon dioxide. He also proved that oleic acid is perfectly isomeric with elaidic acid, formed from it by the action of a little nitrous oxide.

The methods enumerated above were sufficient for fractionating the fatty acids resulting from saponification of fats from many sources, and, in the hands of many chemists, made possible the isolation and study of almost the entire series of both saturated and unsaturated fatty acids which occur in nature. Interest of chemists or physiologists in fats as food substances during the 19th century was essentially limited to the relative digestibility of fats of high and low melting points.

The Discovery of Absorption of Halogens by Unsaturated Fatty Acids

In 1822 Edmund Davy (19), cousin to Sir Humphrey Davy, gave the first account of the action of iodine on unsaturated compounds. He described in detail the phenomenon observed when oil of turpentine is shaken with a solution of iodine in aqueous potassium iodide. He noted the disappearance of iodine color. He observed the same result when oils of lavender, caraway, peppermint, or amber were studied, but concluded that linseed, olive, and castor oils could not take up iodine under these conditions. This error may have been due to failure to add sufficient oil to decolorize the solution when tests of the last mentioned oils were made. The earliest suggestion that absorption of halogen might be used to measure the degree of unsaturation of a fat or fatty acid was made in 1883 by Mills and Snodgrass (20) who proposed a "bromine number." The following year Hübl developed a practical method for determining the "iodine number" of fats, and in 1898 Wijs (21) suggested important improvements in the technic for this operation. These methods determine the number of unsaturated carbon-to-carbon bonds in the molecule of a fat or fatty acid.

The Earliest Attempts to Analyze Fats For Their Components

In 1815 H. Braconnot (22), professor of natural history at the Lyceum at Nancy, said that hitherto chemists had believed that fat of organized bodies consisted of one substance having the same essential properties, and differing only by its firmer or weaker consistence, as in the case of suet, lard, marrow, etc., which were recognized by the Ancients. He was the first who attempted to separate and distinguish between oily fats and solid fats in fats from different sources. His method was to cool the sample and press it between layers of paper. The oily part was imbibed by the paper, while the solid part remained. He then steeped the paper in warm water and recovered and measured the floating layer of oil. He reported the ratio of oil to tallow in the fats examined. The following values were reported:

Vosges summer butter	60 : 40	Duck fat	72 : 28
Vosges winter butter	35 : 65	Turkey fat	74 : 26
Lard	62 : 38	Olive oil	72 : 24
Ox marrow oil	24 : 76	Oil of almonds	76 : 24
Sheep marrow oil	74 : 26	Oil of colza	54 : 46
Goose fat	68 : 32		

In 1823 Traill (23) made the first attempt to determine the fat content of human blood, using the method of Braconnot. He evaporated serum and soaked up the oil on paper, "care having been taken to weigh the paper before and after the soaking up of the oil." He found 4.5 per cent of liquid fat in his sample.

First Use of Organic Solvents for Extracting Fatty Matter

After alcohol became available in the form of spirit of wine (about 85 per cent alcohol) in the 12th century, apothecaries began to extract dried plants with it to prepare tinctures, which were sold for medicinal purposes. H. Boerhaave (1668–1738) was professor at the University of Leyden. In 1732 he published his *Elements of Chemistry,* an extremely successful work. Casper Neumann (1683–1737) (24), a German apothecary, was one of the first to devote himself to the study of the chemistry of vegetable substances. In 1719 he discovered thymol in *Monarda* (horsemint) and in 1760 he published a famous work on chemistry. Both Boerhaave and Neumann employed organic solvents in their studies.

It was Hilaire-Marie Rouelle (1718–1778) (25), who first suggested the *chemical dissection* of vegetable and animal substances by applying successively various organic solvents to the sample, and in the order of the poorest solvent first, the next poorest solvent second, etc., so as to obtain different constituents from the complex mixture in the plant. He employed this technic in discovering urea and hippuric acid in urine. H. M. Rouelle may be justly called the father of physiological chemistry.

Great credit is due Johan Friederich John, professor of chemistry in the University at Nuremberg, for developing methods for chemical analysis of vegetable substances. His work will be considered more fully in Chapter 11, (26), but here attention is called to his employing turpentine, naphtha, ether, and alcohol as solvents for fats and similar substances. As chemists developed an interest in the analysis of food and feeding stuffs, ether extraction became the standard procedure for estimating "crude" fat in these materials.

Waxes

In 1813 Chevreul (27) attempted to make soap from spermaceti, the wax-like substance obtained from the head of the sperm whale. He discovered that on boiling this with caustic alkali he produced a soap, later identified as potassium palmitate, but that no glycerol was present in the water from which the soap was obtained. Instead he separated a white crystalline material, insoluble in water but soluble in alcohol and ether, which he called *cetin.* After recrystallization it melted at 49° C. and came to be known as cetyl alcohol. Spermaceti was eventually shown to be an ester of the palmitic acid with cetyl alcohol.

After years of unsucccessful inquiries by several chemists into the nature of beeswax, Brodie (28) in 1843 identified its principal constituent as myricyl palmitate.

Chinese wax, the secretion of an insect *Coccus ceriferus,* which is deposited on the branches of ash trees in western China, proved to be ceryl cerotate.

The waxes are mentioned here because they are of wide distribution on the surfaces of leaves of plants, fruits, etc., and so came into consideration by the early chemists who sought to determine the components of vegetable food-stuffs. They are soluble in fat solvents and pass into the ether extract of the sample, and constitute a variable portion of the "crude fat" fraction in the food or feed analysis. Since they are inert, and are not absorbed from the digestive tract, chemists of the last quarter of the 19th century realized that their presence in the fat fraction constituted a source of error in their attempts to estimate the nutritive values of foods by chemical methods.

Discovery of the Phospholipids

In 1844 and 1846 N. T. Gobley (29) described the isolation from egg yolk of a substance which contained both nitrogen and phosphorus in addition to glycerol and fatty acids. He called it lecithin (from the Greek, *lekithos,* egg yolk). On hydrolysis it yielded a nitrogenous base, identified by Strecker (30) in 1868 as choline, which he had isolated from bile. In 1908 MacLean (31) showed that not all of the base in lecithin preparations was choline, and he suggested the presence of a lecithin-like substance which instead of choline contained an amino acid. But in 1913 Trier (32) identified the nitrogenous base in *kephalin,* which occurs generally in brain, egg yolk, etc., along with lecithin, as amino ethyl alcohol. Kephalin had been isolated and described in 1884 by Thudichum (33).

These phospholipids, lecithin and kephalin, attracted no special attention of nutrition investigators until 1899 when Zadik (34), and later others, sought by animal experiments to determine whether they were essential in the diet or were the products of synthesis. This type of investigation will be considered more at length in a later chapter.

Cholesterol

In his *Dictionary of Chemistry* Macquer (35) stated that cholesterol, generally called *biliary fat,* was first obtained from gallstones by Poultier de la Salle, although the discovery has been attributed to Gren. He also obtained it from gallstones by dissolving them in hot alcohol, from which, on cooling, it separated in crystals which bore a superficial resemblance to the high-melting fatty acids. Chevreul described biliary fat before the French Institute in 1814, and again in his famous memoir on fatty substances in 1823. Throughout the 19th century it was usually designated cholesterin. Cholesterol has, in general, the same solubility properties as fats, and is, therefore, extracted with them by solvents. Cholesterol was found to occur in brain and in other organs, and was eventually found to be present in egg-yolk, milk, and in nearly all animal fluids. Together with isocholesterol it occurs in wool-fat (lanolin).

In 1862 Benecke (36) isolated from various seeds and vegetable oils substances which were closely similar to cholesterol, but cholesterol itself was never found in plant tissues. Although several investigators extended observations on the wide distribution of plant sterols no close chemical study was made of them until Hesse (37), in 1878–1885, compared the melting points of a number of pure sterols from plants with that of cholesterol. His studies revealed that a number of related sterols occur in plants. The most important sterol ever discovered in plants is ergosterol, which was obtained by Tanret (38) in 1889. It was to be identified many years later as a mother substance or precursor of vitamin D.

Since ether extracts of dried green leaves of plants are bright green, the earliest chemists to extract fatty substances from vegetable materials were aware that chlorophyll is extracted along with fats. As will be set forth in later chapters, nutrition investigators were eventually forced by circumstances to inquire whether the phospholipids and sterols had nutritional significance.

The Problem of Digestion of Fats in the Alimentary Tract

The earliest writers on animal chemistry, among whom Fourcroy, Vauquelin, Prout, Liebig, Dumas, Boussingault, and Mulder were foremost before 1850, saw no reason for supposing that fats underwent any chemical change within the digestive tract. It was recognized that foods contain fats and oils, as also do the bodies of animals. It seemed apparent that food fat was absorbed and deposited in the body without undergoing chemical change. Thomas Thomson (39), writing in 1843 on the processes of digestion, said nothing of any change in fat ingested with the food. In 1846 Simon (40), in a two-volume work on animal chemistry, stated that no one could state with any degree of certainty what part the pancreatic fluid performed in digestion.

C. G. Lehmann (41), writing in his comprehensive work on animal chemistry (1855), examined all the evidence which microscopic examination of the walls of the intestinal tract revealed, during fasting and after ingestion of fatty food, and arrived at the following conclusions:

1. Fats taken with the food are unaltered in the stomach, and are not absorbed into the walls of that organ.
2. During digestion in the duodenum and small intestine the lacteal vessels in the wall, which were clear before, become filled with fat globules. Certain cells in the vicinity of the lacteals take in fat globules. In the duodenum fat is emulsified to fine droplets.
3. The transition of fat from the intestine to the lacteals was, he said, "controversial and obscure because the animal body is everywhere permeated by an aqueous fluid, and fats are absolutely insoluble in water and aqueous solutions. Accordingly they cannot undergo diffusion in the ordinary sense of the word . . . the irresistible evidence of daily experience demonstrates that oily fluids cannot penetrate through membranes moistened with water."
4. "Viewing the case chemically, we may say that the fats are . . . easily decomposable; but . . . that stronger reagents are necessary for this decomposition than we are accustomed to find in the intestine. A closer investigation shows us that the fat found in the lacteals is in precisely the same condition as that which is contained in the chyme, and, consequently, that the assumption that the fat is decomposed during its resorption through the lacteals is inadmissible." He went on to say that the evidence supported the view that certain special cells in each of the intestinal villi are solely devoted to the absorption of fat. He referred to the then recent studies of Bidder and Schmidt (42) which showed the importance of bile in emulsifying fat in the intestine, but affirmed that emulsification of fat was not sufficient to enable the droplets to pass a moist (water) membrane.

Claude Bernard (43), one of the greatest experimenters among the 19th century physiologists, discovered that pancreatic juice performed some function which is indispensable for the absorption of fat. This he conceived to be digestion of fat into glycerine and fatty acid, the latter forming soaps, soluble in water and capable of passing the water-permeated membrane of the intestinal villi. He observed the formation of crystals of "margaric acid" in a mixture of pancreatic fluid and fat. There was vigorous controversy over Bernard's assertion, but his views were eventually accepted. The pancreas contributes to fat digestion by secreting a lipase.

The Controversy Over Synthesis of Fat from Carbohydrate in the Body

There was an obstinate controversy, which began in the year 1843 and was maintained through the following decade, between the French and German investigators of animal nutrition over the question whether the animal body could convert carbohydrates to fats. Dumas and Boussingault (44), Persoz (45), Payen, and Gasparin (46), endeavored to show by direct experiments that herbivorous animals take enough fat with their food to supply their needs for fattening and for milk production, and that, accordingly, the animal organism had no need for generating fat and was incapable of doing so. Liebig and his students maintained that the opposite was true, basing their conclusions on the same kinds of observations. They found that certain animals contained more fat and discharged larger quantities in their milk and excreta than they had obtained in their food; thus Liebig was led to the conclusion that the body must be able to form fat from other substances. A point on which the two schools of thought differed was their definition of fat. The French chemists considered as fats all the substances which could be extracted from foods by ether, while Liebig insisted that only the substances in the ether-soluble matter from foods were fats which possessed all the properties of fats, thus excluding wax, chlorophyll, the bile residues in the feces, etc., all of which entered into the calculations of the French workers. Liebig further supported his views by the results of experiments by Huber, and later by Grundelach (47), which appeared to show that when bees were fed only sugar they were capable of generating wax. But Dumas and Milne-Edwards (48) convinced themselves by experiments that bees cannot survive long when given only sugar to eat; however, when given honey, which contains some wax, they remained healthy and capable of producing wax. The controversy was eventually ended by Boussingault (49) and Persoz (50) who by repeated experiments with pigs, ducks, and cows, proved the correctness of Liebig's view.

The physiological value of fat deposits within and under the skin as an insulator against heat loss from the body, and the usefulness of fat deposits as preventors of friction between muscles, were noted by the early physiologists. The general considerations of the fatness and leanness of men and animals, under different conditions, physiological or pathological, led to the conception that a special administrator under the title of "vital force" caused the body, in times of plenty, to store up fat as a source of fuel to be used in seasons of scarcity.

Liebig propounded the view that fats serve mainly to "the excitement and maintenance of animal heat." He conceived nutrients in animal nutrition to be of two classes: plastic nutrient substances, and food for respiration, the former derived from the albuminous, or nitrogenous, and the latter comprising carbohydrates and fats. Liebig did not entertain so crude a view of the respiratory phenomenon as actually to assert that fuel foods were simply absorbed into the blood and there burned like oil in a lamp or coal in a steam engine. But many physiologists of his time believed he regarded the production of heat in the body as too independent of other bodily processes. It was impossible in his era to comprehend the intricacies of metabolic phenomena. He founded a new era in physiological and pathological chemistry, and in great measure, owing to his aphoristic mode of stating his ideas, which greatly over-simplified physiological phenomena, he aroused in others interest and aggressiveness to formulate better experimental techniques for the purpose of deciding the soundness of his views. Oversimplification has been the characteristic weakness of scientists of every generation.

While physiologists considered fats as friction-reducing deposits around the various organs, and as insulators of the body against cold, nutrition investigators long followed the teaching of Liebig, who regarded fat as fuel food for maintaining body temperature at the normal level. At the end of the 19th century the idea prevailed that fats and carbohydrates, in equivalent caloric quantities, were interchangeable in metabolism. This suggested that fats were not essential in the diet.

In 1913 evidence was brought forward to demonstrate that certain fats carried a hitherto-unsuspected nutrient, later called vitamin A. Experimental inquiry seemed for a short time to support the idea that fats were essential only as carriers of this newly-discovered factor. It was not until 1929 that Burr and Burr showed beyond question that certain highly unsaturated fatty acids are indispensable nutrients. In their absence profound malnutrition of a characteristic type supervened. This outstanding discovery will be discussed more fully in a later chapter.

REFERENCES

1. Lucas, A.: Ancient Egyptian Materials and Industries. 3rd ed. London, 1948.
2. Bryan, C. P.: The Papyrus Ebers, p. 153.
3. Breasted, J. H.: The Edwin Smith Surgical Papyrus, I, p. 100.
4. Haller, A. von: Elementa Physiologie. (1757–1760).
5. Darcet, J. P. J., Lefevre and Pelletier: Cited by Fourcroy, Elements of Chemistry, Edinburgh, 1800, Vol. 3, p. 139.
6. Dioscorides, Pedacious: *De materia medica libri quinque.* Cited from Kremers and Urdang; History of Pharmacy, 2nd ed. 1951, p. 21.
6a. Fourcroy, A.: Elements of Chemistry (1800) 3 vols. Vol. 3, p. 136.
7. Vogel, F. C. R.: Ann. de chim. 58 (1806); Philos. Mag. *26,* 72 (1806).
8. Senebier, J.: Ann. de chim. *11,* 89 (1791).
9. Chevreul, M. E.: Annales de chimie *88,* 225 (1814); *Recherches chimiques sur les corps gras d'origine animale* (1823).
10. Scheele, C. W.: Opusc. ii, 189; Collected Papers of C. W. Scheele, Trans. by L. Dobbin, London (1931).
11. Thomson, T.: Animal Chemistry (1843) p. 135.
12. Berthelot, M.: Ann. de chim. et de phys. (3) *41,* 432 (1854); Chimie organique fondée sur la synthèse. 2 vols. (1860).
13. Redtenbacher, J.: Liebig's Ann. *47,* 113 (1843).
14. Fourcroy, A. F.: Elements of Chemistry, 5th ed. 3 vols. 1800 Edinburgh, Vol. 3, p. 133.
15. Poutet, J. J. E.: Ann. de chim. et de phys. (2) *12,* (1819).
16. Boudet, F. H.: Liebig's Ann. *4,* 1 (1832).
17. Varrentrapp, F.: Liebig's Ann. *35,* 196 (1840).
18. Gottlieb: Ann. de Chem. u.d. Pharm. *57,* 37–67 (1846).

19. Davy, E.: Philos. Mag. *59*, 208–210 (1822).
20. Mills and Snodgrass: J. Soc. Chem. Ind. *2*, 435 (1883).
21. Wijs, J. J. A.: Zeitschr. f. angew. Chem. *11*, 291 (1898).
22. Braconnot, H.: Annales de Chemie *93*, (March, 1815); Ann. Philos. *6*, 156 (1815).
23. Traill, T. S.: Ann. of Philos. (New Series) *5*, 197 (1823).
24. Neumann, C.: The Chemical Works of Gaspard Neumann. Trans. into English by W. Lewis (1760).
25. Rouelle, H. M.: Cited from Thomas Thomson. System of Chemistry (1804), Vol. 4, p. 363.
26. John, J. F.: Chemische Tabellen der Pflanzenanalysen. Nürnberg (1814).
27. Chevreul, M. E.: Annales de Chimie *88*, 225 (1814); Philos. Mag. *44*, 29 and 193 (1814).
28. Brodie: Philos. Mag. 33, 217 (1948).
29. Gobley, N. T.: Journ. de pharm et de chim. *6*, (3) 25, 26 (1844); *9*, 81–91, 161 (1846).
30. Strecker, A.: Ann. de Chem. u. Pharm. *148*, 77–80 (1868).
31. MacLean, H.: Zeitschr. f. physiol. Chem. *57*, 304 (1908).
32. Trier, G.: Zeitschr. f. physiol. Chem. *73*, 383–88; *76*, 496–98 (1912); *86*, 1–32 (1913).
33. Thudichum, J. L. W.: Chemical News *31*, 112, 113 (1875); Die Chemische Konstitution des Gehirns des Menschen und der Thiere. Tübingen (1901) p. xii, 339.
    Thudichum and Kingzett: Ber. d. d. Chem. Gesell *9*, 950 (1876).
34. Zadik, H.: Arch. ges. Physiol. *77*, 1–21 (1899).
35. Macquer, P. J.: A Dictionary of Chemistry, containing the Theory and Practice of that Science: Its Application to Natural Philosophy, Natural History, Medicine, and Animal Economy, 3 vols. Trans. from the French to English, London, 1777.
36. Benecke, F. W.: Liebig's Ann. *122*, 249 (1861).
37. Hesse, O.: Liebig's Ann. *192*, 175 (1878): *228*, 273 (1885); *211*, 283 (1882).
38. Tanret, C.: J. Pharm. Chim. (5) *19*, 225 (1889).
39. Thomson, T.: Animal Chemistry (1843) pp. 586–604.
40. Simon, J. F.: Animal Chemistry, with Special Reference to the Physiology and Pathology of Man. Trans. by G. E. Day. 2 vols. London, 1846, Vol. 2, p. 17.

41. Lehmann, C. G.: Physiological Chemistry, 2nd ed. Trans. by G. E. Day, Edited by R. E. Rogers, 2 vols. Philadelphia, 1855, Vol. 2, pp. 402–405.

42. Bidder, F. and Schmidt, C.: Die Verdauungssaefte und der Stoffwechsel. Mitau (1852) pp. 215–234.

43. Bernard, C.: Compt. rend. *28,* 960 (1849).

44. Dumas, J. B. A. and Boussingault, J. B.: Ann. de chim. et de phys. (3) *12,* 152 (1844).

45. Persoz, J. F.: Compt. rend. *18,* 245 (1843).

46. Payen, A. and Gasparin: Compt. rend. *18,* 797 (1843).

47. Huber and Grundelach: Cited from C. G. Lehmann (Ref. 41) Vol. 1, p. 229; also Playfair, L.: Philos. Mag. (3) *23,* 281 (1843).

48. Dumas, J. B. A. and Milne-Edwards, H.: Ann. de chim. et de phys. (3) *14,* 400 (1845).

49. Boussingault, J. B.: Compt. rend. *20,* 1726 (1844).

50. Persoz, J. F.: Compt. rend. *21,* 20 (1844).

4

Knowledge of Albuminous Substances

THE EARLY CHEMISTS who sought to learn something of the nature of vegetable and animal substances submitted their samples to destructive distillation. Paracelsus (1493–1541) (1) founded a new school of chemists whose ambition was to prepare medicines by their art instead of seeking to discover the "elixir of life" and the philosophers' stone which could transmute baser metals into gold. In his *De Natura Rerum* (Of the Nature of Things) he said: "The separation of those things that grow from the earth and are easily combustible, as all fruits, herbs, flowers, leaves, grass, roots, wood, etc., takes place in many ways. Thus by distillation is separated from them, first, the phlegm, then the mercury, and the oily parts; third, the resin; fourth, the sulfur, and fifth, the salts, which remain. When this separation has taken place by the chemical arts, there are found many splendid and powerful remedies for internal and external use."

Chemists heated organic materials in a closed retort so that air was in great measure excluded, the degree of heat being progressively raised to keep distillate coming over as the more stable substances were decomposed into simpler and more volatile ones. This procedure was applied during the 17th and 18th centuries to many hundreds of plant products by chemists with the motives of the apothecary. In discussing the analysis of vegetable bodies in 1804 Thomas Thomson (2) (1773–1852), professor at Glasgow and distinguished investigator and historian of chemistry, said: "The older chemists confined their analysis to destructive distillation. By this process they obtained the same products from every vegetable. For every plant, when distilled, yields water, oil, acid, carburetted hydrogen (marsh gas), and carbonic acid gas; while a residuum of charcoal remains in the retort."

Analysis of Animal Substances by Distillation

The pioneer in this field of inquiry was Johann Conrad Dippel (1673–1734) a German physician, chemist and mystic, who won a place in history by his discovery of the dye Prussian blue, and his subsistence by the preparation and sale of Dippel's "animal oil," labelled by the apothecaries *oleum empyreumaticum animale.* This preparation was formed by destructive distillation of bones and other animal substances. It was a complex mixture containing much pyridine and pyridine derivatives, and was used as an antiseptic. The analysis of animal matter was described in 1777 by P. J. Macquer (1718–1784), professor of medicine and chemistry at the University of Paris, in his famous dictionary (3) as follows: "At first a pure phlegm, with a degree of heat not exceeding that of boiling water; then a volatile alkaline spirit, which becomes more and more penetrating and strong; a fetid, light thin oil, then a concrete volatile salt (ammonium carbonate) which forms ramifications upon the sides of the receiver, much air, and a fetid oil, which becomes more and more black and thick; and lastly, it leaves in the retort a considerable quantity of almost incombustible coal, from which, after incineration, scarcely any alkali can be obtained." There was nothing of value to physiologists in the results of such analyses of vegetable and animal substances.

Papin's Digestor

Denis Papin (1647–1712) was a French physicist and one of the inventors of the steam engine. His chief claim to fame was his invention of his famous "steam digestor," a vessel with a tightly fitting lid which prevented steam generated in it from escaping, thus generating high pressure by superheated steam. It was equipped with a safety valve, and was the earliest design of a pressure cooker. His chief purpose in designing the instrument was for softening bones in order to extract gelatin from them. Chemists were at once interested in it and soon all sorts of materials were treated with super-heated steam and the end-products were examined. Hitherto, vegetable and animal substances had not been subjected to hydrolytic cleavage, except cartilage in the formation of gelatin by boiling meat or bones. A sample of meat, when boiled with successive portions of water, yields a quota of gelatin, and the quantity secured from successive treatments rapidly decreases, without marked decrease in the material as compared with the original sample remaining when the broth is removed. This showed that only a small part of flesh or bone is convertible into gelatin by boiling with water. When, however, animal substances were treated with super-heated steam in Papin's digestor all kinds of tissues distinguished by anatomists were converted into what superficially resembled gelatin, both when in concentrated glue-like solutions and when dry.

Jelly

Pliny used the term *albumen* to denote the white of egg. Macquer, in the second edition of his dictionary (1777), did not use the term, but did employ the word *albuminous* to include animal substances which coagulate on heating (egg-white, blood serum) and to "animal matter" generally. In his article on *Jelly,* Macquer asserted that the bodies of animals seemed to be chiefly composed of gelatinous matter, since when treated in Papin's digestor, flesh, bones, membranes, tendons, nerves, horn, skin, etc., yield, upon evaporation of most of the water, a liquor which on cooling is a true jelly. "If the evaporation be continued until the matter be dry, but with a heat incapable of decomposing the jelly, it forms first a glue, and afterwards a horny substance, more or less transparent, hard, and solid. The blood, lymph, and seminal fluids of animals are scarcely anything but pure gelatinous matter. Milk contains a large quantity of it."

The famous Swiss physiologist, Albrecht von Haller (1708–1777) (4), in his extensive compilations of existing knowledge published between 1757 and 1765, expressed the belief that half of the animal body is composed of jelly. In 1791 George Fordyce, of the faculty of the College of Physicians in London (5), who employed the term *mucilage* to designate the jelly formed from animal matter in the digestor, concurred in the belief that blood, white of egg, skin, tendon, muscle, mucous membrane, and cartilage are the same substance, modified by being combined with different proportions of water. He further stated that "mucilage," identical with that which occurred in animal matter, was also found in vegetable products, especially in seeds. Macquer said (3), "Hence we ought to conclude that the gelatinous matter of animals is the true animal substance. It constitutes almost entirely the bodies of animals; it is that which nourishes, repairs, and reproduces them; it is in the animal kingdom what mucilage is in the vegetable kingdom, from which it seems to be derived, and which it resembles in many ways in its properties."

"Animalized Matter" in Vegetable Substances

In 1742 I. B. Beccari (6) asserted that ". . . if we except the spiritual and immortal part of our being, and if we take only into consideration our bodies, it must be true that we are composed of the same substances which serve as our nourishment." From his subsequent remarks it is obvious that he considered the glutenous part of flour to be peculiarly of an animal, and the starch of a vegetable nature; for when distilled, the gluten, he said, "affords principles similar to those of all animals, while the starchy part yields products similar to those of all vegetables." In his view Thomas Thomson concurred in 1843 (7) when he stated that "animals are principally formed from the glutenous or albuminous principles of vegetables." Beccari noted that when wheat gluten was kept in water it underwent putrefaction like animal substances.

From very early times mankind had been familiar with the spontaneous effervescing fermentation of fruit juices to form wine, and of cereal decoctions or extracts of sprouted (malted) grains to form beer. The rising of bread dough in panary fermentation, set up by a little leaven, was another example. So also was the spontaneous non-effervescent conversion of wine into vinegar. The earliest characteristic of substances of animal origin observed by chemists was putrefaction, with its attendant fetid odor. The cause of this unwholesome decomposition was, in 1843, a complete mystery. The cause of fermentation of sweet or farinaceous preparations was quite unknown until 1837 when Charles Cagniard de Latour observed under the microscope the budding of yeast cells, which showed yeast to be a living organism, and concluded that fermentation was due to its activity. Following this discovery Schwann tried to demonstrate that putrefaction and fermentation were due not to the oxygen of the air as some believed, but to minute living elements in the air which could be destroyed by heating. The subject of the spontaneous decomposition of organic materials was cleared up dramatically by the genius of Pasteur.

Discovery of Albuminous Substances in Seeds Other Than Wheat

In 1806 Vauquelin and Fourcroy (8) reported a study on germination and fermentation of various farinaceous substances. They frequently used the terms gluten, sugar, farinaceous, saccharo-acid, and starch. They employed infusion of nut-galls (tannin), and alcohol for precipitating "animal matter," and acetic acid for dissolving "animal matter" from residues after the starch had been washed out from cereal meals. They reported the first extensive analysis of barley in which they stated that, in addition to sugar, starch, oil, lime, magnesia, silica, and iron, the grain contained "animal matter" partly soluble in acetic acid, and partly consisting of insoluble glutenous flakes.

Vauquelin and Fourcroy also studied beans, and found them to contain starch and also much animal matter which burnt like horn and was precipitated by nut galls, mercuric, or silver nitrate, lead acetate, and by prussiate of potash. This analysis explained, they said, why beans putrefy so easily "and become infectious"; why beans are so nourishing, and "susceptible of filling the place of all other foods"; why when cooked with the skins on, they are better preserved; and why this article yields at once the aliment, the basis, and the materials proper to form and color the blood and to nourish the bones." No previous analyses of foods and no philosophical speculations on the essentials of an adequate diet were so extensive and profound as were those of Vauquelin and Fourcroy.

At the beginning of the 19th century casein of milk, blood fibrin, white of egg, gelatin, and the coagulum formed on heating blood serum were recognized by chemists as distinct substances, but nothing was known concerning their chemical natures.

Fecula

The term *fecula* was much used by the earliest chemists who investigated vegetable materials. It was never used in an exact sense, and there was no general agreement as to what was meant by it. It was generally applied to the insoluble vegetable fibers which passed into the juice when it was pressed out. But H. M. Rouelle applied the term to the insoluble substances which coagulated from plant juices when the latter were allowed to stand or were heated. These materials he identified with "albuminous" or "animalized" substance. Joseph Louis Proust (1754–1826) wrote in 1803 a memoir on "fecula" (9). Proust, director of the Royal Laboratory at Madrid, is known for his establishment, by numerous analyses, of the law of definite composition of compound chemical substances. It was he who laid the foundation for the law of multiple proportions later promulgated by Dalton. In his memoir on fecula he told of the confusion of thought concerning its nature. He said it must partake of the nature of wool, silk, etc., because when kept in water for a time it "exhales excrementicious putridity." This remark identified his particular samples of fecula with albuminous substances of plants. But as late as 1818 H. A. Vogel (10) presented before the Royal Academy of Sciences at Munich an analysis of farina of wheat, in which he used the term fecula to denote starch.

The Earliest Chemical Distinction Between Proteins

In 1811 Berthollet (11) set a new pattern for determining quantitative differences between proteins when he distilled weighed samples of meat and of old cheese, and collected and measured the amounts of ammonia which distilled over. He found the ratio of ammonia in the samples to be as 19 : 24. It was many years before this type of analysis, in modified form, was applied to individual proteins as a means of discovering their differences in composition.

Of much greater significance was the communication of Braconnot (12) in 1820 of a paper entitled "On the conversion of animal matter into a new substance by the action of sulfuric acid." He called attention to his earlier discovery that by treatment with mineral acid he converted various kinds of vegetable materials into sugar and gum, and said he had resolved to extend the method to animal matter. He dissolved twelve grams of glue (from gelatin) in sulfuric acid, and after some hours diluted the concentrated acid with water and heated the solution for twenty hours. He then neutralized the acid with chalk, filtered off the calcium sulfate formed, and evaporated the filtrate to a syrup. On standing there were formed crystals which he separated and found to have a sweet taste. He called the new substance *sugar of gelatin.* Purified by recrystallization, it tasted nearly as sweet as grape sugar. It was more soluble in water than grape sugar, but less soluble than milk sugar. Braconnot added yeast to the substance in solution and found that it did not ferment. When he heated it strongly the new substance puffed up and gave a fetid smell like that of animal matter. When rubbed with strong potash, ammonia was evolved. Thus, Braconnot had discovered how to prepare an amino acid (glycine) from a protein by acid hydrolysis.

In the same year he described crystals of another kind which he obtained by hydrolyzing muscle tissue, and also wool, with sulfuric acid, and proceeding with the neutralized solution as he had done with glue. From the acid-free solution evaporated to a syrup he secured crystals which did not taste sweet, but gave all of the tests for animal matter which were given by sugar of gelatin. This amino acid he called *leucine* (Greek, *leukos,* white).

The Discovery of Tyrosine

The discovery of a third amino acid as a product of protein decomposition was made twenty-six years after the investigations of Braconnot on sugar of gelatin (glycine) and leucine. In the year 1846 Liebig (13) fused washed curds of milk (casein) with an equal weight of potash, then dissolved the fusion mixture and acidified it with acetic acid. A white crystalline substance separated, which he called *tyrosine* (from *tyros,* Greek for cheese). Liebig did not attempt to study carefully the new substance. F. Bopp, in Liebig's laboratory in 1849, described an extended study of methods for preparing tyrosine and came to the conclusion that hydrolysis of proteins of various origin with hydrochloric acid was the best method. He showed that the new amino acid could be prepared from any of the proteins then recognized. He showed that the neutralized solution after hydrolysis of proteins yielded crystals of both tyrosine and leucine.

The Millon Reaction for Proteins

In 1849 Millon (14) reported that albuminous substances, when treated with a reagent made by dissolving mercury in fuming nitric acid and diluting with water, gave when heated, a brick-red precipitate. Gelatin did not give the reaction unless contaminated with protein. It was not until 1879 that O. Nasse (15) discovered that pure tyrosine gave the reaction with Millon's reagent, and that the test given by proteins was due to the presence of this amino acid. Since gelatin gave a negative test it was concluded that it contained no tyrosine.

Sulfur in Proteins

It was Scheele (16) who showed sulfur to be a constituent of proteins. Using white of egg and milk curd, he identified sulfur by the blackening of silver when these substances were heated on this metal with caustic potash.

Discovery of Cystine

The first sulfur-containing amino acid was prepared in 1810 by Wollaston (17) who found it to be the principal constituent of a urinary calculus. Cystine was first isolated from a protein hydrolysate in 1899 by K. A. H. Mörner (18).

The Studies of Mulder on Albuminous Substances

The experimental studies on albuminous substances related in previous pages of this chapter left the problem of their structure unsettled and puzzling. G. J. Mulder (1802–1880), a Dutch chemist, was the first to propose a theory concerning the causes of the differences between albumin, fibrin, and casein, and other substances more or less similar to them in physical properties and in their chemical behavior toward reagents (19). Analyses of these substances showed that their percentage composition with respect to carbon, hydrogen, nitrogen, and oxygen were so similar as to suggest that they contained one common radical.

The proteins with which he worked all contained sulfur, and apparently all were contaminated with some inorganic phosphate. Mulder treated samples of albumen, fibrin, and casein with water containing 0.25 to 0.5 per cent of caustic potash and dissolved them by heating at 60 to 80 degrees for one hour. He found, as others before him had found, that potassium sulfide was formed from sulfur disengaged from the samples. On acidifying the solutions with acetic acid, there were formed precipitates of gelatinous nature, which appeared to be identical, and were of essentially the same elementary composition. Mulder believed that they were identical, and that they represented a common radical which, at the suggestion of Berzelius, he called *protein* and which he designated by the symbol $\overline{Pr}$. But the sulfur and phosphorus content of his preparations differed, and he concluded that the differences between them derived from the different proportions of sulfur, or of sulfur and phosphorus with which the common radical was combined. He postulated the existence of compounds of *protein* with "sulphamide," H_2NS, and "phosphamide," H_2NP, and therefore designated the albuminous substances *protein compounds*. To *protein* he assigned the empirical formula C_{40} H_{31} N_5 O_{12}. Mulder's analyses of the several well-known *protein compounds* were soon confirmed by Sherer in Liebig's laboratory and by

Dumas in France, and for a few years his view seemed to be established as the most useful concept available for understanding the nature and origin of albuminous substances.

Mulder's method of showing the composition of protein bodies is illustrated by the following:

Albumen of blood	$= 10\ \overline{Pr} + S_2\ P$	Arterial membrane	$= \overline{Pr} + 2HO$
Albumen of egg	$= 10\ \overline{Pr} + S\ P$	Mucus	$= \overline{Pr} + 3HO$
Fibrin	$= 10\ \overline{Pr} + S\ P$	Chondrin	$= \overline{Pr} + 4HO + 2\ O$
Casein	$= 10\ \overline{Pr} + S$	Horny tissue	$= \overline{Pr} + NH_3 + 3\ O$
Globulin	$= 15\ \overline{Pr} + S$	Gelatinous tissue	$=$
Muscular flesh	$= \overline{Pr} + HO + H$		$2\ \overline{Pr} + 3\ NH_3 + HO + 7\ O$

Liebig accepted the views of Mulder concerning the existence of a common radical, *protein,* in all the different albuminous substances then known. For want of a better guide, physiologists and chemists adopted the definitions, nomenclature, and speculations concerning structure proposed by Mulder, and for a decade or more they were the common basis for discussion of the mechanism of certain nutritional phenomena. But after 1830 discoveries of fundamental significance followed one another in rapid succession, and some of these were of kinds which led to new viewpoints concerning the chemistry of albuminous substances.

The Theoretical Significance of the Discovery of Amygdalin

In 1830 Robiquet and Boutron-Charlard (20) carried out a remarkable study on bitter almonds. For years a small industry was based on distilling the marc remaining in the press after expression of the bland fixed oil of almonds, which is a fatty oil. The marc, when treated with water and distilled, yielded volatile oil of bitter almonds (benzaldehyde) which was used for perfuming soap. Pierre Jean Robiquet (1780–1840) was an apothecary and professor of pharmacy in Paris. He was also the owner of a chemical works, and in 1805 published an account of his isolation of asparagine from the juice of asparagus (21). His researches on bitter almonds show him to have been a genius in chemical experimentation. Two years before Liebig and Wöhler studied oil of bitter almonds, he had digested it with potash in contact with air and observed the formation of potassium benzoate. He showed that the oil absorbed ammonia to form a solid substance which retained its ammonia when dried. He also produced benzoic acid by the action of nitric acid on the oil. These facts were available to Liebig and Wöhler when they began their epoch-making investigations on the benzoyl radical which revealed the methods by which this could be converted into benzoic acid, benzoyl chloride, benzoyl cyanide, and benzamide. These researches formed an event of the first importance in the history of organic chemistry. But Robiquet's studies of the behavior of the marc of almonds had already set a new standard for biochemical investigations. Robiquet and Boutron-Charlard asserted that oil of bitter almonds did not exist in the fruit, but was formed during the process of distillation. This conclusion was based on the following observations: When the marc was digested with ether no volatile bitter almond oil was dissolved out. But when it was digested with water, and then extracted with ether, the oil was present in this solvent. Volatile oil of bitter almonds must, they concluded, have been set free from some source during the digestion of the marc with water.

They also found that if the marc was first extracted with ether, then with alcohol, and then with water, no volatile oil was to be detected in any of the three preparations. But the alcohol used in the extraction was found to contain a substance in solution which crystallized, and to this they gave the name amygdalin. They noted that, when heated, it swelled and gave the odor of caramel, suggesting the presence of sugar. When heated with caustic potash it gave out a strong smell of ammonia, indicating that it contained nitrogen. When treated with nitric acid benzoic acid was formed. They overlooked the opportunity to digest amygdalin with the water extract. This was done by Liebig and Wöhler who discovered that there was present in the aqueous solution a ferment, amygdalase, which hydrolyzed amygdalin to volatile oil of bitter almonds, and hydrocyanic acid. The demonstration that amygdalin is a conjugated substance which is readily cleaved into simple derivatives had profound effect on the thinking of chemists. The principle was soon to be illustrated by other examples.

Thus in 1845 Piria (22) described salicin (salicyl alcohol glucoside) from willow bark, and, in 1852, (23) populin (benzoyl salicin) from the bark and leaves of poplar. In 1849 A. Wurtz (24) (1817–1884) accidentally discovered the aliphatic amines by the action of alkali on cyanic and cyanuric esters. In 1850 A. W. Hofmann (25), by the action of ethyl halide upon ammonia, synthesized ethyl, diethyl, and triethylamines. Wurtz (26), in 1850, secured methylamine from casein by treatment with alkali, and Rochleder (27) achieved this by treating casein with chlorine. These observations led to the proposal that methylamine was a proximate constituent of casein.

In 1849 C. G. Lehmann (28), in his comprehensive treatise on physiological chemistry, stated that the discoveries of glucosides and primary amines had great influence in broadening the chemists' conceptions concerning the structure of albuminous substances (p. 293, vol. I), and led scientists to discard Mulder's views as scientific fiction.

Efforts to Study Oxidation of Proteins

It has been mentioned that the early chemists who subjected various albuminous substances to destructive distillation were unable to distinguish any differences in the products of decomposition, hence they believed them to be alike.

Schlieper (29) in 1846, and Guckelberger (30) in 1858, were the first to study the products formed by the action of strong oxidizing chemicals on casein, egg white, fibrin, etc. They hydrolyzed proteins by means of sulfuric acid to which oxidizing agents such as manganese dioxide and potassium dichromate were added. They identified in all cases, among the substances which distilled over, most of the fatty acids of the acetic series, together with valeronitrile, hydrocyanic acid, certain aldehydes, and benzoic acid. They further stated that the distillate from gelatin obtained by their method was characterized by yielding much less acetic acid than did fibrin, and very little "hydride of benzoyl" (benzophenone), whereas gelatin yielded much more valerianic acid than did any of the proteins examined. While the results achieved by Schlieper and Guckelberger clearly demonstrated that the proteins which they compared differed to a marked degree in their yields of certain simple chemicals formed by hydrolysis and oxidation, their technic was not searching enough to hold promise of revealing much useful information about proteins; therefore this procedure fell into disuse.

A Feeding Study Which Revealed Differences in Nutritive Values of Proteins

The earliest animal experiment which clearly showed that proteins from cereal and legume seeds differed in value was made by Lawes and Gilbert at Rothamsted, England in 1854 (30a). They fed two pigs closely similar in weight and condition, *ad libitum,* one on lentil meal (containing 4 per cent of nitrogen) and the other on barley meal (containing 2 per cent of nitrogen). After the animals had been restricted to these diets "for a certain time," a nitrogen excretion study was made on each during a three-day period, and later during a ten-day period. The amounts of nitrogen contained in their food was estimated from the record of food ingested, and the output of urea in the urine was determined. The result was that the pig fed the lentil meal excreted more than twice as much urea-N. as did the one fed barley meal. It was evident that the pigs on these two sources of protein retained very different percentages of their food protein for conversion into body protein. Nevertheless, this highly significant experiment did not fire the imagination of nutrition investigators. It was not until about fifty years later that investigations on experimental animals verified the prediction (based on chemical evidence of great differences in yields of ammonia, the three basic amino acids, arginine, histidine and lysine, and the distribution of two types of sulfur in protein molecules of different species) that proteins so different chemically must also differ in nutritive value.

Measurement of the Ammonia Formed on Protein Hydrolysis

In 1872 O. Nasse (31) stated that R. Thiele had measured the ammonia which was disengaged when proteins were boiled with alkali. Nasse made a thorough study of this method and broke new ground in differentiating the several proteins at that time available. His method was to boil a weighed sample of protein with barium hydroxide and collect the ammonia evolved in standard acid solution for measurement. He found that under his conditions there was quickly evolved about double the amount of ammonia from egg albumen as was obtained from an equal weight of gelatin. After the early rapid evolution there was a prolonged but very slow formation of ammonia from both sources when boiling with the reagent was continued. Successive experiments with coagulated egg white yielded 0.198, 0.184, and 0.187 per cent of ammonia. He published the following table, which clearly showed that there must be great differences in the chemical composition of proteins.

Ammonia yielded by proteins on boiling with alkali

	Per cent of total N.
Casein	11.2
Blood albumen	15.2
Gluten (wheat)	19.4
Serum protein	18.7
Legumin (Pea)	19.5
Fibrin (blood)	20.25
Gelatin	3.35
Muscle syntonin	8.32

Discovery of the Basic Amino Acids

In 1886 Schulze and Steiger (32) observed that a copious precipitate was produced by the addition of a solution of phosphotungstic acid to an extract of germinating lupine seeds. On decomposing this with barium hydroxide they succeeded in isolating the basic amino acid arginine from the filtrate of barium phosphotungstate.

In 1889 Drechsel (33) isolated another basic amino acid, lysine, from the phosphotungstic acid precipitates obtained from acid-hydrolysis products of proteins. In 1896 Kossel (34), professor of biochemistry at Heidelberg, and Hedin (35), professor at Upsala, independently discovered a third basic amino acid, histidine, in the phosphotungstic acid precipitate. The use of this reagent for separating basic amino acids from the acid and amphoteric amino acids marked an important step in the discovery of the great variation among proteins in their yields of total basic constituents, and of the individual basic amino acids which enter into the constitution of proteins from various sources.

In 1900 Hausmann (36), a pupil of Drechsel, combined in principle the idea of Nasse for estimating the ammonia formed on hydrolysis of a protein with precipitation of basic amino acids according to the procedure introduced by Kossel. Hausmann devised a method for determining the nitrogen distribution in respect to ammonia nitrogen (acid amide groups), basic amino acids (arginine, histidine, and lysine), and monoamino acid nitrogen (by difference between total nitrogen and the nitrogen in the combined ammonia and basic

HAUSMANN'S TABLE

In 100 of total nitrogen	*Amide-N forming NH_3 on acid hydrolysis*	*Diamino acid-N (arginine, histidine, lysine)*	*Monoamino-acid-N*
Egg albumen	8.53	21.33	67.80
Serum globulin	8.90	24.95	68.28
Casein	13.37	11.71	75.98
Gelatin	1.61	35.83	62.56
Edestin (hemp seed)	10.08	31.70	57.83

amino acid fractions). He hydrolyzed with acid a sample of protein, filtered off any dark, insoluble "humin," and after neutralizing the filtrate and adding an excess of magnesia, he distilled and measured the ammonia which passed over. The solution in the flask was acidified and precipitated with phosphotungstic acid, and the basic amino acid phosphotungstates were filtered off for nitrogen estimation. The content of nitrogen left in the solution corresponded to the nitrogen present in the protein as monoamino acids. The following table shows the results obtained by this procedure.

	NH_3-N Per cent	*Basic amino acid -N Per cent*	*Monoamino acid -N Per cent*	*Humin-N Per cent*	*Total N Per cent*
Vegetable proteins					
Phaseolin (bean)	10.74	24.50	62.85	1.79	16.20
Zein (maize)	18.41	3.03	77.50	.99	16.13
Gliadin (rye)	23.78	5.49	70.27	.79	17.66
Legumin (pea)	9.40	28.82	60.27	.94	17.97
Arachin (peanut)	11.10	27.13	60.50	1.2	18.28
Animal proteins					
Egg Albumen	7.51	25.82	65.11	1.61	16.11
Vitellin (egg yolk)	7.67	28.56	62.41	1.36	16.28
Chicken muscle	7.45	29.98	50.85	2.43	16.09
Beef muscle	5.50	27.32	64.52	2.65	16.18

Hausmann's method for showing the types of cleavage products of proteins formed by acid hydrolysis was applied by T. B. Osborne (37) to many isolated and carefully purified proteins. Some of his results are shown in the following table.

THE YIELDS OF BASIC AMINO ACIDS BY PROTEINS

Compiled from analyses by T. B. Osborne and by Abderhalden.

Protein	*Histidine Per cent*	*Arginine Per cent*	*Lysine Per cent*
Globulin (buckwheat)	0.88	23.67	8.61
Edestin (hemp seed)	2.19	14.17	1.65
Globulin (cottonseed)	3.46	13.51	2.06
Gliadin (wheat)	0.58	3.16	1.33
Zein (maize)	0.82	1.35	0.00
Ovovitellin (egg yolk)	1.90	7.46	4.81
Beef muscle	2.66	7.47	7.59
Chicken muscle	2.47	6.50	7.24
Halibut muscle	2.55	6.34	7.45
Egg white albumin	2.17	5.07	6.43
Casein (cow's milk)	2.50	3.81	5.96
Lactalbumin (cow's milk)	2.06	3.23	9.16

Differences in the Sulfur Content of Proteins

In 1898 F. N. Schulze (38) described a method for distinguishing two kinds of sulfur in proteins by estimating what he called "loosely-bound sulfur" and total sulfur. By "loosely-bound sulfur" he meant that part of the sulfur which is liberated as hydrogen sulfide when a protein is hydrolyzed with strong sodium hydroxide. He prevented oxidation of sulfur during the hydrolysis by generating hydrogen in the flask by the action of part of the sodium hydroxide upon zinc dust. After completing the decomposition of the protein by alkali, he acidified the solution and distilled. The hydrogen sulfide which passed over was absorbed in a solution of a lead salt for measuring. By this method Schulze found the ratios between the sulfur which did yield hydrogen sulfide and those which did not. He reported the following values:

In serum albumen	3 : 2	Globin	2 : 0.95
Egg albumen	2 : 0.83	Globulin	2 : 0.91
Hemoglobin	2 : 0.88		

T. B. Osborne (39) employed the Schulze method for examination of proteins from different sources, with the following results:

	Total sulfur Per cent	*Loosely-bound sulfur Per cent*	*Ratio between firmly-bound and loosely-bound sulfur*
Legumin (pea)	0.358	0.165	1 : 1
Oxy-Hb. (horse)	0.390	0.190	1 : 1
Globin (horse)	0.420	0.200	1 : 1
Vignin (pea)	0.426	0.214	1 : 1
Amandin (date)	0.429	0.217	1 : 1
Oxy-Hb. (man)	0.568	0.335	1 : 2
Zein (maize)	0.600	0.212	2 : 1
Glycinin (soybean)	0.710	0.320	2 : 2
Hordein (barley)	0.847	0.348	2 : 2
Edestin (hempseed)	0.884	0.347	2 : 2
Gliadin (wheat)	1.027	0.619	2 : 3
Ovovitellin (egg yolk)	1.028	0.348	3 : 3
Excelsin (Brazil nut)	1.086	0.350	3 : 2
Serum globulin (horse)	1.110	0.630	2 : 3
Fibrin	1.100	0.380	3 : 2
Ovalbumin (egg)	1.616	0.491	5 : 3
Serum albumin (horse)	1.930	1.280	2 : 7

By the end of 1902 a sufficient number of analyses of proteins had been reported by Schulze, Kossel, Hausmann, and Osborne, using the methods described, to demonstrate clearly that proteins must differ widely in their nutritive value. It was a necessary conclusion because of the strongly contrasting composition of their hydrolysis products. Nutrition investigators were soon to test the new viewpoint by studies with animals.

Steps in the Progress in the Preparation of Individual Proteins

The few albuminous substances known to Liebig, Mulder, and their predecessors were those which have already been mentioned in these pages. Being pioneers in the study of substances of great complexity which, when moist, were liable to change during the operations to which they were subjected, these early investigators necessarily dealt with preparations which were rather crude and impure when judged by the criteria later employed by chemists. But after the middle of the 19th century a number of discoveries of great importance were made of technics for separating and purifying individual proteins from the complex mixtures in which they occur in vegetable and animal products. A brief account of these is essential to understanding the changing points of view concerning the nature of the protein element in foods from different sources, and of the problems concerning the utilization of proteins in animal nutrition.

In 1858 Maschke (40) employed the technic of precipitating proteins from aqueous extracts of seeds by passing carbon dioxide into the dilute solutions. Copious precipitates were secured by this method from several kinds of seeds. This was a valuable discovery for separating proteins from accompanying impurities. Maschke was first to report success in crystallizing a protein, viz., the protein later called excelsin, from the Brazil nut (41).

In 1859 Denis (42) called attention to the fact that many proteins of both animal and vegetable origin which did not dissolve in water were soluble in solutions of neutral salts. In 1878 Méhu (43) discovered that proteins are quantitatively precipitated from their aqueous solutions upon saturation with ammonium sulfate, and that they are not coagulated by this treatment. The precipitated proteins secured by Méhu's method were again soluble in water or in neutral salts solution and were unaltered from their native state in natural products. Méhu's discovery was confirmed in 1884 by Heynsius (44). These new methods for manipulating proteins with little or no alteration in their properties were of epoch-making importance. They made possible the discovery that each plant, and even each part of a plant such as a leaf and a seed, contains many proteins, each having unique properties. This was a new and astonishing revelation concerning the make-up of natural products in both the animal and vegetable kingdoms from which physiologists and chemists acquired broader views concerning the chemical processes which form the basis of physiology.

In 1875 and 1877 Weyl (45) applied the method of Denis to the separation of proteins of some common cereal grains. In 1862 Heinrich Ritthausen published the first of a long series of careful studies on the separation, purification, and description of individual proteins from vegetable sources.

Ritthausen (46) was one of the outstanding students trained by Liebig. In 1853, while at the Agricultural Experiment Station at Möckern, he began the study of the constituents of animal feeds; later, at Waldau, he devoted himself to the study of plant proteins, and advanced knowledge of these to a notable degree. His method was to extract the seeds first with water, then, successively, with very dilute acid and alkali solutions. He fractionated the naturally occurring mixture of proteins to an extent far in advance of previous investigations, and showed clearly that there were in seeds many more kinds of proteins than had hitherto been believed. From different seeds he prepared proteins having the same solubility, but he did not attempt to study these in detail to discover whether any distinguishing properties could be found when the proteins were derived from different plants.

Denis and Weyl, both of whom used neutral salt solutions as solvents for water-insoluble proteins, claimed that the techniques they devised subjected the proteins studied to less drastic treatment than did the procedure described by Ritthausen in which dilute alkali was the solvent. In 1876 Weyl criticized Ritthausen's method and brought it into disrepute for a time. Later, highly critical studies by T. B. Osborne compared the products obtained by the several methods and vindicated Ritthausen's procedure.

About 1890 T. B. Osborne, at first with R. H. Chittenden (47), took up the study of seed proteins, and in 1891 reported on the isolation of several proteins from the oat kernel. During a period of about twenty-five years he devoted his attention to studying the constant differences in proteins having similar solubilities in neutral salt solutions of several kinds. He achieved distinction by demonstrating that the number of kinds of proteins in plants (in seeds and leaves, for example) greatly exceed what had been hitherto suspected, and that those of each plant, or part of a plant, are unique in their physical and chemical properties. As new analytical procedures were described by others, which served to reveal distinguishing qualities in proteins, Osborne applied them to his ever-growing list of purified proteins from cereal grains, legume seeds, bean, pea, oil seeds, nuts, etc., and later also those from several animal sources. The results of Osborne's studies, and of those by others who contributed on a lesser scale to investigations in this field, had deep significance in changing the views of chemists and biologists concerning the nature of the processes of animal nutrition.

It has already been mentioned that Braconnot isolated glycine and leucine, and Bopp isolated tyrosine from proteins by employing acid hydrolysates of proteins. This kind of hydrolysis proved to be the most satisfactory one for discovery of other amino acids which enter into the constitution of proteins. The following table (48) shows the progress in discovery of amino acids up to 1935 when twenty-two were recognized.

Amino acid	*Discoverer*	*Year*	*Amino acid*	*Discoverer*	*Year*
Glycine	Braconnot	1820	Cystine	Mörner	1899
Leucine	Braconnot	1820	Valine	Fischer	1901
Tyrosine	Bopp	1849	Proline	Fischer	1901
Serine	Cramer	1865	Tryptophan	Hopkins } Cole }	1901
Glutamic acid	Ritthausen	1866			
Aspartic acid	Ritthausen	1868	Oxyproline	Fischer	1902
Phenylalanine	Schulze } Barbiere }	1881	Isoleucine	Ehrlich	1903
			Thyroxine	Kendall	1915
Alanine	Weyl	1888			
Lysine	Drechsel	1889	Oxyglutamic acid	Dakin	1918
Arginine	Hedin	1895			
Iodogorgonic acid	Drechsel	1896	Methionine	Mueller	1922
			Threonine	Rose	1935
Histidine	Hedin } Kossel }	1896			

The kinds of information given in this chapter concerning the differences in composition of proteins from various sources were of great importance in that they forced upon the attention of investigators, after about 1900, the fact that the problems of protein nutrition were actually problems concerning the kinds and amounts of individual amino acids derived from the digestion of food proteins. This new knowledge outweighed all other accumulated facts about proteins in nutrition between 1900 and about 1915. This was a period when the viewpoints of nutrition investigators were changed by evidence that several inorganic nutrients, hitherto given little attention, and unsuspected organic substances were of fundamental practical importance in the study of nutrition. These will be dealt with in later chapters. Throughout the 19th century investigations along two lines not yet mentioned in these pages posed problems which were only vaguely understood in their chemical aspects even near the end of the century. They stimulated much thought and experimenting about digestion and assimilation of food substances, and the significance of gelatin in animal nutrition. These deserve discussion in separate chapters and will next receive attention.

REFERENCES

1. Paracelsus: *De Natura Rerum;* Cited from Fletcher and Stillman, Science Monthly 6, 167 (1918).
2. Thomson, T.: System of Chemistry, Vol. 4, p. 363 (1804).
3. Macquer, P. J.: Dictionary of Chemistry, London, 1777, 3 vols. Vol. I.
4. Haller, Albrecht von: *Elementa physiologie corporis humani,* Lausanne (1757–66), Vol. 2, p. 152.
5. Fordyce, G.: A Treatise on the Digestion of Food, 2nd ed. London (1791), pp. 46–48.
6. Beccari, I. B.: Note on Beccari of Bologna. By D. R. Thompson, Philos. Mag. 23, 321–326 (1843); *Collection Académique,* Vol. x, p. 1, (1742).
7. Thomson, T.: Philos. Mag. 25 (ser. 3), pp. 321–26 (1843).
8. Vauquelin, L. and Fourcroy, A.: Annales de Muséum d'Histoire Naturelle, Tome vii (1806); Philos. Mag. 25, 176–182 (1806).

9. Proust, J. L.: Memoir on Fecula. Philos. Mag. *17*, p. 22–31 (1803).
10. Vogel, H. A.: Annals of Philos. *11*, 314 (1818).
11. Berthollet, C.: Philos. Mag. 37, 63 (1811).
12. Braconnot, H.: Ann. de chim. et de phys. *13*, 113 (1820).
13. Liebig, J.: Ann. d. Chem. *57*, 127–29 (1846); *62*, 257–369 (1847).
14. Millon, N. A.: Compt. Rend. *28*, 40 (1849).
15. Nasse, O.: Sitzungsberichte d. Naturf. Ges. zu Halle, March 8, 1879 Maly's Jahresber. *9*, 2 (1879).
16. Scheele, C.: Chemical Essays, p. 268.
17. Wollaston, W. H.: Philos. Trans. Roy Soc. (1810), pp. 223–230.
18. Mörner, K. A. H.: Zeitschr. f. physiol. Chem. 28, 595–615 (1899).
19. Mulder, G. J.: Ueber die Proteinverbindungen des Pflanzenreiches. J. prakt. Chem. *16*, 129 (1839); *44*, 503–505 (1848).
20. Robiquet, P. J. and Boutron-Charlard, A. F.: Ann. de chim. et de phys. (2) *44*, 359, 376, 552 (1830).
21. Vauquelin, L. and Robiquet, P. J.: Ann. de chim. *57*, 88–93 (1806).
22. Piria, R.: Ann. de chim. et de phys. (2) *69*, 281 (1838); (3) *14*, 257 (1845).
23. Piria, R.: Ann. de chim. et de phys. (3) *34*, 278 (1852).
24. Wurtz, A.: A Short History of Chemistry, Partington, J. R. London, 1951, p. 261.
25. Hofmann, A. W.: Philos. Trans. 1850 and 1851.
26. Wurtz, A.: Compt. Rend. *30*, 9 (1850).
27. Rochleder, F.: Ann. d. Chem. u. Pharm. *73*, 56 (1850).
28. Lehmann, C. G.: Physiological Chemistry (1855), 2 vols. Vol. 1, p. 293.
29. Schlieper: Ann. d. Chem. u. Pharm. *59*, 1–32 (1846).
30. Guckelberger: *Ibid. 64*, 39–100 (1848).
30a. Lawes, J. B. and Gilbert, J. H.: Phil. Mag. *4*, 32–62 (1854).
31. Nasse, O.: Pflüger's Arch. *6*, 589 (1872); 7, 139–55 (1873).
32. Schulze, E. and Steiger, E.: Ber. d. deutschen chem. Ges. *19*, 1177–80 (1886).
33. Drechsel, E.: J. prakt. Chem. *39*, 425–29 (1889).
34. Kossel, A.: Zeitschr. f. physiol. Chem. *22*, 176–87 (1896).

35. Hedin, S. G.: *Ibid. 21,* 155–68 (1895).

36. Hausmann, W.: *Ibid. 29,* 136–45 (1900).

37. Osborne, T. B.: The Vegetable Proteins. (1924), pp. 72–73.

38. Schulze, F. N.: Zeitschr. f. physiol. Chem. *25,* 16–35 (1898).

39. Osborne, T. B.: J. Amer. Chem. Soc. *24,* 140 (1900).

40. Maschke, O.: J. prakt. Chem. *74,* 436–37 (1858).

41. Maschke, O.: Bot. Zeitschr. *17,* 409–413, 417–425, 429–32 (1859).

42. Denis, P. S.: Mémoire sur la sang, etc. Paris (1859).

43. Méhu, M. C.: Journ. de pharm. et de chim. (August, 1878). Maly's Jahresber. *8,* 269 (1878). Also
Wenz, J.: Maly's Jarhesber. *15,* 32 (1885).

44. Heynsius, A.: Pflüger's Arch. *34,* 330 (1884).

45. Weyl, T.: Pflüger's Arch. *12,* 635 (1876).

46. Ritthausen, H.: J. prakt. Chem. *85,* 193–212 (1862); *86,* 257–265 (1862); see Osborne, T. B. The Vegetable Proteins (1924) pp. 142–144, for complete list of references to Ritthausen's studies.

47. Osborne, T. B.: The Vegetable Proteins (1924) London.

48. Vickery, H. B. and Schmidt, C.: Chem. Rev. *9,* 169 (1931).

5

Ideas About Food Utilization Derived from Studies on Digestion

Hippocrates (460–370 b.c.) held the belief that although there are many kinds of foodstuffs, there was but a single kind of aliment. This belief prevailed through many centuries because no knowledge of the chemical nature of organic substances of animal or plant origin existed. Richerand (1), in his *Elements of Physiology* (1813), reiterated the view of Hippocrates; and even William Beaumont (2), famous for his studies on digestion on Alexis St. Martin who had a fistulous opening into his stomach as the result of a gunshot wound, expressed the view that but a single kind of aliment or nutrient was contained in foods.

Galen (130–200 a.d.) studied digestion in swine and concluded that the stomach was the place where food was resolved into particles small enough to be absorbed (3).

The first man to devote constructive thought and experiment to discovering the nature of the digestive process was René Antoine Ferchault de Réaumur (1683–1757) who, in 1731, invented the thermometer which bears his name. In 1752 (4) he published his studies *On the Digestion in Birds.* Réaumur devised methods which were to be employed by later investigators.

Réaumur sought to determine whether the changes which food undergoes in the stomach were the result of trituration only, or whether they were of the nature of fermentation or of solution in some peculiar solvent. Up to the time of Réaumur's experiments, these questions had been answered only on the basis of speculation.

In his experiment, Réaumur employed a kite which, like the owl, swallows its food in the form of large fragments of torn mice and other small animals, and eventually regurgitates pellets composed of the more indigestible parts of the food. He inserted into the stomach of the kite metal tubes, open at both ends, and containing morsels of various foods. The open ends he secured by gratings of fine wire. The tubes were left in the stomach until they were returned by the bird.

Réaumur found that pieces of meat had been partially dissolved, and that the residues in the tubes had no odor of putrefaction. Small pieces of bones were dissolved and larger ones were eroded, and these, when returned to the stomach in a tube, were further reduced in size by solution. He noted that the tubes contained a yellowish, somewhat opalescent fluid which tasted salty and bitter, from which he drew the conclusion that the fluid had caused the meat to dissolve. Since gastric fluid dissolves foods which water does not dissolve, he compared the digestive process to the solution of gold by *aqua regia,* and concluded that the gastric juice had no power to dissolve starch. Thus he propounded the question: "To which of the solvents which chemistry offers can this liquid be compared?"

Réaumur's next step was to collect sufficient gastric juice to enable him to study its properties. This he accomplished by placing in the tubes sponges which were squeezed out when the bird had returned them. He obtained in this way 4 ml of the fluid, which he described as having a taste both salty and sour, and which turned red paper tinted with blue turnsole (litmus). Employing the juice he performed the first *in vitro* digestion experiment. He observed that meat immersed in the juice for twenty-four hours had lost a little weight, and that it had not undergone putrefactive change as did a similar piece immersed in water for the same amount of time. He concluded that gastric digestion was not, as some had supposed, due to putrefaction. The kite died and terminated his experiments.

Réaumur then extended his studies of digestion to experiments on a dog, which he fed bones. He also had the dog swallow tubes containing meat. After twenty-four hours he killed the animal and found that the bones had been eroded and partly disintegrated and the meat in the tubes had been in great part dissolved. He noted that the tubes had been little or not at all distorted by pressure, which ruled out attrition as a digestive factor in the dog. Similar experiments with sheep were not very successful. It appears that Réaumur did not distinguish rumen digestion from true stomach digestion. He did establish, however, the fact that gastric juice possesses greater solvent powers than does water, that certain constituents of the food were dissolved in it, and that gastric digestion is antagonistic to putrefactive change.

Spallanzani's Investigations on Digestion

Twenty-five years after the publication of the studies of Réaumur, Lazaro Spallanzani (5) (1729–99) repeated and extended Réaumur's investigations on gastric digestion. He employed fishes, frogs, newts, serpents, several kinds of birds, sheep, oxen, horses, cats, and dogs. He also experimented on himself. Spallanzani modified the shapes of the tubes which were patterned after those of Réaumur, by perforating the sides to admit entry of gastric juice.

In his experiments, Spallanzani tested the digestibility of meat, bone, wheat, and other foods. Like Réaumur, he recovered tubes from carnivorous birds, but in many experiments he opened the stomachs of his animals at stated periods after eating for examination of their contents. He caused animals to swallow pieces of meat and other morsels attached to a string or wire and after various intervals of time he withdrew the specimens for examination. He himself swallowed little linen bags containing foods. These he allowed to pass through the alimentary tract. He also used sponges to soak up gastric juice. In some studies he forced himself to vomit before breakfast. These studies advanced to some extent the facts brought to light by Réaumur, served to support the view that gastric digestion involves chemical solution of food substance.

In 1777 Dr. Edward Stevens (6) published a thesis in which he described experiments carried on by a man who earned his living by swallowing stones, a practice he had begun when seven years old and had continued for twenty years. Stevens enclosed foods in silver containers 2.5 × 3.25 inches in dimensions with perforations "larger than a crow's quill." His subject swallowed these and they were recovered in the stools after thirty-six to forty-eight hours. In this way he tested beef, pork, cheese, pheasant, vegetables of different sorts, and cereal grains. In general, the foods were found to have been completely dissolved, but unbroken cereal grains appeared not to have been altered. Ivory balls were dissolved and disappeared. Stevens stressed the point that foods were converted into chyme without having come into actual contact with the stomach walls.

The Investigations of Dr. John Richardson Young

John Richardson Young (1782–1804) (7), in 1803, submitted a thesis to the Faculty of Medicine of the University of Pennsylvania on the subject "An experimental inquiry into the principles of nutrition and the digestive process." His work was forgotten for many years until it was brought to light by Kebler. In his thesis, Young referred to the studies of Réaumur and of Spallanzani. He chose for his experiments the bullfrog *Rana Ocellata,* a carnivorous animal whose stomach is easily accessible because of the capacious mouth and wide gullet which enable it to swallow large objects.

Young confirmed previous observations that in the digestive process flesh becomes dissolved and bones eroded, even teeth being decomposed. He found that the hind legs of a living young frog placed in the bullfrog's stomach during five days were not digested, but frogs' legs which were tied off to stop the circulation were digested. He concluded that living tissues are not attacked by the gastric secretion. He compared the rates of digestion in the frog and the snake and confirmed Spallanzani's observation that digestion proceeded faster at higher temperatures than at lower ones, within the range of the body temperatures of warm and cold-blooded animals.

Young questioned Spallanzani's assertion that gastric juice of carnivorous animals cannot digest vegetable foods. Instead, he found that bruised seeds of wheat, beans, and peas, when placed in linen bags and left three days in the frog's stomach had been liquified and disappeared from the bags. He spooned out gastric juice from his frogs and invariably found it acid, and asserted that the acidity did not arise from acetious fermentation, but was a normal constituent of the secretion. He wrongly identified the acid of gastric juice with phosphoric acid. William Prout (8), in 1824, proved that gastric acidity is due to the presence of hydrochloric acid.

Beaumont's Studies on Gastric Digestion

William Beaumont (1785–1853) was the outstanding pioneer in the study of gastric digestion in man. Over a period of several years on, he observed the responses of the stomach of his famous patient, Alexis St. Martin, who had a permanent fistulous opening into his stomach as a result of a gunshot wound.

Beaumont's most important observations confirmed those of Réaumur, Spallanzani, and Young, but went far beyond these in making clear the physiological responses of the gastric mucosa to chemical and mechanical stimuli. He secured generous quantities of human gastric juice from St. Martin and submitted it to some of the most famous chemists of his time for analysis. Unfortunately, at that period chemists did not know what to do with this unique material. Beaumont's studies were published in 1833 (9). His remarkable patience, and the thoroughness, penetration, and discernment manifest in his account of his investigations made his publication of tremendous importance because of the great interest which it aroused in physiologists in Europe as well as in America. Rosen (10) has given an interesting account of the reception of Beaumont's discoveries in several countries.

A direct result of Beaumont's work was the production in dogs, by surgical means, of gastric fistulas by Blondlot (11) and Bardeleben (12). Thus, gastric juice became readily available for study. Many important studies of digestion were made by Tiedemann and Gmelin (13).

Eberle (14) in 1834 discovered that by extracting the gastric mucosa with very dilute acids, a fluid was obtained which possessed digestive powers for coagulated albuminous substances, flesh, etc. Schwann (15) showed that it was only the glandular structure which yielded a digestive extract having the properties of gastric juice. Schwann also made the remarkable discovery that corrosive sublimate formed a precipitate in such extracts, and that on converting the mercury to its insoluble sulfide and filtering, the filtrate possessed a high degree of digestive power. The active substance thus precipitated he called *pepsin*.

A new viewpoint concerning protein digestion was announced by Miahle (16) in 1844, who stated that on digestion of albumen and other proteins, "a single, easily soluble substance" was formed. This substance he named *albumose*. This erroneous conclusion was the landmark from which others explored the properties of intermediate products of protein digestion, as begun by pepsin and hydrochloric acid and completed by other ferments in the alimentary canal.

Ideas which were accepted about midcentury concerning digestion and conversion of food to the uses of the body, were expressed by J. Franz Simon (17) in 1846 as follows: "By the process of digestion we understand the solution and the modifications that the food undergoes in the stomach and adjoining portions of the intestinal canal, together with the absorption and metamorphosis of the nutrient fluid (chyme) contained in the reduced pulpy mass of the food, till it becomes perfect chyle (milky fluid in lacteals)." He continued, "The subject of digestion has attracted much attention for the last seventy years, but unfortunately the results that have been obtained are by no means proportional to the time and labor involved in the experiments instituted in relation to this department of physiology."

In 1853 C. G. Lehmann (18), who made many digestion studies with gastric juice, gave the name *peptone* to the end-product of pepsin-hydrochloric acid action on protein bodies. He was unable to distinguish the peptone formed from albumen, fibrin, casein, etc., so he believed it to be a single substance. Both he and Miahle supported the view that digestion of proteins by gastric secretion involved cleavage, and consequently the formation of a simpler substance. This view seemed conclusively established by the fact that as digestion progressed the amount of coagulable protein decreased and the products formed progressively lost their power to form insoluble derivatives with metallic salts, tannin, etc.

In 1854 Thomas Graham (1805–69) (19) greatly contributed to chemical knowledge by his discovery of the phenomena of osmotic force; then in 1861 he introduced a method for separating crystalline from colloidal substances by means of dialysis, using a semipermeable membrane. This new tool was soon applied to the study of digestion. It could be shown that as digestion progressed the amount of diffusible substances increased, showing that large molecules of proteins were cleaved to simple, diffusible products. This was in harmony with the formation of glycine, leucine, and tyrosine by acid decomposition of proteins.

Albumoses and peptone were found to be diffusible through animal membranes, but it was soon discovered that they did not enter the blood from the alimentary tract as might have been expected. Furthermore, on injecting these substances into the blood, they were found to be highly toxic to animals. On the basis of such knowledge, it seemed justifiable to conclude that peptone and albumoses were recombined in some manner in the epithelial lining of the alimentary canal to form the albumen and fibrin of the blood.

Could Protein Be Synthesized from Peptone?

The concept of peptone as a substance representing the end-product of gastric digestion (pepsin-HCl) became established about the middle of the 19th century. Later physiologists speculated about whether peptone could replace protein in animal nutrition as the sole source of nitrogenous food. The earliest investigator to put the idea to experimental test was Plotz (20) of the University of Budapest. In 1874 he published the results of feeding a dog, over an eighteen-day period, a diet of artificial milk which contained 5 per cent of peptone (prepared from blood fibrin digested with an HCl extract of gastric mucosa), and 5 per cent of a salt mixture which included NaCl and potassium phosphate. The first three days he fed the dog natural milk; for the remainder of the time he substituted an artificial product. At the beginning of the test the dog weighed 1335 grams, and at the end its weight was 1836 grams. The obvious conclusion was that the dog had utilized peptone for protein synthesis.

Plausible as the conclusion seemed then, an investigator forty years later would have held the experiment valueless for the following reasons: At the beginning of the experiment the dog was well stocked with nutrients which the body is capable of storing, and would scarcely have had time to exhaust its reserves in the eighteen-day period, provided the experimental diet supplied minimal amounts of unsuspected nutrients. Since the digestant employed to convert fibrin into peptone was a hydrochloric acid extract of gastric mucosa, it contained "extractive" substances dissolved from glandular tissue. Also, in the absence of assurance to the contrary, there was the possibility that the dog was weighed empty at the beginning and full at the end of the experiment.

The nature of the chemical phenomena of protein digestion remained unexplained until 1871, when Lubavin (21) heated albumen in aqueous solution, in Papin's digestor, at 120–150° C. for twenty-six hours. He precipitated the brown, bouillon-like fluid with lead acetate, and filtered off the precipitate of lead compounds. The filtrate was evaporated to a syrup and shaken with ether. From the aqueous layer he obtained crystalline substances which he identified as leucine and tyrosine. From casein he also secured these amino acids, and concluded that by interaction of the proteins with water alone, cleavage of colloidal substances, indiffusible through animal membranes by Graham's technic, were converted into simple crystalline, diffusible products. From then on the processes of protein digestion in the alimentary tract were regarded as progressive hydrolysis, or decomposition by interaction with water, which is taken up in the reaction. He concluded that digestion of proteins is comparable with the hydrolytic conversion of starch to sugar by the action of acid as shown by Kirchhoff. Lubavin visualized the initial formation of peptone, and later of amino acids by the action of super-heated steam on proteins, as similar to the digestion of proteins by juices in the alimentary tract.

Sustained Interest in Peptones and Albumoses

Throughout the last half of the 19th century investigators sought to determine the course of the intermediary steps in the digestion of proteins into products suitable for absorption into the blood and available for nutrition of the tissues. Peptone was defined as the end-product of pepsin-hydrochloric acid digestion of proteins. Proteose was assumed to be the product of digestion which stood next to protein in complexity and which by further hydrolytic change became peptone. These concepts were generally accepted by chemists and physiologists for want of evidence as to the manner in which the protein molecule is cleaved and the nature of the end-products of digestion by the proteolytic enzymes of the small intestine. As investigations progressed it became apparent that these terms could not with accuracy be applied to single substances, but that there were many kinds of proteoses and peptones.

Early Studies of Pancreatic Digestion

The secretion of the pancreas was first collected from the duct of Wirsung by Regnier de Graaf in 1664, but no studies were made of its properties until 1825 when Tiedemann and Gmelin (13) showed that the juice could digest albuminous substances. In 1878 Méhu (22) discovered that proteins are quantitatively precipitated from their solutions without denaturation by saturation with ammonium sulfate, a technic which was considerably extended by Heynsius (23). The new reagent was made use of by W. Kühne and his pupils among whom R. H. Chittenden deserves distinction. They proposed a new definition for peptone, defining it as the digestion product of protein which was not precipitated by adding ammonium sulfate to saturation. The fact soon emerged that "true peptone" is formed rather rapidly during tryptic digestion, but in very small amounts in peptic-HCl digestion. Many attempts were made to isolate and identify intermediate products of peptic and pancreatic digestion of proteins, but with little success beyond the establishment of the fact that digestion in the alimentary tract resulted in products of progressively smaller molecular weights. The fractions into which, by various devices, digestion products were separated were given such names as meta-, para-, dys-, hemi-, and anti-peptones; hetero-, hemi-, proto-, and anti-albumoses. These could not be characterized as single species of molecules, and had no clear meaning in the chemical sense. Investigators failed to duplicate each other's results and the state of the chemistry of the digestion products of proteins fell into hopeless confusion. Between 1871 and 1900 Maly's *Jahresbericht der Thierchemie* contained 299 references and abstracts of papers devoted to the study of peptones in scientific journals. In 1895, W. D. Halliburton, a distinguished English physiologist (24), wrote, "Although it seems apparent that these bodies represent different steps in hydration of protein, they cannot be identified at present. In spite of the advances of chemistry as a whole, it is practically at a standstill so far as proteids are concerned; nor can we hope to understand the steps in proteolysis until the chemists are able to give us some idea of the chemical constitution of proteids which these digestive juices act upon."

The time had arrived when chemical studies were instituted which were to give the insight into the nature of proteins so much desired by physiologists. By 1900 sixteen amino acids had been discovered, and E. Fischer (25) and his distinguished pupil E. Abderhalden (25) devised methods for uniting these to form peptides of different degrees of complexity from two or more amino acids, eventually succeeding in coupling eighteen amino acids in peptide linkage after the manner in which they occur in proteins.

Erepsin

Biochemists who investigated digestion of proteins by enzymes and attempted to determine the extent to which they were degraded hydrolytically never succeeded in carrying digestion to the amino acid stage in *in vitro* experiments because the accumulation of the simpler products of digestion, unless removed from the system, slows, and eventually stops the process. Kühne made the important discovery that there is an essential difference between the digestive action of trypsin and that of pepsin. He found that tryptic activity does not stop at the peptone stage but continues to cleave peptone to the setting free of individual amino acids. As late as 1900, however, these crystalline products, which could be detected in the digesting contents of the small intestine, were believed to be by-products of natural digestion of little significance and formed in but small quantities. In 1906 O. Conheim (26) discovered in intestinal secretion an enzyme which could hydrolyze peptones to amino acids. To this enzyme he gave the name *erepsin*. Conheim had believed that proteins were synthesized from peptones in the intestinal wall. His discovery of the peptone-digesting enzyme gave a new meaning to intestinal digestion. It became evident that protein cleavage in normal digestion proceeded to the amino acid stage. This meant that in nutrition, so far as the protein element is concerned, extremely complex syntheses result from the mixture of amino acids which arise from successive digestion with pepsin, trypsin, and erepsin. With Conheim's investigations it became apparent that the synthetic powers of the animal body in the building of body proteins from food proteins extended to complete synthesis from amino acids.

In 1912 Folin and Denis (27), by direct chemical analysis, proved that it is amino acids rather than more complex intermediary products of protein digestion which are absorbed by the intestine and enter the blood. They perfected technics for the quantitative determination of minute amounts of urea, ammonia, and total nitrogen in animal substances, but at that time it was not possible to determine the amounts of amino acids by any direct method. Hence they expressed what they believed to be amino acids by the term "non-protein, non-urea, non-ammonia nitrogen." These scientists took samples simultaneously of portal, systemic blood, liver, and muscle from fasting animals, and from others at successive stages of absorption after feeding high-protein food, through the peak, the fall and return to the fasting state; as a result of these tests, Folin and Denis clearly demonstrated that the fraction representing amino acids is at a low level in the blood and tissues during fasting, and that it rises like a tide after absorption of digestion products begins and sinks again when absorption has ceased. Their research represents one of the classics of chemical investigations of the metabolic scheme.

In 1911 Van Slyke and Cullen (28) described a procedure for the direct determination of amino acid (alpha-amino) nitrogen in protein hydrolysates and in extracts of animal tissues, in the presence of various organic nitrogenous compounds which occur in animal tissues. With this new method they were able to confirm the observations of Folin and Denis by direct determination of the distribution of amino acids absorbed from the alimentary tract during digestion. The evidence was conclusive that animals take simple amino acids as they are formed and absorbed by the intestine and are distributed by the blood to all the tissues, and synthesize proteins of unique composition suitable for all the purposes of living tissues.

The results of these investigations as to the manner in which the animal body utilizes food proteins for its nutrition were in sharp contrast to the views of Mulder and Liebig, who believed that protein was a single species of organic compound formed only by plants and utilized by animals without marked alteration.

Theoretical Significance of Formation of Hippuric Acid in the Body

The controversy between German and French investigators over the possibility of synthesis of fats from carbohydrates by the animal body has been noted in an earlier chapter. The first evidence that the animal is capable of synthesizing a complex organic nitrogenous compound from simpler substances resulted from experiments made by Alexander Ure (29), a professor at the Anderson Institute in Glasgow. In 1841 he observed that when benzoic acid was given orally to an animal, hippuric acid was excreted in the urine. One year later Wöhler and Kellar (30) confirmed Ure's findings. In 1845 Dessaigne (31) showed that when hippuric acid is heated with dilute mineral acids it is cleaved into glycocoll (glycine) and benzoic acid. Ure's observation was of considerable importance in influencing the thought of physiological chemists, as Wöhler's synthesis of urea by heating ammonium cyanate influenced thought of organic chemists. The synthetic powers of the animal body continues to the present day to enter into the speculations of biochemists in planning and interpreting their experiments.

REFERENCES

1. Richerand, W.: Elements of Physiology. Philadelphia (1813).
2. Beaumont, W.: Experiments and Observations on Gastric Juice, and the Physiology of Digestion (1833).
3. Galen (Cited by Walsh, J. J.): Ann. Med. History 9, 132 (1927).
4. de Réaumur, R. A. F.: Memoirs of the Acad. Sci. of Paris (1752).
5. Spallanzani, L.: *Dissertationi de fisica animale e vegetale.* 2 vols. (1780).
6. Stevens, Edward: Cited by Thomas Thomson, Animal Chemistry, Edinburgh (1843), p. 593.
7. Young, J. R.: Cited by L. F. Kebler, J. Chem. Ed. *17*, 573–75 (1940).
8. Prout, W.: Philos. Trans. (1824), p. 43.
9. Beaumont, W.: Experiments and Observations, etc. (1833).

10. Rosen, G.: The Reception of Wm. Beaumont's Discovery in Europe. New York (1942).

11. Blondlot, N.: Traité Analytique de la Digestion, Nancy (1843).

12. Bardeleben: Arch. f. phys. Heilk. 8, 1–7 (1843).

13. Tiedemann, F. and Gmelin, L.: Recherches Physiologique, et Chimique pour Servir a l'Histoire de la Digestion. Paris (1825).

14. Eberle, J. N.: Physiologie der Verdauung. Würzberg (1834).

15. Schwann, T.: Müller's Archiv. Berlin and Leipzig (1836); Pogg. Ann. 38, 358 (1836).

16. Miahle, L. F.: Journ. de pharm. et de chim. (3) *10,* 161–67 (1844).

17. Simon, J. F.: Animal Chemistry with Reference to the Physiology and Pathology of Man. Trans. by G. E. Day. 2 vols. London (1846) Vol. II, p. 35.

18. Lehmann, C. G.: Physiological Chemistry. 2nd ed. Trans. by G. E. Day, 2 vols. Philadelphia (1855) Vol. I, p. 450.

19. Graham, T.: Philos. Trans. London, *144,* 177–288 (1854); *151,* 183–224 (1861).

20. Plotz, P.: Pflüger's Arch. *9,* 323 (1874).

21. Lubavin, N.: Compt. rend. 73, 1219 (1871).

22. Méhu, M. C.: Journ. de pharm. et de chim. Series (4) *28,* 159 (1878); Maly's Jahresber. *8,* 269 (1878).

23. Heynsius: Pflüger's Archiv. *34* (1879).

24. Halliburton, W. D.: Sci. Progress 3, 35 (1895).

25. Fischer, E.: Untersuchungen über Aminosauren. Polyeptide und Proteine. Berlin (1906).

26. Conheim, O.: Zeitschr. f. physiol. Chem. 33 (1901); *35* (1902); *36* (1902); 37 (1903).

27. Folin, O. and Denis, W.: J. Biol. Chem. *11,* 87, 161 (1912); *12,* 141, 253 (1912).

28. Van Slyke, D.: J. Biol. Chem. *12,* 275–284 (1912).

29. Ure, A.: Provincial Medical and Surgical Journal, London (1841) ii, p. 317.

30. Wöhler, F. and Kellar: Ann. d. Chem. u. Pharm. *43,* 108 (1842).

31. Dessaigne: Compt. rend. *21,* 1224–27 (1845).

6

Facts Concerning Nutrition Gained From Experiments With Gelatin

EARLY IN THE nineteenth century owing largely to spoilage of cereals from wetness, there was scarcity of food in some parts of Europe, and learned societies concerned themselves with this problem. In 1815 the Gelatin Commission was appointed by the Academy at Paris to inquire whether the gelatinous extract of bones could properly replace meat in one's diet, particularly as food for the poor. Magendie served as chairman of the Commission, and Vauquelin was a member. Its report, presented after many years of careful investigation involving animal experiments, stated that the Commission was favorably disposed toward gelatin as food. It read, in part, (1) that "everyone who is familiar with broth knows that its nutritious qualities are due primarily if not entirely to gelatin." The report went on to say that all who had written on the subject considered gelatin as the most nutritious of animal matter. The question of the nutritive value of gelatin was not limited to the usefulness of this substance when taken alone but extended to inquiry whether, alone or mixed with other substances, it could take the place of meat.

In the year 1817 the Society for the Promotion of the Arts at Geneva investigated the practicability of utilizing for humans the nutriment contained in bones. The report (2) stated that four pounds of bones yielded one pound of gelatin, and that the soup made from it was as nutritious as soup made from six pounds of meat. By the term gelatin the members of both these investigating groups meant the substance formed by boiling meat, tendons, etc. with water, rather than the product of deep-seated hydrolysis with super-heated steam in Papin's digestor.

A second commission, known as the Magendie Commission, with Thenard, Darcet, Dumas, Fluorens, Breschet and de Serres as members, reported in 1841 (3) on the most important animal nutrition experiments which had been conducted at that time. In 1816 Magendie had found that dogs could not survive on non-nitrogenous food (sugar, fats) (4). Then, in 1841, he reported that he found by trial that dogs could not be maintained when given gelatin alone, and that they also failed in health when fed only bread or bread and gelatin. At that time this statement was astonishing to physiologists. Magendie found that dogs restricted to either cooked or raw egg-white as their sole food, steadfastly refused to eat it, notwithstanding the pangs of hunger. He restricted dogs to washed blood fibrin as their sole food and observed that, although they at first refused it, they later ate it freely during a seventy-five-day period. Nevertheless they steadily declined in weight and died with all the manifestations of inanition.

The Commission then restricted dogs to a diet of bones and made the surprising observation that the animals not only survived during three months, but maintained their original weight and soundness of health. Magendie, who presented the report, emphasized his belief that the albuminous nutriment in bones is too small to supply the needs of the animal body. He said, "When, however, bones containing the gelatin-forming material, the marrow fat, and blood salts are eaten together, the health of the animals remains normal." In other words, with a quite inadequate amount of albuminous substance in the diet of bones, the supplement of gelatin-forming tissue enabled the animals to convert the mixture into blood and tissue proteins. It should be mentioned that Edwards and Balzac (5) were the first to declare that gelatin alone could not replace albuminous bodies in animal nutrition.

The conclusions of the Magendie Commission were summarized in the following somewhat condensed declarations.

1. It was not possible by any known process to extract from bones an aliment which, either alone or mixed with other substances, can take the place of meat.
2. Gelatin, albumen, and fibrin, taken separately, nourish animals for a very limited period, and only in a very incomplete manner. In general, they soon excite an insurmountable disgust so that animals die rather than partake of them.

3. The same alimentary principles artificially reunited and rendered agreeably sapid by seasoning are taken more readily and for a longer period than when in a separate state; but they had no better ultimate influence on nutrition, for the animals that ate them, even in considerable quantities, soon died with all the signs of complete inanition.
4. "Muscular flesh in which gelatin, albumen, and fibrin are united according to the laws of organic nature and associated with other matters, such as fats and salts, suffices, even in very small quantity, for complete and prolonged nutrition."
5. "Raw bones can do the same, but the quantity consumed in twenty-four hours must be very much larger than in the case of meat."
6. "Every kind of preparation, such as a decoction with water, the action of hydrochloric acid, and particularly the transformation into gelatin, diminishes, and seems even in certain cases almost to destroy, the nutritive value of bones."
7. The Commission, however, was unwilling to express an opinion upon the employment of gelatin, associated with other aliments, in the nourishment of man. It was believed that direct experiments alone could throw light upon this subject.
8. "Gluten extracted either from wheaten or maize flour satisfies by itself complete and prolonged nutrition."
9. "Fats taken alone sustain life for some time, but give rise to an imperfect and disordered nutrition, fat accumulation in all the tissues, sometimes in the state of olein, and even the most pure stearin."

The Magendie Commission having found that gelatin alone failed to nourish animals, a commission was appointed by the Institute d'Amsterdam (6) to determine whether gelatin increased the nutritive value of other aliments to which it was added. Evidence was derived from the same kind of studies as were made by the Paris Commission on dogs, and the conclusion arrived at was that gelatin was not only of no nutritive value when taken alone, but was not improved nutritively by combination with other substances. This made gelatin appear to be a useless substance.

Conclusions 4 and 8 in the Magendie Commission proved to be erroneous. While it is true that adult dogs may subsist for some weeks on muscle substance and water, they ultimately suffer malnutrition. Young, growing animals cannot thrive on a diet of muscle substance. Physiologists accepted for many years the statement of Magendie, and the nature and extent of deficiency of nutrients in muscle were not discovered until seventy-five years later.

In 1863, W. S. Savory (7), surgeon and lecturer in anatomy and physiology at St. Bartholomew's Hospital, who enjoys the distinction of having been the first to employ rats as subjects in nutrition studies, tested by experiments certain questions concerning nutrition. He restricted two rats to a diet composed exclusively of lean veal containing 1.56 per cent fat. One rat died on the thirteenth and the other on the twenty-third day. Savory was unable to account for their death, and since he had kept a kite in apparent good health for two months on no food other than lean veal, he continued to believe that the veal diet was satisfactory and had nothing to do with the death of his rats.

It is difficult to account for Magendie's reported experience of successfully maintaining health in dogs restricted to either wheat or corn gluten, the product remaining after washing away the starch from the ground kernels. One suspects that an attendant gave the animals other food without reporting it. What Magendie said was (8), "Gluten, notwithstanding that its odor is savorless and sometimes nauseous, while its taste has nothing agreeable, was taken (by dogs) without difficulty from the first day, and the animals continued to use it without distaste for three months uninterruptedly. The dose was 120–150 grams daily, and the animals preserved all the characteristics of excellent health. This fact appeared the more remarkable to us, as it was in opposition to the law which seemed to result from various facts, before stated, that an alimentary substance, especially if it were an isolated immediate principle, is not fitted for support of life beyond a very limited period. Here, however, is a substance hitherto considered as an immediate azotized principle, which without any preparation or seasoning, excited neither repugnance nor disgust, and which alone nourished completely and for a long period."

Magendie subsequently observed that gluten ought not to be considered as an immediate principle (i.e. single proximate principle). "That which we employed undoubtedly contained some traces of fecula. Exclusive of this, we know that it may be resolved into two distinct substances: one of an albuminous nature, the other called glaiadine. The latter is separable likewise into gluten, gum, and mucilage. The dogs, therefore, ate much gluten combined with a little albumen, gum, mucilage, fecula, and even sugar arising from fecula. Thus, this aliment, simple in appearance, was really very compounded: "It is the presence of gluten in wheaten flour that renders it pre-eminently nutritious." Magendie's statement about the separation of wheat gluten into fractions was based on the published account of Taddei (9) that part of wheat gluten is soluble in alcohol. To this material he gave the name gliadin, and to the part insoluble in alcohol, zymom.

The conclusions reached by the Magendie Commission stimulated thought among chemists and physiologists because of the difficulties which arose concerning the explanation of the origin and fate of gelatin in animal nutrition.

William Prout wrote in 1840 (10) that gelatin should be included among the albuminous aliments. He considered it to be a modification of albumen, or "as the least perfect kind of albuminous matter existing in animal bodies."

The Puzzle Concerning Nutritive Failure of Animals Restricted to Isolated and Re-combined Nutrients

The findings of the Magendie Commission, that dogs could not eat egg albumen and suffered inanition when it was the only food available to them, and that when dogs ate freely of washed blood fibrin they failed nutritionally in a short time, showed that these albuminous substances when taken alone were no more effective than gelatin in supporting nutrition. But it was a commonly observed fact that, so far as chemists had been able to show, animals thrive when fed the well-known albuminous substances "united according to the laws of organic nature, and associated with other matters, as fats, salts, etc." Gelatin was, however, a substance which does not occur in the body, but was formed by prolonged boiling with water, and no experiments could be so planned as to unite it with other substances "according to the laws of organic nature."

Since chemists had failed to derive gelatin from any of the albuminous substances known to them, and gelatin does not occur in the vegetable kingdom although the tissues of animals which feed solely on vegetable foods yield gelatin when boiled in water, it was evident that gelatin-yielding substances, such as tendon, bone matrix, etc., must be formed from proteins. In the years following Magendie's report the view was generally accepted that the reverse process-conversion of gelatin into protein was not possible in the nutrition of animals. Liebig suggested that the nourishing powers of gelatin were confined to its conversion into "cellular tissue, membranes, and cartilage." That it had close affinity with proteins was shown by the increase in formation of urea after ingestion of gelatin, as in the case of protein metamorphosed in the body.

The Studies of Voit and Bischoff on Gelatin

In 1872 Carl Voit (1831–1908), professor of physiology at Munich, took up the study of the nutritive significance of gelatin (11). He introduced a new technic into his investigations by determining with his experimental dogs the minimum amount of protein (muscle) which would prevent a deficit of nitrogen when an animal was fed protein alone (lean meat free from visible fat), the same when fed carbohydrate, and when fed fat only. Voit had already established the fact that the nitrogen output in the urine was greater in a fasting animal, deriving energy for heat and work from disintegration and metabolism of its own muscles after depletion of its store of fat and carbohydrate (glycogen), than when these respiratory foods were available as sources of energy. By supplying the energy needs of the dogs with non-nitrogenous foods and determining the minimum of protein which would maintain them in nitrogen equilibrium, and by substituting part or all of the muscle substance in the diet by gelatin, he was in position to test the extent to which it could be utilized to replace protein. At the outset of their experiments Bischoff and Voit were of the opinion that gelatin could completely replace protein in nutrition. As the result of experiments they were forced to the conclusion that "Gelatin exercises its sparing power on the protein both with large and small quantities of protein (meat) fed at the same time and with small quantities in much higher degree than either fat or carbohydrates. Large quantities of gelatin spare more protein from combustion than do small quantities; however, protein is lost from the body even if with large quantities of gelatin the greatest amount of fat be given." Further conclusions were that direct laying down of gelatin, either as gelatin-yielding tissues or the protein-forming tissues, was not possible and that it must be assumed that when elastic and fibrous tissues are formed in the body it is at the expense of protein. Thus it was evident that gelatin could replace only a part of the protein of the food (12).

Pollitzer (13), Munk (14), and Murlin (15) extended the study of gelatin in the hope of establishing the exact percentage of the protein minimum requirement of dogs which gelatin could replace. Their failure to arrive at such quantitative data was later to be accounted for by reason of the differences in the amino acid content of the proteins employed in the basal diets, and perhaps other factors. The fact that gelatin is inferior to commonly employed food proteins was, however, fully established. From his thorough study Murlin made the following conclusion: "On a diet containing one-sixth more than the fasting requirement of nitrogen and ten calories per kilogram more than the requirement of potential energy, of which one-half is supplied as fat, it is possible to replace protein (beef-steak) by gelatin to the extent of fifty-eight per cent without loss of body protein."

Studies of the Nutritive Value of Gelatin Supplemented with Amino Acids

In 1872 when O. Nasse discovered that Millon's reagent for the detection of protein gave the same brick-red precipitate with the amino acid tyrosine and that gelatin did not give this reaction, a new cause for the nutritional inferiority of gelatin became evident. All proteins gave this test, so it might reasonably be assumed that the absence of tyrosine was the chief defect of gelatin as a nutrient. Would supplementing it with tyrosine render gelatin the nutritive equivalent of protein? In 1879 Hermann and Escher (16) put this question to the test by feeding a dog a diet composed of carbohydrate, fat, mineral salts, and gelatin supplemented with tyrosine. They reported that the negative nitrogen balance of the dog when given gelatin unsupplemented was changed to positive balance when tyrosine was provided. This result was in harmony with all the facts at that time known, and it was the earliest experimental evidence that amino acids were of importance in nutrition. However, later investigators were unable to confirm the report of Hermann and Escher, so the problem of the nutritional inadequacy of gelatin remained unsolved.

When, in 1898, Mörner isolated cystine from protein hydrolysates this amino acid assumed interest in speculations concerning the nature of the deficiencies of gelatin. The presence of but a trace of sulfur in gelatin was evidence of its lack of the sulfur-containing amino acid, cystine. In 1900, when Hopkins and Cole isolated and described tryptophan from proteins and showed that gelatin gave a negative test for this new amino acid, nutrition investigators were in position to suggest that deficiency of tyrosine, cystine, and tryptophan were collectively involved in determining the nutritive usefulness of gelatin. These new facts explained why the report of Hermann and Escher could not be confirmed.

In 1905 Kaufmann (17) reported experiments in which he fed dogs a diet in which gelatin, tyrosine, cystine and trytophan were substituted for protein. He stated that the animals maintained nitrogen equilibrium on this mixture, indicating that the protein degraded in the tissues of the animals in the processes of normal metabolism was reconstructed from gelatin and the amino acids provided. However, Kaufmann's short nitrogen balance study led him into error. We now know that gelatin is not made equivalent to proteins by the addition of the three amino acids.

In 1928 Jackson, Sommer, and Rose (18) made a thorough study of the nutritive value of gelatin by means of growth experiments with young rats. They found that the rats could not long survive when fed a diet complete except for protein, but containing 35 per cent of gelatin supplemented with tyrosine, cystine and tryptophan. Hydrolyzed gelatin supplemented with the same three amino acids gave no better results. They found that severe kidney injury followed the consumption of high gelatin diets and attributed growth failure to this injury.

In the period covered by this history no further investigations have been reported concerning the specific defects in the composition of gelatin which account for its inferiority in animal nutrition. The general advance of knowledge of the amino acid content of muscle and blood proteins, which are synthesized from the amino acids absorbed from the digestive tract, and of the amino acids yielded by gelatin, clearly reveal that gelatin is poorly constituted to meet the body's needs for tissue protein synthesis. Information as to the relative amounts of muscle, liver, blood, and other proteins which are normally degraded and which must be replaced by synthesis, is too fragmentary to permit speculation on the first, second, third, etc., limiting amino acid in gelatin which accounts for its poor utilization.

It is perhaps worthwhile to point out that muscle proteins yield on hydrolysis about 3.2 per cent of the sulfur-containing amino acid methionine and 6.0 per cent of isoleucine, whereas gelatin contains but 0.8 per cent of methionine and 1.7 per cent of isoleucine. Both are indispensable amino acids. It seems highly probable that it is the poor constitution of gelatin as respects several amino acids which determines its low biological value. This view is substantiated by the conclusive demonstration of animal studies that relatively small supplements of proteins, complete in their amino acid complement, enable the body to utilize some of the amino acids derived from gelatin.

REFERENCES

1. Philos. Mag. *46,* 17 (1815).
2. Bibliothèque Universal, Sept. 1817.
3. Compt. rend. *13,* 237, 269 (1841).
4. Ann. de chim. et de phys. 3, 66 (1816).
5. Edwards, W. F. and Balzac: Ann. sci. nat. *26,* 318 (1832).
6. Gazette Médicale *12,* 176 (1844), Paris.
7. Savory, W. S.: The Lancet, i, 383, 412 (1863).
8. Compt. rend. August (1841).
9. Taddei, G.: Giornale de fisica, chemica, e storia-naturale, Brugnatelli (2) 2, 367–374 (1819).
10. Prout, W.: On the nature and treatment of stomach and urinary diseases (1840), pp. xii and xiii. 3d edition.
11. Voit, C. and Bischoff, T. L. W.: Die Gesetze der Ernährung des Fleischfressers (1860).
12. Voit, C.: Zeitschr. f. Biol. *5,* 344 (1869).
13. Pollitzer, S.: Pflüger's Arch. 37, 301 (1885).
14. Munk, I.: *Ibid., 58,* 309 (1894).
15. Murlin, J. R.: Amer. J. Physiol. *19,* 285–313 (1907).
16. Hermann, L. and Escher, Th.: Maly's Jahresber. d. Thierchemie *9,* 2 (1879).
17. Kaufmann, M.: Pflüger's Arch. *109,* 440 (1905).
18. Jackson, R. W., Sommer, B. E., and Rose, W. C.: J. Biol. Chem. *80,* 167 (1928).

7

Advances in Nutritional Research to 1845

THANKS TO THE GREAT CONTRIBUTIONS of Lavoisier, Black, Priestley and Cavendish, by the year 1800 chemists knew that combustion involved the union of oxygen with carbon and hydrogen to form carbonic acid gas and water. Respiration in animals was known to represent oxidation within the body. The earliest chemists had accumulated knowledge of fats, carbohydrates, and albuminous substances, as related in preceding chapters.

The Earliest Animal Experiment in Which A Control Was Used

In 1791 Dr. George Fordyce, Fellow of the Royal Society and of the College of Physicians in London, and reader on the practice of physic, published the second edition of a book on nutrition (1). He was the earliest experimental investigator of note in animal nutrition. Fordyce conducted experiments with large numbers of young chicks to determine whether they could be reared without using gravel for grinding seeds in their gizzards; he concluded that small stones are essential to their survival. By giving chicks small pieces of stones of different kinds, he further proved that they exercised choice in the kinds they ate or rejected.

Fordyce's most important experiment, however, was to determine the need of birds for calcareous substances. He observed in his canaries that the hen "at the time of laying requires a quantity of calcareous earth, otherwise she is frequently killed by the eggs not passing forward properly." He divided his canary hens into two "parties." To one group he gave a piece of old plaster, the other he kept for a control. Both groups were fed the same kinds of seeds. He noted that the birds eagerly broke down the mortar and ate it.

Whereas many of the control group died, the hens which received the supplement of mortar all passed through the laying season in good health. Fordyce therefore concluded that canaries require a calcareous supplement to the seed diet ordinarily provided them.

The Earliest Nutrition Study Based Upon Chemical Analysis

At the beginning of the 19th century chemists generally believed that inorganic matter could be formed by plants in the process of vegetation. This belief was subjected to experimental inquiry by several men, and an account of their inquiries is given elsewhere (Chapter 21). Vauquelin (2) conducted an experiment designed to discover whether the animal body, like the plant, might transmute or perhaps generate inorganic substances. He analyzed fowls to determine their "fixed parts" (inorganic matter) and compared the result with the fixed portions of the food they ate. In one experiment a hen consumed in ten days 11,111.8 grains Troy of oats, which contained 136.509 grains of phosphate of lime and 219.548 grains of silica, a total 356.057 grains.

In the ten days covered by the experiment the hen laid four eggs, the shells of which contained 98.776 grains of phosphate of lime and 453.417 grains of carbonate of lime. The excrement during the experimental period contained 274.305 grains of phosphate of lime, 511.911 grains carbonate of lime, and 185.266 grains of silica. The total given out was 971.482 grains, while the total taken in was 356.057 grains. From these data he calculated that 34.282 grains of silica were retained by the hen, while an excess of 137.796 grains of phosphate of lime was excreted. Thus, Vauquelin concluded that a transmutation of elements had occurred in the metabolism of the hen. Fourcroy (2) reported this study without criticism. In 1838 Thomas Thomson, one of the best informed chemists of his generation, stated his belief that inorganic elements could be generated by growing plants. He went on to say, however, that Vauquelin's experiment should be repeated to confirm his findings.

A chemist of a century later might have pointed out that Vauquelin's hen must have had one egg completed in her oviduct at the start of the experimental period and another on the way to completion, both of which had been made from food not taken into account in the calculations. Even the third egg laid in the ten-day period was in the yolk stage on the ovary at the start of the period. It is also probable that during part of the time when the hen was restricted to oats she drew on her skeletal reserves and was in negative calcium and phosphorus balance.

Earliest Inquiries Into Sugar as Food

Fourcroy (3) said of cane sugar: "It is a food which, taken in too large a quantity, is capable of heating the animal system." He said, further, "It may even be considered a medicine, since it is incisive, aperient, slightly tonic, and stimulant; and there are, accordingly, instances of disorders, arising from obstructions, which have been cured by the habitual use of sugar."

The Experiments of John Curwin

In 1808 the Committee of West India made its fourth report to the House of Commons on the efforts which had been made to feed animals with sugar (4). A prize had been offered: "To the persons who shall make and report to the Board of Agriculture the most satisfactory experiments to ascertain the quantity, the effect, and the value, of brown muscovado, i.e. unrefined sugar, in feeding or fattening oxen, cows, hogs or sheep; a piece of plate of the value of 25 guineas." Mr. John Curwin, M.P., reported that he had tried feeding sugar and molasses to calves without success. He added that he conceived "that it may be applied for the rearing of stock, giving part skim milk."

The Committee, with commendable zeal for increasing the market demand for the most important agricultural product of the West Indies, stated in its report (p. 285) that "The great Dr. Rush, of Philadelphia, is reported to have said that 'sugar contains more nutrient in the same bulk than any other known substance'" and further "That eminent physician Sir John Pringle remarked that the plague had never been known in any country where sugar composes a material part of the diet of the inhabitants."

Magendie's Feeding Experiments with Sugar and Fat

In 1816, eight years after Curwin's report, F. Magendie (1783–1855) (5), a famous French physiologist, conducted a series of experiments in which he fed dogs a diet of sugar or olive oil and water. The animals soon exhibited the symptoms of inanition, suffered malnutrition, and died. In the course of these experiments,

Magendie observed the occurrence in his sugar-fed animals of ulceration of the cornea, a condition which a hundred years later was proven to be characteristic of deficiency of vitamin A. Hence, Magendie was the first to describe a symptom of a dietary deficiency disorder in an experimental animal.

Magendie was unable to explain the cause of nutritive failure in the experimental dogs, but he did state that it was due, in part, to a lack of albuminous matter (nitrogen) in the diet. He pointed out further that human subjects were unable to subsist on a diet of sugar. In this connection he cited the experience of five sailors whose ship, carrying a cargo of sugar, was wrecked in 1793. The men were rescued after nine days, during which time they had subsisted on sugar and rum alone. They were found to be in a weakened condition due to starvation. In further support of his belief that albuminous (nitrogenous) substance was indispensable in the diet, Magendie reported the case of an eccentric man who subsisted for a month solely on potatoes and water. At the end of the month the man was extremely feeble, but his condition showed marked improvement as soon as nitrogenous food was added to his diet, and within a few weeks he had completely recovered.

In 1681, before Magendie's time, Sir Christopher Wren (6) had stated that the potato, as a steady diet, was incapable of sustaining one's health. In his report before the Royal Society of London, Wren said that "in Ireland, where the people feed much on potatoes, they help themselves by drinking milk, soured. . . ." Pereira (7) quoted Sir Christopher as commenting that the black slaves of the West Indies, when fed a diet consisting largely of potatoes, were apt to suffer from dropsy, and that to prevent this disorder their diet was supplemented with milk and bread.

Thomas Thomson, writing in 1838 (8), said, "Sugar has now become an essential part of the food of the Europeans. It contains perhaps a greater proportion of nourishment than any other vegetable substance in the same bulk. . . . If we believe Dr. Rush, the plentiful use of it is one of the best preventatives of the diseases occasioned by worms. It has long been supposed to have a tendency to injure the teeth; but this prejudice is now given up."

The Views of William Prout on Animal Nutrition

Before the time of Liebig and Mulder, William Prout (1785–1850) shared with Magendie the leadership in constructive thought about foods and nutrition. Prout practiced medicine in London, but spent much of his time in chemical investigations relating to physiological problems. He attained lasting fame by proposing that the atomic weights of all the elements were multiples of hydrogen. Although this theory fell into disfavor as refined determinations showed that fractional atomic weights were a reality, Prout's views have attained new importance in the light of the discovery of isotopes and the fusion of hydrogen to form helium.

Prout's fame as a biochemist rests in great measure on a declaration which he made in the first of a series of three lectures "on the ultimate composition of simple alimentary substances," which he delivered before the Royal Society (London) in 1827 (9). He said that in examining foods, the objective was "to determine the saccharine, oily, and albuminous divisions in which the alimentary substances of the higher animals may be comprehended, and then to inquire into the changes which are induced in them during the subsequent stages of assimilation by the stomach and other organs." Prout included water as an essential but neglected to mention inorganic substances. The above quotation has often been referred to by writers on nutrition as the earliest attempt to define the adequate diet in terms of chemical substances.

In his lectures Prout said very little about foods other than the technics and the results of analysis for their content of carbon and hydrogen, on which basis he discussed sugar, starch, lactose, manna, gum, fat, woody fiber and the organic acids, oxalic, citric, tartaric, mucic and acetic. Although he mentioned nitrogenous nutrients, he did not go into detail.

As early as 1819 (10) Prout stated his observation that the contents of the stomachs of animals fed on vegetable substances, even when fully digested and about to pass the pylorus, exhibited no trace of an albuminous principle; while the chymous mass in the stomachs of animals fed on animal food contained albumen. This assertion about vegetable food seems astonishing, since Beccari, Parmentier, Fourcroy, and Vauquelin had all shown the presence of "animalized" or albuminous substances in plant products, and the subject had been discussed in well-known chemical treatises by Fourcroy and Thomson. But Prout was convinced by his own tests of the stomach contents that albuminous substances were absent toward the end of the gastric digestion of vegetable foods. He suggested that a secretion of nitrogenized matter of unknown nature by the duodenum converted non-nitrogenized foods into nitrogenized albuminous constituents of the body. In the third edition of a book (11) on therapy, published in 1840, he wrote, "That the oleaginous principle, may be converted into most, if not all, the matters necessary for the existence of animal bodies, seems to be proved by the well-known fact that the life of an animal may be prolonged by the appropriation of the oleaginous and other matters contained within its own body." In a footnote he said (p. xxvii), "The azote (nitrogen) may, in some instances, be derived from the air, or *generated,* but my belief is that, under ordinary circumstances, the azote is principally furnished by a highly azotized substance, secreted from the blood, either into the stomach or duodenum, or into both these localities; and that the portion of the blood thus deprived of its azote is separated from the general mass of the blood by the liver, as one of the constituents of the bile, which secretion, as a whole, is remarkably deficient in azote." This view as directly opposed to that of Liebig who maintained that in animal nutrition no nitrogen was derived from the air, and that herbivorous animals secure from their vegetable food sufficient albuminous food for their needs.

Prout's Idea of How Food Is Converted to Animal Tissues

Dr. Prout had observed that minute quantities of foreign bodies (i.e., impurities) prevented the crystallization of substances in solution. The presence of such foreign bodies changed profoundly the properties of substances capable of crystallization. This he conceived to be the result of union of the foreign bodies with crystallizable substances and the transformation of the latter into *organized* substances such as occur in animal tissues. Union of simple crystallizable substances with a little more or a little less water and with minute amounts of foreign bodies, whose nature he did not specify, seemed to him to answer the important question of how food substances might become organized into living tissues.

Prout proposed to adopt the word *merorganized* to designate substances formed essentially of the principles of crystallized bodies which are incapable of assuming the crystalline form, probably because of the presence of foreign bodies. Starch from wheat, he said, appeared to be an example of this merorganized state. He believed that starch contained a certain amount of water and that when this was removed it was identical with cane sugar.

This idea embodied the same concept as that of Mulder with respect to *protein compounds.* Prout's concept that food was metamorphosed into blood or flesh was a distinct advance beyond the concept of Haller, Macquer, Fordyce, and others, who reasoned that the fundamental nutrient was gelatin, which appeared in many different and contrasting states depending on the extent to which it was combined with water. In the earlier philosophy of nutrition there was no suggestion of the role of minute amounts of foreign bodies.

First to criticize the speculations of Prout on foods was H. Bence-Jones, famous for his discovery of the peculiar protein known as Bence-Jones protein (12) which appears in the urine of patients having multiple myelomas. He asserted in 1842 that common salt was an indispensable article of diet (13). The ravenous appetite of herbivora for salt had been observed from time immemorial. Some regarded this as an abnormal craving, others as a need. The subject is discussed elsewhere (Chapter 21).

Thaer's Hay-Equivalents

Contemporary as an experimenter with Magendie and Prout, was Albrecht Daniel Thaer (1752–1828), an eminent writer on subjects relating to farming. His father was Court physician at Hanover, Germany, and Thaer succeeded his father in this position in 1778. He bought an estate near Celle and constructed buildings for agricultural investigations. Notwithstanding he was physician in ordinary to George III, King of England and Hanover, he reduced his medical practice to devote himself to experimentation and teaching. In 1802, the year before Liebig was born, and when Prout was seventeen years old, Thaer converted his estate into an agricultural institute, the first institution of its kind. Here he gave lectures on farming in which he discussed chemistry, physics, and geology in their relation to agriculture. He employed Einhof whose chemical analysis of barley, a pioneer advance in food chemistry, has already been mentioned.

In 1804 Thaer was made Privy Counsellor and head of a new State Agricultural Institute established at Möglin by Frederick William III, King of Prussia. Between 1809 and 1812 he published four volumes on Principles of Rational Husbandry (14). Most of Thaer's experiments were devoted to fertilizers, crop rotation, agronomy, etc. He is remembered by nutrition investigators for his attempt, the earliest of its kind, to determine the relative feeding values of different farm crops. Thaer had observed that when farm animals such as cattle, horses, and sheep, are given only well-cured hay to eat, they remain in good condition for a long time. From this observation he conceived the idea of determining by feeding experiments the amount of one feed which was the equivalent of a given amount of hay, in maintaining good nutritive condition in animals. He adopted as his unit, 10 lbs. of meadow hay. The following table shows the results of his experiments.

THAER'S "HAY EQUIVALENTS" (14)

Meadow hay	10 lbs.	Pea straw	13 lbs.
Clover hay	9 lbs.	Potatoes	20 lbs.
Wheat straw	45 lbs.	Turnips	52 lbs.
Barley straw	40 lbs.	Wheat (grain)	6 lbs.
Oat straw	40 lbs.		

It is interesting to note that Thaer's method of inquiry did not include the idea of chemical composition as determined by analysis.

Several practical feeders undertook to verify the hay-equivalents published by Thaer. Their results were recorded in Johnston's book (15). There was no agreement in the values as determined by different farmers, as is shown, for example, by the equivalents for turnips. Thaer assigned the value of 52 lbs. of turnips as equivalent to 10 lbs. of hay. Six other investigators reported for turnips the values 45, 53, 60, 45, 29, and 80 lbs. Johnston expressed his belief that the method recommended by Liebig (i.e., Mulder), was superior to that of Thaer. However, after Liebig became the outstanding authority on almost all questions relating to chemistry, Thaer's method fell into disuse.

Sinclair's Analysis of Grasses

In 1844 Johnston (15), lecturing at the University of Durham, stated that an elaborate examination of some of the dried grasses of England had been made by the late Mr. Sinclair, gardener to the Duke of Bedford. His method was to boil in water equal weights of each species of hay until everything soluble was dissolved out, and then to evaporate the solution to dryness. The weights of the dry matter thus obtained he considered to represent the nutritive values of the grasses from which the several samples of hay were made. Johnston pointed out that because of three known factors, Sinclair's experiments were of questionable value: first, the proportion of soluble matter yielded by any species of grass varies not only with the age of the grass when cut, but with the soil, climate, season, rapidity of growth, and variety of seed sown. Second, animals can digest a greater or lesser proportion of their food which is insoluble in water. Even the woody fibre of hay is not entirely useless as a source of nourishment, since the manure of animals had been found to contain less of it than was ingested in their hay. Braconnot's experiments had shown that woody matter could be converted into gum and sugar by sulphuric acid. And third, substances such as vegetable fibrin, albumen, casein, and legumin are either wholly insoluble in water or are coagulated by boiling water into insoluble forms. These defects in Sinclair's method undermined confidence in its reliability.

Liebig's Views on Animal Nutrition

The outstanding investigator and teacher in the field of chemistry during the first half of the nineteenth century was Justus von Liebig (1803–1873), professor at Giessen and at Munich. His investigations illuminated organic, physiological, and agricultural chemistry. It appears that his interest in the chemistry of proteins was inspired by the work and speculations of Mulder, a brief account of which has been given in Chapter 4. It will be recalled that Mulder deduced from his analytic data that there existed a single radical, to which he gave the name protein. This substance, he said, was present in a number of compounds with sulphur, phosphorus, or both in greater or less proportions, and the variety of such compounds therefore accounted for such differences as were manifested by casein, gluten, fibrin, and albumen.

Mulder's most noteworthy pronouncement on the subject of animal nutrition was published in 1838 (16). At that time he stated that bread and other foods which contain protein definitely have a nutritive value. They supply the most essential constituents of the animal body in forms suitable for utilization and without having to undergo changes in digestion. Liebig did not, as many have written, originate this idea. However, he did accept it without reservation, and by his extensive writings gave it wide publicity.

At Liebig's request, his assistant Scherer (17) made analyses of all the protein substances available and in 1841 both he and Liebig (18) published their first papers on proteins. Since Liebig assumed that nearly all the nitrogenous matter in natural foods was in the form of protein, he thought the nutritive values of different foods with respect to protein could be assessed on the basis of their content of the element nitrogen.

Liebig accepted the fact, first demonstrated by Lavoisier, that the phenomenon of respiration involves oxidation of substances within the body for the production of heat. He concluded that all the heat produced in the body arose from oxidation. This being the case, the carbon dioxide exhaled by an animal was an index of its heat production. On this fact many later investigations on respiratory metabolism were based. Fats and carbohydrates, Liebig taught, were fuel foods; he termed as plastic food the nutrient which formed new body tissues during growth, replaced them as they were degraded in physiological processes (e.g., muscular work), and supplied protein for milk secretion.

Liebig drew up a table showing the nutritive values of a list of foods based on his concept (19). His students, especially Schlossberger, Scherer, and Horsford, made many analyses of foods, and these form the basis of the table.

	Plastic constituents	*Non-nitrogenous constituents*
Cow's milk	10	30 (8.8 fat, 10.4 milk sugar)
Woman's milk	10	40
Lentils	10	21
Horse beans	10	22
Peas	10	23
Fat mutton	10	27 (11.25 fat)
Fat pork	10	30 (12.50 fat)
Beef	10	17 (7.08 fat)
Veal	10	1 (0.41 fat)
Wheat flour	10	46
Oatmeal	10	50
Rye meal	10	57
Barley	10	57
White potato	10	86
Rice	10	123
Buckwheat	10	130

Liebig believed that work was accomplished by the breakdown of muscle substance, and that repair or restoration of the muscle to its normal condition required rest and plastic food (protein). He further stated that muscular activity resulted in increased formation and elimination of uric acid and urea. This supposition was not supported by later investigations.

He conceived the idea, without supporting evidence, that the extractives of muscle possessed unusual physiological significance. As a result of this belief, Liebig recommended beef extract (20) for patients suffering from exhaustion or weakness, and from cerebral depression and despondency. Because of Liebig's pronouncement, beef extract was widely popular for many years, until it was proved that the only value was in its flavor.

Liebig's Equivalents Among Foods

A table based on Liebig's teachings was included by Jonathan Pereira in the most critical work on diet (20) published before 1850. The table, showing the *nutritive equivalents* of various foods determined on the basis of their nitrogen content and compared with wheat flour, is reprinted below.

	Equivalents		*Equivalents*
Wheat flour	100	Potatoes	613
Oats	117	Potatoes (10 mos. old)	894
Rice	177	Carrot	757
Buckwheat	108	Carrot (dried at 212°)	95
Maize	138	Jerusalem artichoke	539
Beans	44	Turnip	1335
Peas	67		

Commenting on the table Pereira (21) said, "It will be observed, that in this table 44 parts of beans, or 67 parts of peas, are represented as being equal in nutritive power to 100 parts of wheat flour. Surely this cannot be correct. Liebig admits that although lentils, beans, and peas surpass all other vegetable foods in the quantity of nitrogen they contain, they possess but small value as articles of nourishment because they are deficient in the component parts of bones (superphosphate of lime and magnesia); they satisfy the appetite without increasing the strength. If this explanation be correct, it suggests the use of bone-ashes with either beans or peas as constituting a most nutritive and economical food."

Pereira (1804–1853) deserves to be better known to students of nutrition. He was a physician, a Fellow of the Royal Society, Licentiate of the London College of Physicians, and a member of the Council of the Sydenham Society. Moreover, he was the first to make a study of institutional diets. In his book he pointed out that Alexander Ure's recent discovery (1841) that benzoic acid fed to an animal is synthesized into hippuric acid by union with glycocoll was not in harmony with the prevailing belief that only degradative chemical processes occurred in the animal body.

Pereira also said, "No plausible explanation has hitherto been offered by Liebig of the necessity for the variation of diet, and for the use of succulent vegetables or fruits, which experience has shown to be necessary for the preservation of human life and health. Liebig has shown that food must contain both a plastic element of nutrition and an element of respiration; but it is well known that a diet (as of salt meat and biscuit) which fulfills both these conditions, is not always sufficient to preserve health and life." This was the type of diet which had long been known to cause scurvy among sailors.

Pereira listed as "classes of alimentary principles," aqueous, mucilaginous, saccharine, amylaceous, ligneous, pectinaceous, acidulous, alcoholic, oily or fatty, proteinaceous, gelatinous, and saline. He discussed as nutrients, carbon, hydrogen, nitrogen, phosphorus, sulfur, iron, chlorine, sodium, calcium, magnesium, potassium, and fluorine. At the time of the publication of his treatise, no other writer had so carefully examined and weighed all the experimental evidence available concerning the essential constituents of an adequate diet.

Eben Horsford's Comments on Liebig's Evaluation of Foods

In 1846 Eben M. Horsford (1818–1893), a pupil of Liebig and later professor of chemistry in the Lawrence Scientific School of Harvard University, wrote a full account of the status of the Liebig system (22). His was the first critical appraisal of the variables involved in the Liebig system, namely, that of attempting to apply chemical methods in farm practice to solve the problems of economical animal production. Horsford's conclusions were:

1. The same species of farm crops grown on different soils may yield unequal percentages of nitrogen.
2. One-seventh of fresh ripe cereal grains is moisture, which can be expelled by heating at 100° C.
3. Wheat and rye flours which look alike may differ by 1 to 0.3 of their whole content of nitrogen.
4. Root crops grown on different soils yield unequal percentages of nitrogen.
5. The nutritive values of peas, beans, and lentils correspond with each other (i.e., are essentially alike).
6. More aliment is contained in a given weight of peas than in an equal weight of any other vegetable analyzed.
7. In the several grains and roots analyzed there are organic bodies beside those identical in composition with gluten and starch.
8. Ashes of carrots, beets, turnips, and potatoes contain carbonates.
9. Iron is present in the ashes of all grains and roots examined.
10. Differences between the theoretical equivalents, as estimated from the percentages of nitrogen and those ascertained by experiments of stock-growers, and particularly the results of different stock-growers, may be attributed to the following reasons:
    a. The percentages of nitrogen and carbon in fodder grown on different soils are unequal.
    b. The prominent test has been the increase or diminution in weight of the animal fed. *Increase* in weight may arise from formation of fat, derived from sugar or starch of the plants. *Diminution* in weight may follow unusual activity, increasing the consumption of fat already present.
    c. The experiments, in but few instances, were undertaken with substances whose percentage of water and nitrogen had not been ascertained.
    d. Theoretical equivalents have been employed in conditions unequally suited to digestion. The same food, coarse or fine, fresh or prepared for easy digestion, yields unequal measures of nutrition.
    e. The conditions, whether the animals were exposed to severe weather or protected in stalls, whether they were

subjected to labor of uniform severity, influenced food requirements. Sheep kept outdoors in winter ate more and gained less than controls kept in fold.

f. Finally, as above mentioned, some animals by nature differ greatly from others in the facility with which fat and muscle are developed, even when the circumstances are precisely the same.

Horsford's appraisal of the variables involved, and the shortcomings of analysis of nitrogen content alone as a basis for comparing foods, indicated failure of the Liebig system. Even if it were true that the protein moiety in different plants was of constant value nutritionally, the variable composition of the same plant grown under different conditions introduced serious error into calculation of rations. Conclusion 7 was especially important, since in it there was admission that serious error could result from using total nitrogen as a measure of the plastic (blood-forming, tissue-forming) nutriment in foods.

Mulder and Liebig's Contribution to Nutrition

The account here given of the investigations and teaching of these two great pioneers is not intended to detract from the value of their work. Both explored new fields of science and were devoted experimenters and teachers. They broke new ground and offered logical conclusions from their limited data. Their assertions stimulated the imagination and thought of many of the best minds in science in their generation, and fostered the development of new methods for chemical analysis and animal experimenting with foods. Progress in understanding the chemical nature of food substances and the nutritive needs of the animal was only to be achieved by a long series of trials and errors. Over-simplification of the problems involved in nutrition has been a weakness of every investigator right down to the present. To be mistaken does not call for reproach or faint praise. The great merit of these two men of genius was their attempts at constructive thought, and their strong motivation to test the truth or falsity of their working hypotheses. The investigator who is enthusiastic, aggressive, and honest, but who misinterprets his experimental findings, has not infrequently stimulated clearer thought and more effective experimental work in another. In so doing, he may attain success which he could not have realized had his imagination not been fired by a predecessor or contemporary. Liebig and Mulder deserve unstinted admiration of later nutrition investigators.

REFERENCES

1. Fordyce, G.: Treatise on the Digestion of Food. 2nd ed. London (1791).
2. Vauquelin, L. N.: Ann. de chim. *29,* 61 (1799).
3. Fourcroy, A. F.: Elements of Chemistry and Natural History. iii, p. 118 (1800).
4. Philos. Mag. *31,* 281 (1808).
5. Magendie, F.: Ann. de chim. et de phys. 3, 66 (1816).
6. Wren, Sir Christopher: In History of the Roy. Soc. London by James Birch, vol. iv, p. 93 (1681).
7. Pereira, J.: Treatise on Food and Diet (1849).
8. Thomson, Thomas: Organic Chemistry of Vegetable Bodies (1838), p. 648.
9. Prout, W.: Philos. Mag. (2) *2,* 144 (1827); *3,* 33, 107 (1828).
10. Prout, W.: Annals of Philosophy *13* (1819).
11. Prout, W.: On the nature and treatment of stomach and urinary diseases. 3d ed. London (1840) p. xxvi.
12. Bence-Jones, H.: Philos. Trans., London, 1848, pp. 55–62.
13. Bence-Jones, H.: On Gravel, Calculus, and Gout. London, 1842.
14. Thaer, A. D.: Principles of Agriculture Crops, Animal Husbandry (1812) vol. iv, English trans. by W. Shaw, and C. W. Johnson (1844) contains a Memoir on Thaer; also see Source-Book of Agricultural Chemistry (1944) pp. 178–183.
15. Johnston, J. F. W.: Agricultural Chemistry, New York (1844) p. 526.
16. Mulder, G. J.: Bulletin des sciences physique et naturelles en Neerlande *1,* 104 (1838).
17. Scherer, J.: Ann. Chem. *40,* 1 (1841).
18. Liebig, J. von: Ann. Chem. *39,* 129 (1841).
19. Liebig, J. von: Letters on Chemistry, London (1851) p. 361.
20. Volhard, J.: Justus von Liebig, Vol. ii, p. 430 (1909).

21. Pereira, J.: A Treatise on Food and Diet. With observations on the dietetical regimen suited for disordered states of the digestive organs, and an account of dietaries of some of the principal metropolitan and other institutions for paupers, lunatics, criminals, children, the sick, etc. Ed. by C. A. Lee, New York 1849.

22. Horsford, E. M.: Philos. Mag. (3) 29, 365–397 (1846).

8

The Nutritional Investigations of Boussingault

MULDER AND LIEBIG themselves did not test by animal experiments their speculations on the chemical nature of protein and the processes of nutrition. After Magendie, the next man to take up animal experimentation on an extensive scale was Jean Baptiste Boussingault (1802–1887).

Boussingault was one of the outstanding men of his generation. Born in Paris, he studied mining, and at the age of twenty went to South America where for ten years he engaged in mining engineering. He then returned to France and taught chemistry for a time at Lyons. After settling on his wife's estate in Alsace at Bechelbronn, he at once began, at his own expense, to apply chemistry to the study of agriculture. Boussingault deserves the title of founder of scientific agriculture because he studied problems both in the field and in the laboratory. He conducted experiments on soils, crops, fertilizers, the assimilation of atmospheric nitrogen by plants, and changes in composition of seeds during germination, as well as in the utilization of food by animals, and applied all available knowledge in the planning and conduct of his experiments. He was the friend and collaborator of Dumas, one of the greatest French chemists of all time. All of his studies bear the stamp of philosophic insight.

Boussingault's Demonstration of Nitrogen Fixation by Plants

Farmers had from very early times observed that crops grown on soil where beans had been the preceding crop developed better than on land previously yielding crops of other kinds of plants. Pliny (1) said that the growing of beans fertilized the ground in which they were grown as well as did application of animal manure. That the improved fertility was due to increase of nitrogen in the soil was not suspected until chemical science developed to the stage where it emerged, in the studies of Vauquelin and Fourcroy, that peas and beans were much richer in albuminous (animal, nitrogenous) substance than were cereal grains (p. 45).

The source of the abundant nitrogen in legume seeds, although suspected to be the air, was a mystery until Boussingault demonstrated that its only possible source was atmospheric nitrogen. This he accomplished by incinerating clay soil to destroy all organic matter, and growing weighed amounts of seeds in this soil. The soil was kept in porcelain dishes and wet with distilled water. During the growth of the plants, Boussingault kept the dishes in a glass house hermetically sealed, but with good sunlight illumination. Control samples of seeds he dried, weighed, and analyzed by the combustion method, for carbon, hydrogen, and nitrogen. His results clearly showed that peas, lucerne, and red clover brought about in the vegetative process a marked increase of nitrogen in the harvested plants over that contained in the seeds, whereas neither wheat nor oats, when studied in the same way, added any nitrogen to the crop over that contained in the seeds sown. It was proved half a century later by Helriegel and Willfarth that the property of "fixing" or incorporating atmospheric nitrogen into plant substances (proteins) was due to the action of certain bacteria which multiply in the nodules on the roots of leguminous plants.

Boussingault's Studies to Determine Whether Animals Use Atmospheric Nitrogen as Food

Boussingault was the first to institute experiments to show, by chemical analysis, the effects on animals of foods inadequate in quality. Thus he found that when fed *ad libitum* as the sole food potatoes or beet roots, both of which are deficient in protein, were incapable of preventing loss of weight in cows. (2) These were the first chemical studies in which animals were restricted to rations derived from a single plant source. From these observations Boussingault drew the conclusion of fundamental importance, that animals could not use nitrogen from the atmosphere to supplement inadequate protein in the rations for synthesis of nitrogenous animal matter (blood, flesh).

Boussingault's Table of Nutritive Values of Feeds

Boussingault accepted the teachings of Mulder and Liebig, that the nitrogen content of food could be used for comparison of their nutritive values for such purposes as formation of blood, muscle, and milk. On the basis of his own analyses, using the combustion method of Dumas which was the only one then available, Boussingault drew up the following table of *theoretical quantities of different kinds of vegetable feeds which will produce equal effects on the growth of muscle.* (3) Like Thaer, he adopted ten pounds of hay as his unit for comparison.

BOUSSINGAULT'S TABLE

Hay	10	Potatoes	28
Clover, hay, in flower	8	Old potatoes	41
Lucerne, in flower	8	Carrots	35
Green lucerne	35	Turnips	61
Wheat straw	52	White cabbage	37
Rye straw	61	Vetches	2
Barley straw	52	Peas	3
Oat straw	55	Maize	6
Pea straw	5	Wheat	5
Vetch straw	7	Rye	5
		Barley	6
Potato leaves	36	Oats	5
		Bran	9
Carrot leaves	13	Linseed oil cake	2

The First Nitrogen-Balance Animal Nutrition Experiments

On the basis of the respiration studies reported by Valentin and Brunner (4) and by Regnault and Reiset (5), it appeared that the expired air is richer in nitrogen than the inspired air. Boussingault accepted their experimental evidence and their interpretation, which was that a part of the nitrogen ingested with the food in the form of protein was eliminated by way of the lungs. Unfortunately, the work of these early students of respiration was not accurate. They were content with measuring the carbon dioxide and the volume of a few respirations, and then calculating from the rate of respiration the output of carbon, nitrogen, and water vapor during a twenty-four hour period.

Marchand (6), using colorless hematoxylin as indicator, asserted that he could detect ammonia in every individual respiration. Boussingault reasoned that if the nitrogen ingested as food and that excreted in the urine and feces and secretion, as of milk, were accurately determined, the difference between intake and output would represent the amount of nitrogen lost from the body through the lungs. He tested this idea of indirect determination of nitrogen elimination by respiration with a horse and a cow (7). In the horse experiment, which lasted twenty-four hours, 17.2 per cent of the nitrogen ingested could not be found in the excreta; and in the cow experiment, which was continued for three days, 13.5 per cent less nitrogen was found in the urine, feces, and milk than in the ingested feed. Boussingault believed that these amounts were lost by excretion through the lungs of the animals. He realized, however, that this method could not give trustworthy results in a growing animal, but he believed that they were reliable when adult animals were used.

Reuling Demonstrated That No Ammonia Is Lost Through the Lungs

In 1854 Reuling (8) published his prize essay on the amount of ammonia in the expired air in health and in disease. He tested all available indicators and concluded that logwood paper was the most sensitive of all for the detection of ammonia, and that he could by its use detect one part in sixty-four millions of water. Reuling stated that the exhaled air of everyone contained ammonia, but that the quantity depended on the amount of ammonia in the inspired air. He asserted that in healthy men there is neither absorption nor elimination of ammonia by the pulmonary mucous membrane, but that, invariably, ammonia was found in expired air of persons with dental caries and with septic tonsils.

Boussingault's Further Studies on Ammonia Loss in Respiration

The conflicting results of Marchand and Reuling led Boussingault to perform a series of experiments with a view to settling the question whether nitrogen was exhaled through the lungs (9). He employed turtle doves, which he fed millet. One experiment lasted five days and the other seven. Having analyzed the millet and determined the amount consumed by the birds, he collected the excrement, dried it, and analyzed it. The average loss of nitrogen which was attributed to excretion through the lungs of the doves was 35.04 per cent of the amount ingested. It seems probable that this large loss was occasioned by ammonia formation in the feces by microbial action, and its volatilization before they were dried for analysis.

Whatever the source of error may have been, Boussingault's conclusion was wrong, as was soon shown by an experiment made by Bidder and Schmidt (10). They settled the question for all time so far as most chemists and physiologists were concerned. Their results were far better controlled and the experimental conditions more exacting than were those of Boussingault or any other previous workers. They employed a full-grown cat which was fed all the meat it would eat during a period of seven days. They found that with the exception of 0.7 per cent of the nitrogen ingested as meat, all was contained in the feces and urine of the cat. They attributed to experimental error their small deficit of nitrogen.

Boussingault's Studies on Digestion and Absorption of Food

Boussingault made a number of experiments to determine the rate of disappearance by absorption of the different constituents of food from the digestive tract. In one study (11) he made a duck swallow 50 grams of gum arabic, and after nine hours recovered 46 grams of the gum from the digestive tract and in the excrement. The gum was neither digested nor absorbed. He adopted this method for the study of the amounts of different foods which could be digested and absorbed into the blood from the digestive tract of the duck within a given time. He first fasted his ducks, then fed them carefully measured quantities of a single food, and killed them after certain periods. He carefully collected and measured the excreta and the material still remaining in the alimentary tract. With these data he calculated the amount of each food which could be absorbed by the duck's digestive tract in one hour. From this unit, as found for different foods, he assumed that the amount which could be digested and absorbed into the blood in twenty-four hours represented the food capable of metamorphosis by a duck in one day (11).

From his experimental values obtained with birds of the amount of

Amount of Food Digested and Absorbed in One Hour By a Duck

	Grams
Dry rice (8.68% albumen and 89.2% starch)	4.20
Dry cheese (70.68% fat)	2.50
Bacon (96.3% fat)	0.88
Cacao seed (48.4% fat)	1.77
Starch	5.26
Sugar	5.62
Boiled egg-white	1.25
Casein of milk, dried	1.37
Gelatin (dry)	4.40
Beef, boiled and free from visible fat	1.41
Albumen 0.92 grams mixed with 4.26 grams gelatin	5.18

carbon, as carbonic acid gas, which was expired during a day, and from the data which he secured on the quantitative capacity of ducks to digest and absorb protein and carbohydrates, he drew two important conclusions: that it was not possible for the birds to secure sufficient carbon from these sources to cover their requirements "for the metamorphosis of matter" within their bodies, and that it was, therefore, necessary that some fat be included in the diet to prevent a deficit of carbon.

Boussingault deduced that animal rations might be inadequate (a) because of inability of the animal to eat enough of the food (e.g., potatoes or beet-root) to provide sufficient nitrogenous matter to replace the organic particles rendered effete by metamorphosis of body tissues; (b) because certain diets (namely, those too largely composed of protein compounds, and carbohydrates) might not contain sufficient digestible, absorbable carbon to meet the needs of the animal for respiration; (c) because the ration may supply insufficient amounts of salts, especially phosphates; and (d) because it supplied too little fat to prevent a deficit of carbon. It was his opinion that the experimental results available indicated that there were certain proportions among these nutrients which distinguished good from poor or bad rations.

Boussingault's Experiments On the Mineral Requirement for Bone Growth

Boussingault experimented on pigs to determine the rate of growth of the skeleton, and the amount of ash constituents of bone which were assimilated by the pig during growth (12). From these experiments, he made the following observations:

1. A new-born pig weighed 650 grams, its dried skeleton 48.25 grams, and its ash weighed 20.73 grams.
2. A pig 8 months old weighed 60,055.0 grams, its dried skeleton 2,901.0 grams, and its ash constituents 1,349.5 grams.
3. A pig 11.5 months old weighed 67,240.0 grams, its dried skeleton 3,407.0 grams, and the ash constituents 1,686.0 grams.

These data afforded the earliest estimate of the minimum amount of calcium phosphate which the diet of a pig must provide for normal skeletal development.

Boussingault's Analytical Distinction Between Urea and Ammonia Nitrogen in Urine

In 1850 Boussingault (13) devised the first method for distinguishing quantitatively between nitrogen as ammonium salts and nitrogen as urea in urine. He added lime water to alkalinity, warmed the solution to 40–50° C., and collected and measured the ammonia evolved. Ammonia, he found, was not evolved from urea solutions under these conditions.

Boussingault's Contribution to Use of Iodine in Goitre Prevention

Courtois discovered iodine in 1811 and nine years later Coindet (14), in Geneva, prescribed it as a remedy for the cure of goitre. Because of overdosages patients were injured by iodine administration, its use was condemned by physicians and it fell into disrepute. In 1824 Alexander Humboldt described the occurrence of goitre in Colombia, South America, and stated that the native Indians knew of a salt deposit which they believed to be remedial for the disease, a property which they did not attribute to other salt sources. A young physician, Dr. Roulin, who had learned in Paris of Coindet's therapeutic use of iodine, went to Colombia, and, having learned of the belief in a special curative value of the salt deposit mentioned by

Humboldt, secured samples of this and other sources of common salt, and requested Boussingault to analyze them. He found that the highly prized salt contained iodine, which was absent from the other sample (15). Boussingault attributed the curative power of the salt to its iodine content, and in 1831 he advised the Colombian Government to provide for the general distribution of the naturally iodized salt in the interest of the health of the population (16). It was not until a hundred years later that the use of iodized salt for the prevention of goitre was placed on a firm foundation and supported by medical authority.

The Importance of Boussingault's Researches in Nutrition

Boussingault was the earliest great innovator in animal experimentation on nutrition problems. He sought, for the first time, to apply the technics of the chemical laboratory to determine the magnitude of the "metamorphosis" of food substances, in terms of carbon and nitrogen, in the fasting and the normally fed animal, using both mammals and birds. He shared with Liebig the appreciation of the significance of inorganic elements in animal nutrition. In his writings on nutrition he considered common salt, which he demonstrated by tests on farm animals, to be indispensable for their well-being, and also included potassium, calcium, and phosphate as necessary nutrients.

With the exception of his experiments on pigs to determine the rate of growth of the skeleton, he conducted his studies with adult animals. His nutrition studies scarcely advanced understanding of the metabolic processes or solved any economic problems of animal production. But his were the pioneer efforts to apply nutrition investigations to farm animals. In so far as knowledge of the processes of nature were available to him from the work of his predecessors, he thought with admirable clarity. His writings during the period of about twenty years, based on unprecedented enthusiasm and industry, stimulated the curiosity of several superior men to take up where he left off, and to advance both the science of physiology and the economics of farm crop and animal production. Boussingault's nutrition investigations were followed by the monumental program carried out in England by John Lawes, and his associate J. H. Gilbert, both of whom were later knighted. Their studies form the subject of the following chapter.

REFERENCES

1. Pliny, The Elder: Natural History, Book 18, Chapt. 30.
2. Boussingault, J. B.: Ann. de chim. et de phys. *12,* 153 (1844).
3. Boussingault, J. B.: Economie Rurale, Paris 1844, p. 483.
4. Valentin, G. and Brunner, J. C.: Arch. f. physiol. Heilk. 2, 372–417.
5. Regnault and Reiset: Compt. rend. *16,* 17 (1842); Ann. de chim. et de phys. (3rd. Ser.) 27, 32 (1849).
6. Marchand: Journ. f. prakt. Chem. 33, 148 (1846); *44,* 35 (1847).
7. Boussingault, J. B.: Ann. de chim. et de phys. (2nd Ser.) *61,* 128 (1836).
8. Reuling: Ueber den Ammoniakgehalt der expirten Luft, und seiner Verhalten in Krankheiten. Ein Beitrag zur Kenntniss der Uraemie. Giessen (1854).
9. Boussingault, J. B.: Ann. de chim. et de phys. (3rd Ser.) *11,* 433 (1844).
10. Bidder, F. and Schmidt, C.: Die Verdauungssafte und der Stoffwechsel. Mitau (1852).
11. Boussingault, J. B.: Ann. de chim. et de phys. (3rd Ser.) *18,* 444–478 (1846).
12. Boussingault, J. B.: Ann. de chim. et de phys. (3rd Ser.) *16,* 486–493 (1846).
13. Boussingault, J. B.: Ann. de chim. et de phys. (3rd Ser.) *29,* 472 (1850).
14. Coindet, J. R.: Ann. de chim. et de phys. *15,* 49 (1820).
15. Marine, D.: Chemistry in Medicine. Chemical Foundation, Inc. New York, 1928, p. 287.
16. Parra, H.: Am. J. Pub. Health 38, 820 (1948).

9

The Investigations of Lawes and Gilbert in Animal Nutrition

CONTEMPORARY WITH THE notable experimental studies of Boussingault in Alsace, two men in England undertook to apply science to agriculture. They were John Bennett Lawes (1814–1900) and Joseph Henry Gilbert (1817–1901). Upon the death of his father in 1822 Lawes inherited the Rothamsted estates, and while he was still a student in Oxford University started investigations on the growing of medicinal plants. In 1837 he undertook to compare the effects of different fertilizers on plant growth. In 1835 Escher (1) had discovered that the fertilizing value of bone meal was greatly improved by treatment with sulfuric acid. Lawes applied this acid to natural rock phosphate and found that its value as a source of phosphate was greatly enhanced because of its increased solubility. He secured a patent on the process of making "superphosphate" in this way and established a profitable business in its manufacture. With this source of income he began to experiment with various farm problems such as crop rotation, soils, fertilizers, and animal feeding. In 1843 he acquired as a collaborator in research J. H. Gilbert, who had been a student of Liebig. Gilbert served as director of the laboratories at Rothamsted for fifty-eight years.

Soon farmers were so enthusiastic about the results of the studies of these men that they contributed funds for the erection of a suitable building in 1855. Hitherto the laboratory studies had been carried out in a barn. In his will Sir John left a large endowment for the permanent support of the Rothamsted Agricultural Experiment Station, which proved to be one of the greatest benefactions to advancement in agricultural practices.

Lawes and Gilbert's Objectives in Animal Nutrition Studies

Lawes and Gilbert first experimented with potted plants, but as their research continued they worked with plants in the field. In 1847, after thirteen years of ever expanding experimentation with plants and their response to fertilizers, the two men began a comprehensive program of studies on animal nutrition which continued through nearly half a century. Their objectives were primarily the economic factors in animal production, but their results had value as contributions to animal physiology.

In 1891 Robert Warrington, who was for many years a member of the staff at Rothamsted, delivered a series of lectures before the Association of American Agricultural College and Experiment Stations (2) on the nutrition studies at Rothamsted. He listed the following points which were given consideration in planning the studies:

1. The effect of the amount of food consumed and of its several constituents in relation to production of a given live weight of animal within a given time.
2. The relation of the amount of food consumed and its several constituents to production of a given increase of live weight.
3. The proportion and relative development of the different organs or parts of different animals.
4. The proximate and ultimate composition of the animals in different conditions as to age and fatness, and the probable composition of their increase in live weight during the fattening process.
5. The composition of the solid and liquid excreta in relation to that of the food consumed.
6. The loss or expenditure of constituents by respiration, and the cutaneous exhalations, that is, in the mere sustenance of the living "meat-and-manure-making machine." This was not determined by the respiration apparatus, but by calculations based on the amounts of dry matter, ash, and nitrogen in the food, feces, and urine.
7. The yield of milk in relation to the food consumed to produce it, and the influence of rations of different composition on the quantity and composition of the milk.

Warrington said that the results of the experiments also supplied data for the consideration of the following questions:

a. The characteristic demands of the animal body for nitrogenous and non-nitrogenous constituents of the food in the exercise of muscular power.
b. The sources in the food of fat produced in the animal body.
c. The comparative characters of animal and vegetable food in human dietaries.

The Experimental Technics of Lawes and Gilbert

In order to secure answers to the several questions which they propounded, Lawes and Gilbert determined the weights of each of the internal organs and some other separated parts in several hundred animals, including oxen, sheep, and pigs in different states of nutrition, viz., a fat calf, a half-fat ox, a moderately fat ox, a fat lamb, a lean lamb, a half-fat old sheep, a fat sheep, a very fat sheep, a lean pig, and a fat pig. They estimated the moisture, dry matter, fat, nitrogen, and ash content in the bodies and parts into which they dissected carcasses for analysis.

Having established these standards of composition of animals in different states of fatness and leanness, they proceeded, in their fattening studies, to deduct the respective constituents of lean animals from the corresponding constituents of the half-fat and fat ones to find the amount of each constituent gained during the experimental feeding period. From the composition and amount of the food consumed by the animal being studied, the efficiency of conversion of food into animal, and of constituents of the animal (fat, muscle, organ, skeleton) could be calculated. The magnitude of this undertaking is shown by the fact that the two men applied these measurements to 98 fattening oxen, 349 fattening sheep, and 80 fattening pigs.

The Utilization of Food by Cattle, Sheep and Hogs

The data obtained by Lawes and Gilbert from years of experimenting led to the following conclusions concerning the utilization of food by animals:

A sheep liberally fed on a mixed dry and succulent ration stored less than 3 per cent of the mineral matter consumed, about 5 per cent of the consumed nitrogenous compounds; it gained about 10 pounds of fat for each 100 lbs. of non-nitrogenous substances in the food (fat and carbohydrates). For 100 parts of dry substance consumed, there were, in the sheep, about 8 or 9 parts of dry matter in the body increase.

The experimental pigs utilized for increase a much larger proportion of the organic constituents of the food than did sheep. This Lawes and Gilbert accounted for, in part, by the fact that there is more woody, indigestible fibre in the food of sheep than in that of pigs.

The average results for pigs showed that for every 100 lbs. of dry matter consumed, 17 lbs. of dry substance was stored as gain. For 100 lbs. of non-nitrogenous organic constituents of the food, about 20 lbs. were stored as fat. When the food consisted of about equal proportions of legume seeds (peas, bean) and cereal grains, from 5 to 8 pounds of the nitrogenous constituents were stored for each 100 lbs. consumed.

In their pig growth studies Lawes and Gilbert found that when legume seeds formed the source of a major part of the nitrogenous food, and cereal grains the minor part, the storage of nitrogenous matter in the bodies of the animals was less than when the reverse was true. In a previous chapter (p. 52) it has been mentioned that in metabolism experiments with growing pigs, Lawes and Gilbert found the protein of legume seeds to be much less efficiently utilized than that derived from cereal grains. Their data also showed that in the fattening pig there was formed four or five times as much fat as was contained in the food. Thus they added to the support of Liebig's assertion that fat may be synthesized in the body from carbohydrates. This question was already settled, but it continued to be debated on the basis of successive experiments by animal nutrition investigators for another half century.

Starch Equivalent For Fat In Animal Feeding

Lawes and Gilbert called attention to the fact that their calculations, based on analytical data from pigs, showed that if the fat content of the body be multiplied by 2.5 the result will be the *starch equivalent* of the non-flesh-forming matter in the food.

Error Arising From Experimenting With Inferior Animals

Lawes and Gilbert's observation that a growing pig could store food protein derived from a mixture of legume seeds and cereal grains only to the extent of 5–8 per cent for conversion into body protein, calls for comment. Deficiencies other than protein, or genetic inferiority might prevent an animal from growing, notwithstanding its innate capacity to store protein for growth of its tissues. Before the middle of the nineteenth century a high percentage of farm animals in Europe and America were inferior genetically and were chronically stunted by restriction to inadequate diets. They had small impetus to grow as compared with the improved breeds of the twentieth century. For example, Dryerre (3) stated that in 1780 in Scotland, even after attempts to fatten them, cattle brought to market did not weigh more than 220 to 264 pounds. At that time cows gave so little milk that farmers estimated a calf could be reared on the milk of two cows.

Conditions of animal production had greatly improved by the middle of the nineteenth century when Knapp (4) recorded a study conducted with cows by Boussingault. At his farm in Bechelbronn Boussingault conducted experiments to ascertain the quantity of milk produced by seven cows for a period of one year. Each cow received daily thirty lbs. of hay or of roots similar in composition. The total yield for the seven cows was 3,837 quarts of milk. The average lactation period was 302.5 days. Thus the average daily yield per cow was 1.8 quarts. In July and August the average yield per cow per day was 2.64, and for February and March 1.1 quarts. In 1844, according to Knapp (4), a good Holstein cow would produce in a 300 day lactation period 2,600 quarts of milk, an average daily yield of 8.6 quarts. In 1953 the milk production for one year by the champion Holstein cow in America was 41,800 lbs. or an average daily yield of 69 quarts during the lactation period of 303 days.

In an article written in 1843 J. von Liebig (5) made an illuminating comment on the inferiority of animals in Germany and the ignorance of farmers in feeding swine. He said, "When a pig is a year old it weighs between 75 and 80 pounds, and if the fat is to be used as lard, it must be fed daily during thirteen weeks with 20 to 25 lbs. of boiled potatoes and two liters of peas. Toward the end of the time, the food may be somewhat diminished. A pig so fattened weighs from 160 to 170 lbs., and contains fat and lard, taken together, from 50–55 lbs." It thus would appear that at the time of von Liebig's article most of the farm hogs were runts from bad feeding.

The extent of runtiness of the pigs described by von Liebig may be judged by comparing them with animals described in 1915 by Burk (6). A sixty-two-day-old pig (initial weight about 60 pounds) when kept daily on green pasture and fed milo chop soaked in skimmed milk, gained 305.5 lbs in six months. Today a typical American farm hog one year old weighs 315 pounds.

Considering the sources of error in the experimental work of Lawes and Gilbert, it is evident that their studies did not contribute much to the solution of the problems at hand, but they did represent a logical step forward toward understanding the cost of production of animals on the farm. An early effort in this direction was made in 1820 by the Secretary of the Board of Agriculture of Scotland (7). He reported to the Board the cost of cultivation, harvesting, and yield of farm crops, and the value of the animals produced. Data obtained from feeding trials indicated that carrots could be used to replace part of the oats and hay required by horses. Similar studies were also reported for barley, oats, turnips, clover, wheat, potatoes, and rye.

The studies of Lawes and Gilbert were intended to contribute new and more detailed information as to how food was converted by the animal. The era of the agricultural experiment station was at hand when they had finished a decade of study. Chemical methods, which will be described in the next chapter, had been discovered and had aroused expectation that far more accurate assessment of the food value of vegetable products could be made by laboratory methods. This idea was to prevail among investigators during the next fifty years.

REFERENCES

1. Escher: Cited by C. A. Browne, in Source-Book of Agricultural Chemistry, Chronica Botanica, 1944, p. 270.
2. Warrington, R.: Exper. Sta. Rec. (Washington, U.S.A.) 3, 73 and 77 (1891–92).

   Lawes, J. B. and Gilbert, J. H.: Phil. Mag. (4) *17*, 145, (1859); also various papers in the Journal of the Royal Society, London, in Vols. *12* to *21* (1851–1860).
3. Dryerre, H.: Proc. of the Nutrition Soc. Cambridge *1*, 168 (1944).
4. Cited by Knapp, F.: Phil. Mag. (3) 32, 456 (1948).
5. Liebig, J. von.: Phil. Mag. (3) 23, 22 (1843).
6. Burk, L. D.: Texas Agric. Exp. Sta. Circular #9, New Ser. pp. 3–6 (1915).
7. Philos. Mag. *56*, 416–427 (1820).

10

Respiration and Calorimetry

THE PROCESS OF BREATHING has been associated with life from man's earliest observations. Thus, in Genesis ii, 7: "God molded man out of the dust of the ground, and breathed into his nostrils the breath of life, so that man became a living being." Breath was from early times associated with combustion, as witness Job xli, 20–21: "Like a pot on a blown fire of rushes, His breath kindles live coals."

Plato, in his *Timeus,* said that "as the heart might be easily raised to too high a temperature by hurtful irritation, the genii placed the lungs in its neighborhood, which adhere to it and fill the cavity of the thorax, in order that their air vessels might moderate the too great heat of that organ, and reduce the vessels to an exact obedience." This view was generally adopted by philosophers and medical men until the time of Joseph Black, late in the eighteenth century.

The function of respiration could not be understood until after the discovery of the nature of combustion, and the discovery by Harvey of the circulation of the blood. The earliest observation on the danger of breathing vitiated air appears to have been made by Pliny (1) who stated that men were sometimes overcome by descending into wine-vats. He said that in the interest of safety a light should be lowered into the vat before going in; if it was extinguished there was danger.

The earliest experiment with the atmosphere seems to have been made by Philo of Byzantium (2) (150 B.C.). He burned a candle in a flask which was inverted with the mouth immersed in water, and noted that after a time the candle went out and water was sucked into the flask. His explanation was that the flame of the candle transformed some of the particles of air to such small dimensions that they could pass through the glass wall of the flask.

Van Helmont (3) (1577–1644) found by experiment that stoppage of breathing caused sudden death of animals. He identified the gas formed in beer and wine fermentation with that formed when charcoal was burned, and with that which occurred abundantly in the Grotto del Cane, near Naples, which issued a gas capable of extinguishing a flame. Dogs were sometimes suffocated when near the mouth of the grotto. Van Helmont made no chemical tests to support his conclusions.

Robert Boyle (4) (1627–1691) and his versatile associate Robert Hooke (1635–1703) discovered that a candle flame under a bell-jar was extinguished when the air was sucked out by an air-pump. Boyle thus asserted his belief that combustion was impossible without air. He further discovered that combustible substances, when mixed with nitre (KNO_3), would burn in a vacuum when heated. Although Boyle and Hooke knew that nitre when heated gave off a gas, they failed to identify it with oxygen, which was later discovered independently by Scheele and Priestley.

In 1665 Hooke (5) published a theory of combustion. He stated that ordinary air contains a small amount of a peculiar matter identical with a substance which exists in nitre. This substance had the property of rapidly dissolving combustibles, and the phenomena of combustion were occasioned by their rapid motion. Hooke called the gas derived from nitre, *nitre air*.

Hooke (6) gave a demonstration before the Royal Society to show that the function of the respiratory movements was to draw in and expel air. He used as an example a dog whose chest wall was opened so as to prevent respiratory movements. The dog remained alive when a vigorous stream of air was kept moving through its lungs by a tube placed in the trachea. As further example of this theory, Hooke enclosed a burning lamp and a chick in a long glass tube. After a time the lamp went out, but the chick continued to breathe; this, Hooke said, showed that air sufficiently vitiated as to extinguish a flame still sufficed for animal respiration. Richard Lower (7) in 1669 injected venous blood into insufflated lungs and observed that it became bright like arterial blood.

John Mayow (1643–1679) (8) demonstrated that only a part of the ordinary air is capable of supporting combustion. In repeating the experiment of Philo of Byzantium he noted that the residual air in the flask after the candle had burned out would not support combustion of either sulfur or camphor, even when these were strongly heated by focusing the sun's rays upon them with a burning-glass.

In another significant experiment Mayow placed a mouse in a flask which he sealed with a bladder over the mouth and tied tightly around the neck. As the mouse respired the bladder was pulled inward, showing that the air in the flask was diminished in volume. A mouse lived only half as long in a flask in which a candle was burning, as in one without a candle. As in Hooke's experiment with the chick, a mouse could still survive after the candle burned out. Like Lower, Mayow observed that venous blood brightened to look like arterial blood when in contact with air. As a result of his experiments he expressed the belief that the ingredient in ordinary air which caused this change was identical with the *nitre air* of Hooke.

Scheele (9) distinguished two constituents of the atmosphere by allowing air to stand in contact with several substances in closed vessels. Liver of sulfur (a mixture of potassium polysulfides and potassium thiosulfate) absorbed about one-fourth of the volume of air exposed to it, and the residual air would not support combustion. Similar results were secured in experiments in which air stood in contact with linseed oil, or iron filings moistened with water. Scheele called the residual air *foul air*, and the constituent which supported combustion he called *fire air*. Fire air was later to be known as oxygen.

The Discovery of Oxygen and its Function in Respiration

C. W. Scheele obtained fire-air, or oxygen, by heating mercuric oxide. Combustible objects burned vigorously in this gas. In one experiment he placed two bees in a little glass box which was fitted to the top of a glass cylinder, the mouth of which was immersed in limewater. He placed honey in the box for the bees to eat. Both the insects were dead in eight days, and the fire-air had been partly used up, as shown by the rise of limewater in the cylinder. Scheele could not explain why the bees died, although he thought it may have been from thirst. The limewater became turbid from absorption of "fixed air" (carbon dioxide) which the bees had given off. Scheele did not understand the phenomena of respiration, because he believed in the phlogiston theory of combustion.

According to the phlogiston theory of Stahl (1660–1734), when bodies burn or are calcined phlogiston escapes from them. Zinc, when heated strongly, burns with a brilliant flame, and there remains calx of zinc (ZnO). In this operation phlogiston was supposed to escape. Zinc was, therefore, conceived to be a compound of calx of zinc with phlogiston. Charcoal, oil, and wax, for example, were supposed to be extremely rich in phlogiston, and when calx of zinc was heated with charcoal, phlogiston was restored. For a century this erroneous view of the nature of combustion was widely accepted by chemists.

Priestley's Discovery of Oxygen

Priestley discovered oxygen independently of Scheele. He heated red oxide of mercury in a closed glass vessel by means of a burning glass (10), thus producing oxygen. He found it to be nearly insoluble in water and that it supported combustion much more vigorously than common air. Animals survived in it much longer than when they respired in a like volume of ordinary air. Priestley further showed that the quality of air was deteriorated by breathing, precisely as in combustion. In 1776 Priestley seemed not to have been aware, however, of the formation of carbonic acid gas during respiration, although this fact had been discovered by Joseph Black in 1757.

Joseph Black (1728–1799) (11) was professor of chemistry at Glasgow and Edinburgh. One of his most notable researches was his demonstration that when magnesium carbonate or calcium carbonate was heated, carbonic acid gas was evolved; then the "mild alkalies," as the carbonates were called, were converted into magnesium oxide and calcium oxide (quicklime) respectively, and these, in contact with water, generated "strong alkalies" (hydroxides). He identified the carbon dioxide thus prepared with that formed in combustion by showing that either, when passed into limewater, regenerated carbonate of lime. Furthermore, he was the first to breathe into limewater and observe the formation of a precipitate of calcium carbonate. The limewater turbidity test was employed by all subsequent investigators of respiration to detect carbonic acid gas.

Steven Hales' Contribution to Analysis of Air

Steven Hales (1677–1761) (12) was curate of the parish of Teddington. He devoted much effort to experimenting in plant physiology, and in 1727 published his famous treatise *Vegetable Statiks* in which he described his measurements of leaf area, water transpiration, and sap pressure by plants. He attempted to analyze atmospheric air, and made the notable observation that when phosphorus was burned in air enclosed in a vessel, part of the air was absorbed in water.

Cavendish, in 1766, described "inflammable air," later called hydrogen by Lavoisier. He obtained it by the action of hydrochloric acid on iron, zinc, or tin. He observed that when "inflammable gas" was mixed with air an explosive mixture was formed. After exploding such a mixture in a flask, he noted that the walls were covered with moisture; Cavendish thus drew the correct conclusion that water had been formed by the union of "fire air" with "inflammable air."

In the language used by Priestley, Scheele's "foul air" was phlogisticated air, later called nitrogen, and his "fire air" was oxygen. Daniel Rutherford (13) was the first to obtain nitrogen in a state of comparative purity. He burned a candle in a closed vessel and when it was extinguished, absorbed fixed air by alkali. There was some residual oxygen in his nitrogen. The first method for nearly completely removing oxygen from nitrogen was by burning phosphorus in the mixture, as Hales had done.

Black's proof that calcium carbonate was precipitated when expired air was bubbled through limewater led Lavoisier to conclude that respiration involved combustion within the body.

Lavoisier's Investigations on Combustion

From the investigations of his predecessors Lavoisier knew that atmospheric air consisted of two kinds of "air," or gas. It was established that nitrogen and oxygen were slightly soluble in water, whereas fixed air (from combustion, fermentation, calcination of limestone, and from expired air) was much more soluble in water, and was completely absorbed from its mixtures with other gases by alkalies. Hales' observations had proved further that by burning phosphorus in air, in "fire air," or in oxygen, that this gas was completely removed. Lavoisier confirmed the observation first made by Jean Rey, in 1630, that tin and lead increased in weight when calcined (14).

In 1777, Lavoisier published his experiments on the respiration of animals (15). In it he stated his theory that ordinary air was a mixture of oxygen and nitrogen gases. He showed that during respiration the nitrogen fraction remained unchanged, but the oxygen was diminished, and that which disappeared was replaced by carbonic acid gas. Thus he verified the discovery of Black and corrected the statements of Priestley, who held that when atmospheric air is completely deprived of phlogiston, it became oxygen gas, and when completely saturated with phlogiston, it became nitrogen gas. Blood exposed to air acquired a florid red color, while at the same time the air was deteriorated for respiration. Hence Priestley (16) assumed that the function of respiration was to deprive the blood of phlogiston. Lavoisier clarified the situation once for all.

In 1783 Lavoisier (15) published an account of his studies on the respiratory metabolism of a guinea pig. The animal was kept in an air-tight box through which was passed a current of air. The incoming air was freed from carbon dioxide by passing it through a bottle containing a potash solution. The outgoing air was passed through a similar potash bottle to absorb the carbon dioxide which was given off from the lungs of the guinea pig during the experiment. In this bottle carbonic acid gas equivalent to 3.33 grams of carbon was collected in a ten-hour period. A second guinea pig was placed in a well insulated box containing ice. The heat given off by the animal in 24 hours melted 13 ounces of ice. Lavoisier calculated from these data that the amount of ice which would be melted by the oxidation of 3.33 grams of carbon was 10.4 ounces. This was the earliest attempt to determine quantitatively the magnitude of the combustion involved in respiration, and the amount of heat produced by the body in the process.

In 1785 Lavoisier, working with Seguin as subject, as well as with animals, established the fact that of every 100 grams of oxygen absorbed in respiration, only 81 parts reappeared as carbonic acid gas. He concluded that the remaining 19 grams were combined with hydrogen to form water and that respiration was, therefore, accompanied by combustion of both carbon and hydrogen. Oxygen in inspired and expired air was determined by loss of volume when phosphorus was burned in the sample in a closed vessel.

With Seguin as his subject, Lavoisier demonstrated that oxygen was absorbed and carbon dioxide expired in proportion to the mechanical work performed. When fasting, Seguin absorbed a greater amount of oxygen at a temperature of 12° C. than at 26° C. When he took food but remained at rest, he absorbed more oxygen than when without food. But the greatest stimulus to oxygen absorption during respiration resulted from doing mechanical work. The amount of oxygen utilized during respiration as the result of work rose to two or three times that absorbed when he was taking his ordinary amount of food and resting.

By these experiments Lavoisier revealed the basic facts regarding energy metabolism. Basal metabolism (at rest and without food) was increased 10 per cent by exposure to cold; 50 per cent by taking food; and 200 to 300 per cent by the combined effects of food and exercise. Later investigators were to find that Lavoisier's results were far from accurate; however, they sufficed to support conclusions fully confirmed by other more accurate experiments.

The Principle of Cooling By Evaporation

Apparently Benjamin Franklin (17) was the first to call attention to the cooling effect of evaporation of liquids. In a letter written in 1757, he described the sudden fall of the mercury in a thermometer when it was moistened with alcohol and the fluid allowed to evaporate. The process of cooling the bulb was hastened by blowing upon it. This discovery showed that heat was required to evaporate liquids, and that in the process of evaporation of liquids heat is absorbed. Franklin expressed the belief that the bodies of humans and animals are kept warm by combustion of the food eaten.

Crawford's Observations on Animal Heat

The pioneer in the study of animal heat was Adair Crawford (1748–1795) (18). He was a pupil of Joseph Black who, in addition to his great achievement in the study of carbonic acid gas, discovered the specific heats of substances. Using Black's data on specific heats, in his own calculations, Crawford employed the following technic for the study of animal heat:

He burned charcoal in oxygen (Priestley's dephlogisticated air) in a closed vessel by igniting it with a burning-glass, and noted that no water was formed. However, when he burned a candle in oxygen, water condensed in the vessel. This showed him that the candle contained what Cavendish had termed inflammable air, whereas carbon did not. When he took 100 ounce measures of oxygen, and altered by the combustion of either wax or charcoal, or by the respiration of a guinea pig, the quantity of heat transferred to 31 pounds of water in his insulated vessel (calorimeter), the temperature of the water was raised in three experiments by 2.1, 1.93, and 1.73 degrees F. respectively. He concluded that the quantity of heat produced when a given quantity of oxygen was altered by animal respiration was nearly equal to that yielded when the same quantity of oxygen was altered by combustion of wax or charcoal. Crawford concluded that the heat thus derived had its source in the conversion of oxygen into fixed air (carbon dioxide) or into water.

Studies on the Magnitude of Carbon Metabolism in Man

Allen and Pepys (19) concluded from many observations on human subjects that the volume of oxygen lost in respiration was exactly replaced by the carbonic acid gas generated.

Among those who devoted much time to estimating the rate of breathing and the volume of air expired at each breath by different individuals (20) were Allen and Pepys, Prout and Menies, and H. Davy. Their objective was to accumulate statistical data as a basis for calculating the total volume of air inspired and expired during twenty-four hour periods. Coathupe (21) made numerous determinations of the per cent of carbon dioxide in expired air of many people and found it to vary between 3.63 and 4.37 per cent. From data on the rate and volume of respirations accumulated by several investigators, Thomson calculated that in twenty-four hours an adult man used 8,957.76 cubic inches of oxygen gas for conversion into carbonic acid gas. This corresponded to an output of carbon dioxide equivalent to 2.66 ounces of carbon exhaled by the lungs.

Edward Smith's Studies of Energy Metabolism

In 1857 Edward Smith (22) published his numerous observations on the effects of different conditions of life on the magnitude of energy requirements of human subjects. His studies included about 1200 observations, many on himself. Smith collected the air expired during short periods; then, using average values for volume of air expired and rate of breathing, he calculated the amount of carbon dioxide formed in the body in one hour. His studies included data on the effects on respiration of day and night, sitting, lying, standing, riding a horse, riding in first- and in second-class coaches, rowing, swimming, walking, running, weight-carrying, ascending and descending stairs, laboring on a treadwheel, reading aloud, singing, bending forward while sitting, and other exercises. He also took into consideration the effect of exposure to sunlight, to darkness, increase or decrease of artificial heat, cold bathing, sponging, shower bathing, and the influence of meals at various times of day.

Smith analyzed his urine and stated that the amount of urea passed corresponded with the concurrent variations in the amount of nitrogenous substance in his food. He noted comparatively little change in the amount of urea voided during wide variation in the amount of labor performed, whereas the carbonic acid gas evolved increased in proportion to the amount of exercise. In 1859 (23) he reported the following results:

	CO_2 *expired per hour*
During sleep	19.0 grams
Lying down and approaching sleep	23.0 grams
In sitting posture	29.0 grams
Walking at rate of 2 miles per hr.	70.0 grams
Walking at rate of 3 miles per hr.	100.0 grams
On treadwheel, ascending at rate of 28.65 feet per minute	189.6 grams

Treadwheel Experiment on Source of Muscular Energy

Smith's respiration studies had a significant effect on the thoughts of physiologists and chemists concerning the source of muscular power, however they failed to secure the attention they deserved because of the high authority of Liebig. In 1842 (24) Liebig had stated his views concerning the chemical phenomena occurring in muscles during exertion: "As an immediate effect of the manifestation of mechanical force, we see, that a part of the muscular substance loses its vital properties, its character of life; that this portion separates from the living part, and loses its capacity for growth and its power of resistance. We find that this change of properties is accompanied by the entrance of a foreign body (oxygen) into the composition of the muscular fibre (just as the acid lost its chemical character by combining with zinc); and all experience proves, that this vitality is accelerated or retarded according to the amount of force employed to produce motion. Nay, it may be safely affirmed, that they are mutually proportional; that a rapid transformation of muscular fibre, or, as it may be called, a rapid change of matter, determines a greater amount of mechanical force; and conversely, that a greater amount of mechanical motion (mechanical force expended in motion) determines a more rapid change of matter. . . .

The amount of nitrogenous food necessary to restore the equilibrium between waste and supply is directly proportional to the amount of tissue metamorphosed."

Edward Smith (25) attempted to test the validity of Liebig's theory by an experiment with human subjects. He devised a treadwheel with which the weight lifted and the distance lifted could be determined. Four prisoners, designated A, B, C and D, climbed eight-inch steps on the treadwheel. They worked in alternate quarter hours, resting during the intervening quarters in a sitting posture. The period of actual labor was 3.5 hours daily. The total average ascent per hour was 2,160 feet or 1.432 miles per day. The nitrogen eliminated in the urines of the men was established during twenty-four-hour periods beginning with the day's work. The following results were obtained:

TREADWHEEL EXPERIMENT OF E. SMITH

Wt. Kg.	*Ascent in meters*	*Days of work*	*External work done in Kg.-Meters*	*Total N eliminated (grams)*	*Wt. of dry muscle corresponding to nitrogen eliminated.*
A 47.6	23,045	10	1,896,942	171.3	1181.2 grams
B 49	23,045	10	1,129,205	174.5	1121.7 grams
C 55	20,741	9	1,140,755	168.0	1080.1 grams
D 56	20,741	9	1,161,496	159.3	1024.3 grams

From the data in the table, Smith calculated that: The average external work per man per day was 119,605 Kg.-meters. The average nitrogen output per man per day was 17.7 grams. The weight of dry muscle corresponding to the average nitrogen evolved per day was 114.0 grams.

Smith could not estimate the energy equivalent of muscle substance, and therefore could not assert, on the basis of his nitrogen excretion data and energy expended, that the energy for muscular work could not have been derived from muscle degradation as Liebig claimed. But his experimental demonstration of the striking increase in carbonic acid gas output during respiration as the work performed increased was almost conclusive evidence that the muscles were deriving energy from non-nitrogenous food.

In 1860 Bischoff and Voit (26) published the results of their experiments with a dog. In the tests the dog was subjected first to hunger periods, and then to periods of eating greatly contrasting amounts of nitrogenous food. They observed that the output of urea ran proportional to the nitrogen ingested. However, because they believed the theory of Liebig, they concluded that the greater output of urea when the dog was fed a high protein diet must have been due to greater internal work (greater metabolism of the internal organs, digestion, and peristalsis). In their great publication "The Laws of Nutrition of Carnivores" Bischoff and Voit had stated their conclusion that fat and carbohydrate when metabolized in the body yield only heat, never motion. They stated that their results supported Liebig's assertion that foods were divided into two classifications: *plastic* and *respiratory*.

Bischoff and Voit were compelled to change their views when they found that the urea output of a dog fed a certain amount of protein was no greater when the animal was subjected to severe exertion than when it was at rest, while the carbonic acid expired in the breath increased progressively as work was done. They tentatively offered the explanation that the muscles derived force from non-nitrogenous food, but the subject still remained controversial.

The Mountain Climbing Experiment

A. Fick and F. J. Wislicenus were professors of physiology and of chemistry, respectively, at Zurich. In 1866 they conducted an experiment in mountain climbing to test the validity of Smith's treadwheel experiment, with the objective of putting Liebig's theory of muscular work to a crucial test (27). They abstained from nitrogenous food for seventeen hours before beginning the ascent of the Faulhorn, a peak in Switzerland with an altitude of 1656 meters. The climb to the summit required six hours. During this time and for another seven hours afterward, taking only carbohydrate and fat as food, they collected their urines and analyzed them for nitrogen content. During the thirteen hour period Fick lost 5.74 grams of nitrogen and Wislicenus lost 5.54 grams.

Fick and Wislicenus pointed out that when going on long and fatiguing expeditions, the chamois hunters of Western Switzerland took only bacon-fat and sugar as provisions; they said these substances were more nourishing than meat. The professors said, "What they mean by this expression is that they have learned by experience that in the form of fat and sugar they can most conveniently carry with them a rich provision of force-producing oxidizable matter." Discussing their own experiment they stated, "We can assert, from our own experience in the ascent of the Faulhorn, that in spite of the amount of work and the abstinence for thirty-one hours from albuminous food, neither of us felt in the least exhausted. This could hardly have been the case if our muscular force had not been sustained by the non-nitrogenous food of which we partook."

At the time of this mountain climbing experiment the caloric values of individual foodstuffs had not been determined, so only general conclusions were possible. It seemed clear to them, however, that the amount of nitrogenous substance necessary to supply the nitrogen lost from their bodies during and after the climb were entirely inadequate to supply their energy needs.

Lawes and Gilbert's Discussion of the Fick-Wislicenus Experiment

Immediately following the publication of the mountain climbing experiment two important criticisms of Liebig's theory of the source of muscular energy appeared. The first of these statements was by Lawes and Gilbert (28), in which they cited their report made in 1852 concerning the source of muscular force. This report had stated that they had provided evidence that during exercise of ordinary and extraordinary muscular force, an animal requires non-nitrogenous rather than nitrogenous food. This belief was based on their observation of the immediate and pronounced response of the respiratory system to effect more rapid and deeper breathing when physical effort was made. They had observed this behavior in hunting horses, cab-horses, fox-hounds, pugilists, and others who underwent extreme exertion. One of their experiments employed two pigs, both regularly in a state of relative inactivity, but one fed double the amount of nitrogenous food given the other. The nitrogen eliminated as urea paralleled roughly the protein intake, and was quite independent of muscular activity, which was the same in the two animals. Hence they asserted that the nitrogen eliminated could not be considered as a measure of muscular work.

Edward Frankland's Studies on the Origin of Muscular Power

The second and most important discussion of the experiment of Fick and Wislicenus was by Edward Frankland (1825–1899). At the time of the mountain climbing experiment he was Professor at the Royal Institution (London), the successor of Faraday, and at the Royal College as successor of Hofmann. He had been a pupil of Bunsen and of Kolbe, and was notable for his discovery of organometallic compounds of tin and mercury, and for the synthesis of hydrocarbons by the zinc alkyl reaction. The omission of his name from even comprehensive treatises on nutrition indicates that he is not generally known as the first to study foods for the quantitative energy values which they yielded on combustion.

Frankland (29), in commenting on the Fick-Wislicenus experiment pointed out that its results could be interpreted only by taking into account the amount of energy evolved in the combustion of a unit of muscle substance, and by considering the work-equivalent of this heat energy. The energy of different foods as derived from combustion had not hitherto been determined, a void in the knowledge of foods in relation to muscular force which Frankland sought to fill. He further pointed out that the energy which the body derived from protein was equal to the difference between the total heat of combustion less the heat of combustion of urea, the principal substance in which the nitrogen of protein foods was eliminated. But since both uric and hippuric acids were also contained in urine, he determined their combustion energy release.

Frankland's Calorie Values of Foods and Metabolic Products

Frankland employed a combustion calorimeter which he said had been devised by Lewis Thomson. It consisted of a copper tube into which a sample of two grams of a food mixed with potassium chlorate was charged. The tube was equipped with a fuse made of a thin cotton thread soaked in potassium chlorate and dried; one end of the thread was buried in the explosive charge while the other end extended outside the open end of the tube. Frankland used a calorimeter which contained two liters of water in an insulated vessel. The closed end of the copper tube containing the charge was submerged in the water, the fuse was lighted, and while it was burning he submerged a diving bell over the upper end to collect the gases evolved after the charge was fired. The hot gases were thus confined in the bell until they dissipated their heat from the explosion to the water and bell. The water in the calorimeter was stirred by moving the bell about. The temperature of the water before and after the combustion of the sample had taken place was the basis for calculation of the heat generated from oxidation of the sample. He determined the heat evolved from igniting the potassium chlorate alone and made other necessary corrections, e.g., the heat loss by the escaping gases, and the work done by the gases generated in overcoming the pressure of the atmosphere.

By this procedure Frankland ascertained the heats of combustion of twenty-nine foods in common use. His values were the mean of three determinations. The following is a list of values for heat units determined on foods dried at 100° C., and also some metabolic end products.

FRANKLAND'S HEAT-UNITS (SMALL CALORIES PER GRAM)

Egg white	4896	Beef muscle (fat-free)	5103
Lean beef	5313	Beef fat	9069
Butter	7264	Purified albumen	4998
Ham, lean, boiled	4343	Hippuric acid	5383
Isinglass	4520	Uric acid	2615
Cod liver oil	9107	Urea	2206
Lump sugar (not dried)	3348		

In his calculation Frankland used the Joule mechanical equivalent of heat, viz., 1 kilogram of water raised 1° C. equals 423 kilogram-meters of energy. For the purpose of interpreting the data of Fick and Wislicenus he calculated the actual energy in kilogram-meters of force developed by oxidation of one gram of the following substances:

Beef muscle (fat-free)	2161 Kg.-Meters	Hippuric acid	2280 Kg.-Meters
Beef fat	3841 Kg.-Meters	Uric acid	1108 Kg.-Meters
Purified albumen	2117 Kg.-Meters	Urea	943 Kg.-Meters

Summary of Conclusions Derived from Frankland's Data

	Fick	Wislicenus	
Weight of dry muscle equivalent to urinary nitrogen excreted	37.17	37.00	
Energy capable of being derived from their muscles	68,690	68,376	Kg.-Meters
Minimum external work performed in ascent	129,096	148,656	Kg.-Meters
Calculated circulatory and respiratory work performed during the secent (internal work)	30,541	35,631	Kg.-Meters
Total ascertainable work performed	159,637	184,287	Kg.-Meters

By introducing the quantitative energy concept of foods and body tissues Frankland solved the problem. He confirmed the conclusions already reached by Lawes and Gilbert, Edward Smith, and Fick and Wislicenus; namely, that muscles work at the expense of energy derived from the oxidation of non-nitrogenous foods, viz., fats and carbohydrates.

Determination of the Respiratory Quotients with Different Foods

In competition for the prize offered by the Academy at Paris for the best essay on animal heat, Despretz and Dulong in 1823 attempted to determine the quantitative relations between oxygen absorbed, carbon dioxide excreted, and energy released by the body as heat or work. Their results did not bring to light any new concept or viewpoint.

The respiration studies of Regnault and Reiset (30) (1849) were more important because of the greater refinement of their technic. They were first to devise a closed system for respiration studies, and with this apparatus they determined with considerable accuracy the relation between oxygen absorbed and carbonic acid gas excreted during respiration. This relation became known as the *respiratory quotient* (R.Q.) $= \left(\frac{\text{Vol. } CO_2}{\text{Vol. } O_2}\right)$. Regnault and Reiset experimented with dogs, rabbits, frogs, reptiles, beetles, silkworms, earthworms, and hibernating and awakening marmots. The R.Q.

values varied from 0.62 to 1.04 when different foods were given. In 1840 H. V. Regnault (1810–1878) became professor of physics and chemistry at the University of Paris.

Frederick Bidder (1810–1894) and Carl Schmidt (1822–1894) at the University of Dorpat taught and investigated the physiology and chemistry of nutrition. They surpassed their predecessors in the accuracy and scope of their studies. Their objectives were to determine oxygen absorption, carbonic acid, and urea elimination in fasting animals, and then to observe on the same animals the effects on metabolism of the ingestion of protein, fat, and carbohydrate individually. Bidder and Schmidt used cats and dogs in these experiments. They were first to study extensively the functions of bile in digestion and metabolism. In 1852 they published their famous book *Die Verdauungssäfte und der Stoffwechsel,* which had great influence on the thinking of physiologists for many years.

Pettenkofer and Voit's Studies with Their Respiration Apparatus

Max von Pettenkofer (1818–1901) was the first professor of hygiene in any university. He was at one time assistant to Liebig, and taught a course in practical chemistry. Among his contributions to physiological chemistry was a qualitative test for bile salts (1845) which is described in textbooks today. He also devised the first test for free carbonic acid in water by its action on rosolic acid (1862), and a qualitative test for strophanthin (1862). Pettenkofer's greatest achievement was the designing of a respiration apparatus large enough to accommodate a man. With this he and his famous associate Carl Voit conducted more critical metabolism studies with men and animals than had any of their predecessors. They determined with considerable accuracy the respiratory quotients of protein, carbohydrate, and fat when metabolized in the body.

Max Rubner's Metabolism Studies

Max Rubner (1854–1932) was one of Voit's most illustrious pupils. He determined the calorific values of urine and feces under different dietary conditions, and perfected the methods for computation which have been used in modern animal calorimetry (31). He refined the experimental technics which enabled him to fully establish the relation between skin surface and food requirements of animals (32). He showed that the heat value of metabolism in a resting animal is proportional to the area of the body surface. The idea was not new, having been predicted in 1839 by Robiquet (33).

The Discovery of the Specific Dynamic Action of Foods

Later Rubner became professor of physiology at the University of Berlin. For many years he devoted himself to the study of the magnitude of energy exchange in the bodies of men and animals. He established the fact that carbohydrate and fat were interchangeable in metabolism on the basis of energy-equivalents. One hundred calories in fat are the nutritive equivalent of the same number in carbohydrate. This was called the isodynamic law of Rubner. When foods of different classes were given to an animal in moderate quantities, Rubner found that 100 grams of fat were equivalent to 211 grams of protein, or 232 grams of starch, or 234 grams of cane sugar, or 256 grams of glucose (34).

In 1902 Rubner published his observations on the influence of foodstuffs on metabolism (35). He found that when 100 calories in the form of meat were ingested by a dog the heat production (energy metabolism) was increased by 30 calories over the values obtained with the same animal at rest and without food. When 100 calories were given as cane sugar the increase in metabolism was only 5.8 calories. The increase in metabolism when 100 calories in fat was given amounted to about 4.0 calories. Any increase in the ingestion of protein led to proportionate increase in the magnitude of metabolism. Rubner defined this effect as the "specific dynamic action" of the various foodstuffs.

Magnus-Levy's Observations On the Basal Metabolic Rate

In 1895 Magnus-Levy (36) first applied respiratory quotient measurements in the study of persons suffering from diseases. He employed a portable respiration apparatus which had been designed by N. Zuntz. With this he made observations at the bedside in hospitals. His most important discovery resulted from tests on subjects who suffered from abnormal thyroid function. In those with hyperthyroid activity he noted a marked elevation in the metabolic rate, whereas in those who suffered from myxedema and underfunctioning of the thyroid gland, there was a marked lowering of the metabolic rate. This was the beginning of the use of basal metabolism studies in clinical work for diagnostic purposes.

As far as fundamental concepts were concerned, respiration and calorimetry studies had made their major contribution to nutrition investigations with the publication of these pioneering investigations of energy metabolism. In clinical work, basal metabolism studies have become of great value. From the standpoint of practical dietetics the knowledge of calorie requirements and the factors that influence them is of great importance.

REFERENCES

1. Pliny: The Natural History of Pliny. 6 vols. Vol. 3, p. 482. Bostock, J. and Riley, H. T. London, 1855–57.
2. Philo of Byzantium. Cited by Robert Fludd: Technica Macrocosmi Historia (1618) p. 471.
3. Van Helmont, J. B.: Ortus Medicinae (1652) p. 88.
4. Boyle, R.: Cited from A Short History of Chemistry, by J. R. Partington, 1951, pp. 73–76.
5. From Birch's History of the Royal Society, London. (1756–57). 4 vols. Vol. 1, p. 180.
6. Hooke, R.: Micrographia (1665). Alembic Club Reprint No. 5.
7. Lower, R.: Tractus de corde, 1669, pp. 61–166. Cited from T. Thomson: Animal Chemistry, Edinburgh (1843) p. 607.
8. Mayow, J.: Tractus quinque medico-physici (1674). From F. G. Donan's trans. in Ostwald's Klassiker No. 125.
9. Scheele, C. W.: Alembic Club Reprint No. 8.
10. Priestley, J.: Experiments and Observations on Air (1775), ii, 30; iii, 55.
11. Black, J.: Lectures on the Elements of Chemistry (1803). Edited by John Robison.
12. Hales, S.: Vegetable Statiks. London (1727); Ramsey, W. The Gases of the Atmosphere, London (1896) p. 33.
13. Rutherford, D.: Trans. by Crum Brown. J. Chem. Ed. *12,* 370 (1935).
14. Rey, J.: Trans. in Alembic Club Reprint No. 11.
15. Lavoisier, A. L.: Mémoires de l'Académie de Sciences, 1777, p. 185.

16. Lavoisier, A. L. and Seguin: Ann. de chim. *91,* 318 (1814).

17. Franklin, B.: Letter from Benjamin Franklin to Dr. L. at Charlestown, So. Carolina, April 14th, 1757, cited by H. Boynton; The Beginnings of Modern Science, Pub. for the Classics Club, J. Walter Black, New York, 1948, pp. 162–167.

18. Crawford, A.: Experiments and Observations on Animal Heat. London, 1778, p. 18. Also, J. S. Haldane: J. Physiol. *16,* 123 (1894).

19. Allen, W. and Pepys, W. H.: Schweigger's Journ. *1,* 182 (1811); Philos. Trans. *2,* 410 (1809).

20. Thomson, T.: Animal Chemistry. Edinburgh, 1843, p. 610.

21. Coathupe, C. T.: Philos. Mag. (3rd ser.) *14,* 401 (1839).

22. Smith, Edward: Philos. Mag. (4th ser.) *14,* 546 (1857).

23. Smith, Edward: Philos. Trans. for 1859, p. 709.

24. Liebig, J. von: Organic Chemistry in its Applications to Physiology and Pathology. 1842, pp. 220–221.

25. Smith, Edward: Experimental Inquiries into the Chemical and other Phenomena of Respiration and their Modifications by Various Physical Agencies, Philos. Trans. London, *149,* 681–714 (1859).

26. Bischoff, T. L. W. and Voit, C.: Die Gesetze der Ernährung des Fleischfressers, Leipzig (1860).

27. Fick, A. and Wislicenus, F. J.: Philos. Mag. (4th ser.) *31,* 159 (1866).

28. Lawes, J. B. and Gilbert, J. H.: Philos. Mag. (4th ser.) 32, 55–64 (1866).

29. Frankland, E.: Philos. Mag. (4th ser.) 32, 182–199 (1866).

30. Regnault, H. V. and Reiset, J.: Ann. de chim. et de phys. *26,* 299–519 (1849).

31. Rubner, M.: Zeitschr. f. Biol. *19,* 535 (1883).

32. Rubner, M.: Zeitschr. f. Biol. *21,* 250–334, 337–410 (1885); Calorimetrische Methodik. Marburg (1891) pp. 1–36.

33. Robiquet, P. J.: Bull. Acad. Roy. de Med. (1839) III, 1094.

34. Rubner, M.: History of the development of energy utilization in vertebrates. Sitzungsber. d. Preussischen akad. d. Wissensch. Physikal. u. Math. Klasse. *17,* 313 (1931).

35. Rubner, M.: Energiegesetze (1902).

36. Magnus-Levy, A.: Berliner Klin. Wochnschr. 32, 650–52 (1895); Von Noorden's Handbuch der Pathologie des Stoffwechsels, Berlin *1,* 207 (1906).

11

The Evolution of the Chemical Analysis of Foods

CHEMICAL ANALYSIS OF FOODS means the determination of their constituents. After more than two centuries of effort, chemists are still seeking to determine which among the chemical substances present in our numerous natural foods have significance in animal physiology. The end is not yet in sight. The identification of essential constituents of the adequate diet and their chemical detection and quantitative determination are problems which have confronted chemists since the beginning of the effective study of nutrition problems. This chapter presents a discussion of the investigation of these problems, the ways in which chemists reasoned and experimented, and the results derived from the research.

The first clear concept of analysis of naturally occurring materials of the vegetable and animal kingdoms was expressed in 1660 by Nichasius le Febure (1610–1674), a French apothecary and author of the famous work *Traité de Chymie.* In this book he said that it was the objective of chemists to separate "homogenial" from "heterogenial" substances. Le Febure was not interested in foods but in ingredients of vegetables, root, bark, flower, or leaf which had medicinal values. What he said about separating pure substances from mixtures applies as well to nutritional investigation of foods as to his stated objectives. In fact, food analysis — the quantitative determination of components of foods which were believed to have physiological importance — was for many years based in great measure upon a body of knowledge which has been accumulated by chemists whose interest was in medicinal drugs.

In chronological sequence the quantitative determination of the percentage composition of organic substances in terms of carbon, hydrogen, and nitrogen deserves first consideration. This order of discussion is justified because, in the view of chemists during the first quarter of the nineteenth century, the provision of carbon and hydrogen for respiration, and of nitrogenous (albuminous) material for construction and repair of muscles and organs of animals represented the essential features of the nutrition problem.

The Combustion Method of Analysis of Organic Substances

Of outstanding importance to the advancement of physiology was the completion by A. L. Lavoisier (1743–1794) (1) of the experimental studies of Joseph Black, Priestley, and Cavendish on carbonic acid gas, oxygen, and hydrogen, and his masterly demonstration of the nature of combustion. He proved that respiration in animals is a process of oxidation of the carbon and hydrogen of food. Lavoisier attempted to determine the composition of alcohol by burning a known quantity of it to carbon dioxide and water, and measuring the amounts of these which were formed. Unfortunately, because Lavoisier could not devise a technic which caused complete oxidation of his sample he failed to secure accurate results. He detected acetic acid as a product of incomplete oxidation of alcohol.

The problem of determining the content of carbon and hydrogen in organic substances was solved in 1811 by Gay-Lussac and Thenard (2). They mixed the sample to be analyzed with potassium chlorate, and collected for analysis the gases evolved in combustion of the heated mixture. It was this method which William Prout (3) employed for the analysis of the foods discussed in his famous lectures (1827) before the Royal Society on "The Ultimate Composition of Simple Alimentary Substances."

Liebig criticized Prout's apparatus (4) and improved upon it by using lead chromate instead of copper oxide, which had previously been employed as the oxidizing agent. However, it was not until 1835 when J. B. A. Dumas (5) showed how properly to prepare copper oxide for combustion analyses and described a method for carrying out the procedure, that satisfactory results were secured. In 1841 Varrentrapp and Will (6), both students of Liebig, described an improved method for determining the content of nitrogen in organic substances which replaced all others for many years. It was based on the observation that when any organic substance tested was heated strongly with an excess of potassium hydroxide, its nitrogen was converted into ammonia which could be accurately measured.

This was the method employed generally by nutrition investigators for the next forty-two years.

In 1883, however, J. Kjeldahl (7) described his method, which depended upon the easy and complete conversion of the nitrogen of most organic substances into ammonia; this conversion was achieved by boiling the substances with concentrated sulfuric acid and a catalyst. Because of its simplicity, speed, and accuracy Kjeldahl's method became the one most widely used by food analysts. It is used even to this day.

In our account of the studies of Boussingault it was pointed out that the influence of Mulder and Liebig was so great that for some decades their followers, with but few murmurs of dissent, accepted the idea that the nutritive value of foods for tissue formation (growth, repair of waste, milk, egg or wool production) could be assessed on the basis of their nitrogen content. Although the theory that proteins were alike in different natural foods was found to be progressively more disappointing decade by decade, it was not completely discredited until about the year 1900, as related in Chapter 4.

The Earliest Steps in the Study of Naturally Occurring Organic Substances

The writings of investigators in this field afford abundant evidence that every item of new knowledge concerning the composition of vegetable foods entered into the speculations of some investigator. It is important, therefore, that the story of progress in separating and identifying the individual chemical constituents of natural products be here related. The advances in knowledge in this field were in great measure made possible by the application of organic and other special solvents to food and drug plants. By this means various individual chemical substances were isolated and their properties studied. Progress by the earliest chemists who studied vegetable materials was determined largely by the discovery of suitable solvents for such fractionations. The following items are of importance in this connection.

Discovery of Alcohol

The discovery of a method for the large-scale production of alcohol was an important event in the history of pharmacy and of organic chemistry. It was unknown as an isolated substance until about the year 1100 A.D., when chemists learned to attach a cooled condenser to the vessels in which they distilled various materials. This enabled them to collect volatile products which hitherto had been allowed to escape. Progress was not rapid, however, and it was not until the fourteenth century that alcohol was obtained in abundance in the form of a distillate called "spirit of wine," which contained about 85 per cent alcohol. In addition to wine, fermented beverages of the beer type were sources of alcohol. An unknown alchemist who wrote under the name of Raymundus Lullus (1235–1315) said of the distillate from wine, then called *aqua vitae* (water of life), "Its taste exceedeth all other tastes, and its smell all other smells."

Spirit of wine was employed by Arnaldo de Villa Nova about the end of the thirteenth century as a solvent for drugs, to secure "tinctures" for medicinal purposes. He taught philosophy and medicine in Barcelona and Paris. His new method for making tinctures was adopted by apothecaries.

Ether

Ether was first prepared by Valerius Cordus (1515–1544), a German youth famous also for his studies in botany. He made ether by heating alcohol with sulfuric acid, as is done today. Eventually it became a commonly used solvent for extracting fatty substances from plant and animal materials.

Steam Distillation

From early times, apothecaries found it profitable to distill water in which fragrant herbs were immersed, and to condense the steam which passed over carrying with it the odorous principles to form fragrant "waters" for medicinal and cosmetic purposes. This method was effective in separating from other constituents of plants the pure "essential" oils (essences). From different plants were secured pure hydrocarbons of the type called by organic chemists *terpenes,* such as oil of turpentine, juniper, peppermint, and lemon. Certain plants yielded alcohols such as methanol, benzyl-alcohol, menthol, and geraniol. Some yielded cyclic hydrocarbons such as cymine, myrcine, and pinine, while still others yielded phenols such as thymol; or aldehydes such as geranial, citronellal, benzaldehyde, and vanillin; or ketones such as camphor and menthol. From valerian, valerianic acid was obtained, and from certain plants were extracted acetate of benzyl-alcohol, cynnamyl-alcohol, and methylbenzoate. By means of steam distillation of plants of various kinds these different classes of organic compounds were made available in pure form for study by the earliest organic chemists. Their value for the development of theory, interconversion, and synthesis was incalculable.

While these volatile-with-steam constituents of plants were never considered to be nutrients for animals, their preparation was an epoch-making step in illuminating the bewildering complexity of organic nature. Steam distillation was popularized among apothecaries by Jean Beguin. About the year 1604 Beguin opened in Paris a school for teaching pharmacy. He wrote for his students two notable books, *Novum Lumen Chymicum* (New Light on Chemistry) (1608) and *Tyrocinium Chymicum* (Chemistry for Beginners). Beguin had great influence in disseminating knowledge and stimulating investigations for separating medicinal principles in concentrated form.

The Discovery of Formic Acid

John Ray (1628–1705), the father of English natural history, was intrumental in bringing about the discovery of formic acid (8). Much of Ray's experimentation was based on the findings of other investigators. Samuel Fischer told him that "when ants are distilled with water, they yield a spirit like that of vinegar, or rather like spirit of *viride aeris*" (sulfur dioxide). Dr. Hulse had written Ray to say that he had found in Lanham's Garden of Health the statement "Cast the flowers of chicory among a heap of ants, and they (the flowers) will soon become as red as blood." Dr. Hulse said he had tried the experiment and that it succeeded. Fischer had further contributed the information that "If you stir a heap of ants so as to rouse them, they will let fall on the instrument you use a liquor which, if you presently smell to, will twinge the nose like newly distilled oil of vitriol."

In 1749 Andreas Sigismund Marggraf (1709–1782) obtained formic acid by distilling ants with steam (9). He neutralized the acid distillate with potash and also with ammonia, and found that he had prepared crystallizable salts. The acid distillate, he discovered, would attack metals and form salts. Marggraf was Court apothecary in Berlin from 1735 until 1754, when he became head of the chemical laboratory in the University of Berlin.

Acetic Acid

Acetic acid was the only acid known to the ancients. It was not isolated until toward the end of the twelfth century because distillation technic was in too primitive a state. But in the fourteenth century concentrated solutions of acetic acid were secured from vinegar. The first to study the properties of acetic acid in different dilutions with water was Pierre August Adet (1763–1832) (10), at one time Ambassador to the United States from France. "Glacial" acetic acid was first prepared in 1703 by Stahl, of phlogiston fame, by freezing vinegar and decanting the unfrozen solution. The liquor poured off was much more acid than the solution before separation of ice crystals. Repetition of the freezing process yielded crystallizable acetic acid.

Chemicals Obtained by Destructive Distillation

Ammonia water containing some ammonium carbonate was prepared from early times by apothecaries, and sold for medicinal use. Usually it was prepared by destructive distillation of horn, and was known as spirit of hartshorn.

Wood distillate, known as pyroligneous acid, was first obtained by Johann Rudolph Glauber (1604–1668) by heating wood in a closed retort and collecting the more volatile products which passed over. This material became an important source of acetic acid, acetone, and wood alcohol (methanol).

Hennig Brand (11), a merchant of Hamburg who entertained himself with experiments in alchemy was the first to procure phosphorus. In 1669 he destructively distilled the solids of urine remaining in the retort after the water had passed over. From the phosphates in the urine, phosphorus was set free by the reducing action of the decomposition products of the organic compounds, and elemental phosphorus passed over and condensed under the liquid in the retort.

Early Discoveries Made by Sublimation

In 1546 George Agricola, also known as George Bauer (1490–1555), described succinic acid which he obtained by heating amber to the point of decomposition when succinic acid sublimed and settled as pure crystals. Agricola was physician to the miners of Joachimsthal, and was known as the "father of mineralogy."

Benzoic acid was first produced by Blaize de Vigenere (1523–1599) by sublimation from gum benjamin (gum benzoin). Later, in 1608 it was prepared by Turquet de Mayerne, French exile and physician to James I of England. Scheele discovered its presence in urine in 1785, and Robiquet first prepared it in 1831 by oxidation of volatile oil of bitter almonds (benzaldehyde).

Rouelle's Systematic Analysis of Vegetable Substances by Menstruums

In his *System of Chemistry,* Thomas Thomson (12) stated that Hilaire Marie Rouelle (1718–1778), the younger, was the first to recommend to chemists the separation of the constituents of plants by the successive application of different solvents, applying them in the order first the poorest and most selective, then the next most selective, and so on. The use of ether, alcohol, and water successively is an illustration of his method. Employing alcohol as solvent, Rouelle discovered urea (1773) by dissolving it out of the complex mixture of substances contained in the dried residue from the evaporation of urine. On cooling the hot alcoholic solution, urea crystallized out. Rouelle also discovered hippuric acid in urine (1776). Aqueous acid and alkaline solutions dissolved many substances which were not soluble in the above mentioned solvents.

The Classification of Organic Substances in 1804

In his comprehensive work on chemistry, published in 1804 (13), Thomas Thomson said that twenty-six genera of vegetable principles were known, but that three of these were alkalies, alkaline earths, and metals, and that these occur in such small proportions that they were scarcely entitled to the name of vegetable principles. "Besides," he pointed out, "it is highly probable that they are taken up ready formed, and deposited without alteration, in the vegetables which contain them; whereas the other twenty-three genera consist of substances which owe their formation to the processes of vegetation. It is of them that vegetables are formed; they are the substances which come into view when vegetables are analyzed." Thomson then listed the substances known to him and the properties by which they were to be recognized by the chemist.

1. Sugar: Soluble in water; insoluble in alcohol. Tastes sweet. Crystallizable.
2. Gum: Soluble in water; insoluble in alcohol, is precipitated by silicate of potash. Tastes insipid. Forms mucilage.
3. Sarcocoll: Soluble in water and alcohol. Tastes bitter-sweet. Uncrystallizable. (Author's note: This was an exudate from a shrub, *penoea mucronata,* which came from Persia and Arabia. It resembled gum arabic.)
4. Tan: Soluble in water and alcohol. Precipitated by gelatin,

muriate of alumina and by muriate of tin. Tastes astringent.

5. Bitter principle: Soluble in water and alcohol. Precipitated by nitrate of silver. Bitter. Usually yellow.
6. Narcotic principle: Crystallizes. Sparingly soluble in hot water and in alcohol. (Author's note: This was narcotine, an opium alkaloid, isolated in 1803 by Derosne.)
7. Starch: Insoluble in cold water and in alcohol. Forms a paste with hot water. Tastes insipid. Is converted into a jelly by alkalies.
8. Indigo: Color blue. Insoluble in water, alcohol, and ether. Soluble in sulfuric acid.
9. Extractives: Soluble in water and in alcohol. Insoluble in ether. Precipitated by oxymuriatic acid, muriate of tin, and muriate of alumina. Not precipitated by gelatin. Color fawn and dyes fawn.
10. Albumen: Soluble in cold water, coagulated by boiling water. Insoluble in alcohol. Coagulated by alcohol and by acids.
11. Gluten: Only soluble when extracted from the plant. Coagulated by heat, acids, alcohol, and by salts. Very elastic. By fermentation acquires the flavor and smell of cheese. Burns like horn.
12. Fibrina: Insoluble in water and alcohol. Soluble in acids. Burns like muscle fibre. (Author's note: This was washed blood fibrin.)
13. Volatile oil: Strong smell. Insoluble in water; soluble in alcohol. Liquid, volatile, oily.
14. Fixed oils: No smell. Insoluble in water; soluble in alcohol, ether, oils. Forms soap with alkalies. Is coagulated by earthy matter and by metallic salts.
15. Wax: Insoluble in water; soluble in alcohol, ether, oils. Forms soap with alkalies. Fusible.
16. Resins: Insoluble in water; soluble in alcohol, ether, oils, alkalies, nitric acid. Solid, fusible, burns with much smoke.
17. Camphor: Strong odor; crystallizes. Insoluble in water; soluble in alcohol, oils, acids. Insoluble in alkalies. Burns with a clear flame, and volatilizes before melting.
18. Caoutchouc: Very elastic; insoluble in water and alcohol. When steeped in ether is reduced to a pulp which adheres to everything. Fusible, and remains liquid. Very combustible.

19. Gum resins: Form milky solutions with water, turning transparent with alcohol. Soluble in alkalies and in nitric acid. Strong smell, brittle, opaque, fusible.
20. Acids: Easily detected by the salts which they form.
21. Sandaracha: Insoluble in water and alcohol; soluble in ether, and in sulfuric acid. Brittle, very combustible. (Author's note: This was the resin, sandarac.)
22. Suber: Burns bright and swells. Converted by nitric acid into suberic acid and wax. Insoluble in water and alcohol. (Author's note: Suber was cork.)

Thomson expressed the belief that these were not the only substances which occur in the vegetable kingdom, although chemists had not yet succeeded in obtaining the others in the separate state and in ascertaining their characters with precision.

It will be apparent from Thomson's compilation of what chemists in 1804 knew of vegetable substances, that there was nothing which had any significance for the physiologist who wished to learn about the nature of animal nutrition.

John's Analyses of Vegetable Substances

A decade after the publication of the classification of vegetable substances by Thomson, there appeared a book on the analysis of vegetables by Johan Friederich John, professor of chemistry in the university at Nürnberg (14). He compiled the results of analyses made by himself and other chemists of more than seven hundred kinds of plants, and the analyses of the ashes of 135 plants. His objectives were those of the apothecary. The constituents estimated were principally those listed by Thomson, but with the addition of such names as "Schleim" to denote sticky, viscous principles, and inulin, prunin, hematoxylin, alcanin, picrotoxin, and lac, pollinin; "Thierisch-animalische Substanz" (protein); and "Tabacsubstanz" (nicotine), myricin, cerin, fungin, and medalin. The divisions among the vegetables listed in his tables included such terms as starchy substances, gummy or slimy substances, sugar-containing, inulin-containing, dyestuff-containing, tannin-containing, resinous, protein-rich substances, and a score of others.

Einhof's Analysis of Barley

When Thaer, of "hay-values" fame, established his Agricultural Institute at Möglin, he invited Heinrich Einhof (1778–1808) to take charge of the chemical work and instruction. Although Einhof died at the age of thirty years, he is known as one of the notable pioneers in agricultural chemistry. The investigations of John and Hermbstaedt on vegetable analysis were motivated by the interests of the apothecary, whereas Einhof's lay in determining the nutritive values of common foods. He applied all available knowledge of analytical processes to the quantitative estimation of the constituents of potato, barley, soy bean, and pea. The following analysis of barley (15) shows that Einhof's thinking was far ahead of his time.

EINHOF'S ANALYSIS OF BARLEY
(8-OUNCE SAMPLE = 3840 GRAINS)

Volatile matter	360 grains	Gluten	135 grains
Albumen	44 grains	Husk (some gluten and starch)	260 grains
Saccharine matter	200 grains	Starch	2580 grains
Mucilage	176 grains	Undetermined and loss	76 grains
Phosphate of lime	9 grains		

Vogel's Analysis of Cereals

In 1818 Heinrich August Vogel (b.1778) reported to the Royal Academy of Sciences at Munich (16) his analyses of wheat, oat, and rice. He used the term fecula to denote starch.

VOGEL'S COMPARATIVE ANALYSES OF CEREALS

	Wheat flour	*Oat*	*Rice*
	Per cent	*Per cent*	*Per cent*
Fecula	68	59	96
Gluten	24	—	—
Gummy matter	5	3.5	—
Vegetable albumen	1.5	4.3	0.2
Fat	—	2.0	1.5

Gorham's Analysis of Maize

Three years after Vogel's report, John Gorham, a pupil of Liebig and professor of chemistry at Harvard University, reported the first chemical analysis of the maize kernel. He was the first to mention the presence in maize of an alcohol-soluble protein, to which he gave the name *zeine*. His results are presented in the following table:

ANALYSIS OF MAIZE KERNEL

	Per cent
Water	9.0
Starch	77.0
Zeine	3.0
Albumen	2.5
Gummy matter	1.5
Saccharine matter	1.45
Extractives	0.8
Cuticle and fibre	3.0
Phosphate, carbonate and sulfate of lime, and loss	1.5

Hermbstaedt's System of Food Analysis

Sigismund Friederich Hermbstaedt (1760–1833) was a German apothecary, and in his later years professor of chemistry at the University of Berlin. He was the first to use the term agricultural chemistry, and one of the most effective teachers and disseminators of the new chemical philosophy of Lavoisier. In 1804 he founded the first journal devoted to agricultural chemistry (*Archiv der Agriculturchemie*). Later, in 1831, he published *Short Directions for the Chemical Analysis of Vegetables According to Physicochemical Principles*. This book had great influence in placing phytochemistry on a systematic basis.

Hermbstaedt's method, first published in 1816 (18), may be illustrated by his analysis of wheat. He determined moisture by drying the sample, weighing before and after. He then soaked the wheat to loosen the bran layer, and removed the bran by macerating the wet grains on a sieve. The wheat kernels minus the bran were then dried and extracted with 80 per cent alcohol to dissolve the oil. The oil, recovered by distilling off the alcohol, remained as a layer floating on the water left in the flask and was separated mechanically and measured. Then Hermbstaedt washed out the starch by kneading dough under a stream of water, after the manner of Becchari. Hermbstaedt used five kilograms of wheat for an analysis.

Horsford's Method for Estimating "Fibre" in Vegetable Substances

While working in Liebig's laboratory in Giessen, Eben M. Horsford (1818–1893), who later became professor of chemistry in the Lawrence Scientific School of Harvard University, published a description of his technic for the quantitative estimation of vegetable fibre (19). This method he applied to oat, barley, and wheat. It was based on extraction of the sample first with hydrochloric acid and then with potassium hydroxide, each reagent having the concentration of 1:100 in water. Microscopic examination of the extracted material revealed that this procedure removed all other constituents from the vegetable fibre. The fibre was washed on a filter and dried for weighing. Vegetable fibre thus separated consisted principally of lignin and cellulose.

Horsford developed this method as a means of securing material from foodstuffs in form suitable for analysis for carbon, hydrogen, nitrogen, and oxygen. The Horsford technic was included in the system devised by Henneberg and Stohman for the analysis of human and animal foods about the year 1860. This system soon became standard practice, especially in the study of the coarse herbage fed to herbivora. The early investigators of the nutrition of farm animals believed that vegetable fibre was unaltered in the alimentary tract and had, therefore, no nutritive value. Later experience disproved this theory. (See Chapter 12.)

The State of Food Analysis in 1850

In Chapters 2, 3, and 4 an account was given of the progress in the isolation and study of the properties of carbohydrates, fats, and proteins respectively. Familiarity with these primary constituents of vegetable products was the basis for development of methods for systematic analysis of foods and drugs, and of any substances which were important industrially. The earliest pioneers in systematic analysis of plant products were Vauquelin and Fourcroy, who attempted to express quantitatively the constituents of beans and smutty grain. Their notable successors were John, Einhof, Vogel, Hermbstaedt and Gorham, all of whom had as their objective the determination of the constituents of the naturally occurring substances with which they were familiar. These men published analytical studies of the kinds described previous to 1821.

Liebig's standing as an authority on all scientific matters was so great that his assertion that the nitrogen content could be used as a measure of nutritive value with respect to "plastic" or body-forming food caused nutrition investigators of several decades to overlook the importance of the type of chemical analysis employed by Einhof, Vogel, and Hermbstaedt. Thirty years after the analyses by these three men, Boussingault, Lawes, and Gilbert ignored their type of results, and followed the simpler procedure advised by Liebig of accepting as food equivalents quantities of different foods which furnished equal amounts of nitrogen.

Prout, in his famous lectures of 1827, took account only of the content of carbon, hydrogen, and nitrogen in his concept of food values. The only new idea concerning planning of rations for farm animals which was brought out by nutrition investigators prior to 1850 related to the so-called nutritive ratio. This referred to the quantitative relation between the blood-forming or muscle-forming nitrogenous substance and the sum of the fat and carbohydrate moieties, conceived as solely of value as heat-producing foods. It was evident that the nutritive ratio for a growing animal, which was adding body tissue, differed from that of a mature one which required nitrogenous food only to replace the small amount of "metamorphosed" tissue indispensable to the processes of life. According to Liebig's concept, a horse doing hard work employed energy derived from muscle breakdown, and therefore required more "plastic" food than a resting horse. Appropriate nutritive ratios in rations for lactating and non-lactating cows, and for other farm animals, assumed primary importance in the minds of students of animal nutrition for many years. On the basis of the above assumptions, and on the basis of the accepted view that all proteins were alike except in their *compounds,* as asserted by Mulder, there was formulated a system of calculation of rations for farm animals which held the confidence of nutrition experimenters for more than sixty years.

R. D. Thomson's System of Ration-Planning for Farm Animals

Robert Dundas Thomson (1811–1864) was lecturer in chemistry at the University of Glasgow. While there he devised a method for calculating rations, using data from chemical analysis of foods and excreta of animals. Thomson was the first to show by analysis that at the height of absorption, after a meal rich in fat, the blood contained more fat than at other times. His subject was a young man from whom he drew large samples of blood for analysis (20).

In a lecture given in 1848 (21) Knapp, professor of technological chemistry in the University of Giessen, said that "in order to judge the values of different kinds of foods for practical purposes, it must be ascertained in what relation the blood-forming or nutritive constituents stand to the calorifient. The kind of food must also vary with the kind of employment, way of living, climate, . . . Thomson has traced out a very simple and ingenious method of supplying this defect in our knowledge. He ascertains the weight and composition of the food given in a certain time and also the excrement thrown out. From both factors he is enabled to calculate the quantity of food assimilated, also the relation of the calorifient to the blood-forming (albuminous or plastic food of Liebig) constituents."

Knapp continued, "He found that a cow, stall-fed, assimilated daily 15.28 lbs. of rye-hay, which contained 1.56 lb. of blood-forming and 13 lbs. of calorifient matter. They thus stand in the relation of 1 to 8.2, a proportion which, it is highly probable, is much more nearly related to man, as the relation in various farinaceous foods is about 1 to 5 or 1 to 6. We know with certainty that in the infant the relation, as in milk, must be 1 to 2.5."

In a lecture in 1849 Remegius Fresenius, professor of chemistry in the Agricultural Institute in Wiesbaden, cited R. D. Thomson for having devised the system for calculating rations. Fresenius stated that describing the composition of the ration best suited to animals under different conditions, such as growth, work, milk, wool or egg production, marked the beginning of the consideration of the nutritive ratio idea.

Henneberg's Contributions to Nutritional Investigations

The Agricultural Experiment Station at Weende, near Göttingen, was established in 1857. William Henneberg (1825–1900) became the Director of the Station, and was for many years an indefatigable investigator and prolific writer on the nutrition of farm animals. Associated with him was Frederick Stohmann, and together, by combining the chemical methods of previous workers, they devised a system of food analysis which became known as the Weende method. The essential features of this method were determination in the sample of moisture, fat, nitrogen, ash, "crude fibre," and, by difference, a fraction which was known as "nitrogen-free extract." Agricultural experiment stations multiplied rapidly after 1860, and the analytical technic recommended by Henneberg and Stohmann was widely adopted as standard procedure in every country.

Henneberg was the founder (1853) and editor of the *Journal für Landwirtschaft.* In 1860 appeared the first number of *Beiträge zur Begründung einer rationallen Fütterung der Wiederkäure,* by Henneberg and Stohmann. In it they described the earliest experimental studies with mature cattle kept under well-defined conditions and fed known amounts of analyzed feeds. Urine and feces were carefully collected and analyzed. It was believed that from such data the important problems in animal nutrition could be solved. In the article Henneberg stated the specific questions which he proposed to answer by experiments. They were:

1. "What are actually the nutritive ingredients in different feeding stuffs, and in what proportions do they occur in each?"
2. "In what proportions must their nutritive ingredients be fed in order to produce from a minimum of food the maximum of flesh (lean), or fat, or both?"

For the solution of these problems Henneberg with his associates, among whom Stohmann, G. Kühn, H. Schultze, and E. Schulze deserve special mention, undertook investigations of the chemical analysis of foodstuffs, the digestibility of each ingredient, and the nutritive effects as shown by feeding experiments. Analysis was limited to determination of crude cellulose (including lignin), crude fat (ether extract), crude protein ($N \times 6.25$), and "nitrogen-free extract."

There was nothing strictly new or novel in the speculations of Henneberg, since they included ideas already expressed by Liebig, Mulder, Lawes and Gilbert, Boussingault, and R. D. Thomson. However, Henneberg's merit as an investigator lay in the scope of his undertaking and the persistence with which he prosecuted his investigations. It was for these reasons that he exercised great influence among nutrition investigators interested in animal husbandry. Since agricultural experiment stations became numerous in Europe and America and had greater resources than did laboratories devoted to chemistry and physiology, their volume of output of experimental data was enormous.

From the publication in 1812 of the final volume of Thaer's *Principles of Rational Husbandry* to the early contributions of Henneberg, half a century of experience had been gained in experimental animal nutrition studies. The summary of defects in food analysis and feeding studies published in 1846 by Horsford represented accurately the state of knowledge twenty years later. No significant advance had been made.

The objectives of all investigators of animal nutrition had been to discover how to assess the nutritive values of foodstuffs, and to find a method for using chemical data in planning rations composed of one or more farm crops, so as to achieve in farm practice the best results in the animal industries. Advice had been offered by each experimentalist on some aspect of this question, but farmers were often disappointed when they attempted to feed animals according to recommended practice, which was based on the assumption that animal rations from different sources having like composition as shown by the chemical methods in use were equivalent in nutritive values. The agricultural chemists were forced to acknowledge that something was wrong with their theory and that their technics of analysis had been overvalued.

Henneberg soon concluded that chemical methods as he applied them in feeding and digestion studies fell short of the desired results. In perplexity, he turned to respiration studies as a supplement to chemical methods in his nutrition experimentation. In doing this he was influenced by the highly important work on the nutrition of carnivora by Bischoff and Voit, which appeared in 1860 (23). This book on metabolism of nitrogen and energy, together with Pettenkofer's paper on respiration (24) in 1862, seemed to Henneberg to afford the means for obtaining greater insight into the processes of nutrition. Quantitative respiration and calorimetric investigations with animals resulted in great advance in knowledge of the energy requirements, gaseous exchange, and the respiratory quotients of animals burning carbohydrate, fat, and protein respectively. But no new insight into the nature and number of essential nutrients was obtained by the comprehensive studies carried out by Henneberg or stimulated by him in other laboratories. In this field Henneberg was a follower of Pettenkofer and Voit, but his work with herbivora represented pioneering studies, and greatly influenced teachers and investigators in animal husbandry. However, it did not advance knowledge of foods and the nutritive needs of animals.

Investigations of the Energy Values of Foods

The beginning of the analysis of foods and of metabolic end products for their energy (caloric) value was made in 1866 by Sir Edward Frankland (1825–1899) (25), successor of Faraday as professor at the Royal Institution. He used a bomb calorimeter, and with it provided analytical data which refuted Liebig's theory that muscle does mechanical work by energy derived from breakdown of its protein substance. Frankland's role in the interpretation of the mountain-climbing experiment of Fick and Wislicenus is described in Chapter 10. The expression of the calorie needs of human subjects under different conditions of life became a prominent item of practical dietetics.

Following Frankland's lead, Stohmann (26) provided the caloric values for one gram of the most important derivatives produced in "the metabolism of proteins in the organism." These included several amino acids, fatty acids, fats, nitrogenous constituents of urine, starch, and several sugars.

Efforts to Discover the Defects of Food Analysis

Between 1860 and 1900 there was little advance in knowledge of how to assess the nutritive values of foods by chemical analysis, although there was steady but slow progress in discovery of the nature of metabolism. As the years passed, there was increasing awareness by agricultural chemists of the unreliability of the advice given in bulletins and textbooks used by farmers as a guide to the feeding of animals. Efforts to better the situation were directed mainly toward discovering the inadequacies of current analytical methods and their interpretation.

It was pointed out that some foods, especially hay made from immature forage plants, and root crops such as turnips and beets, contained much nitrogenous substance which was not protein, but, rather, simpler compounds such as asparagine, glutamine, betaine, and lecithin. Nitrogenous substances representing such simple compounds were referred to as "amide" compounds, or "amide nitrogen."

It therefore seemed worth while to devise chemical methods for distinguishing the proportion between these and "true protein." In 1878 Wagner (27) tried to accomplish this by dissolving the entire nitrogenous material from a sample of food by means of dilute alkali, and from this solution precipitating "true" protein by adding tannin. He determined the nitrogen content of the precipitate and designated it protein. This nitrogen was subtracted from the total to give a fraction which was supposed to be nutritionally inferior to protein. In the same year Sestini (28) first coagulated the protein materials by heating extracts of foods, but before filtering off the coagulum he added lead acetate to precipitate uncoagulated protein. The nitrogen in the combined precipitates he called protein. Kellner (29) modified the procedure by using phosphotungstic acid as reagent for precipitating protein from suitably prepared extracts of foods. Dehmel (30) used copper sulfate as a precipitating agent.

E. Schulze (31) was the most notable investigator of his time of non-protein nitrogenous substances in plants. He described an elaborate method for designating the different classes of nitrogenous compounds in foods. In the "protein-free" fraction of plant extracts, he discriminated by analysis between "peptone," nitrate, and ammonia fractions.

The investigators just named assumed that by differentiating between "true protein" and other nitrogenous substances they were making a more accurate appraisal of the nutritive value of the nitrogenous materials in foods. This was immediately contested by Weiske (32), who proved by experiment that for the rabbit the "amide" type of compound, as exemplified in asparagine, was of nutritive significance as a substitute for protein. The fact that the rabbit is a ruminant, and that ruminants utilize simple forms of nitrogen through the synthetic powers of microorganisms in the alimentary tract was not at that time understood. This is discussed in Chapter 12. Weiske showed clearly that a rabbit, when restricted to a diet composed of starch, fat, salts, gelatin, and asparagine, utilized the asparagine as a source of protein. The new efforts to improve chemical analysis of foods on the basis of distinguishing different sorts of nitrogenous compounds now appeared of doubtful value.

Advancing knowledge of the chemistry of natural products revealed that the fraction of a food sample extracted by ether contained not only fats, but also waxes, chlorophyll, and sterols, which were believed to have no nutritive significance. Hence, the accuracy and usefulness of calculations of caloric values of foods based in part on the crude fat fraction were questioned. Respiration studies revealed that a large part of the cellulose and pentosans in forage plants, hay and seeds, disappeared from the alimentary tract of ruminants and reappeared among the products of respiration. From these studies it was concluded these materials have nutritive value for these species. Voit (33) used a diet in which he substituted asparagine for meat-meal. He could not detect any protein-sparing effect of asparagine when rats were used for experiment. The contrasting results secured by Weiske with a ruminant could not be duplicated by Voit with the omnivorous rat.

Agricultural Chemists Discuss Methods for Food Analysis

Thus, in September of 1889 there were many theories on food analysis. At this time there occurred a memorable discussion of the inadequacy of the Official Methods of Food Analysis, so called because the methods had been adopted by the American Association of Official Agricultural Chemists. So general was the disappointment with the results of employing data from chemical analyses for calculating rations for farm animals, that it was felt the situation must be remedied. A committee was formed consisting of W. O. Atwater, G. C. Caldwell, E. H. Jenkins, W. H. Jordan, and H. W. Wiley (Chairman), all prominent names in agricultural chemical work. The committee was instructed to consider ways and means for securing more thorough chemical study of foods and feeding stuffs. The group had available a compilation of analyses of 3,273 samples of American foods and feeds which had been prepared at the Connecticut Agricultural Experiment Station by E. H. Jenkins and A. L. Winton. In addition, there were far more data from analyses of foods and feeds grown in other countries. All analyses considered had been made by the original Weende method of Henneberg and Stohmann, up until 1884 when the procedure was somewhat modified by the American Association of Official Agricultural Chemists.

The fifty-page report of the Wiley Committee (34) reads in part, "In vegetable materials, by our present methods, we determine, or assume that we determine, one group which we call protein, by multiplying the total nitrogen by 6.25; a second which we call fats, or crude fats, by extracting with ether; a third, which we call fiber, or crude fiber, by extracting with dilute acid and alkali; a fourth, which we call ash, by incineration; and a fifth, which we call carbohydrates, or 'nitrogen-free extract,' by subtracting the sum of the first four from the total water-free substance, which latter we get by subtracting from the whole weight, the weight of water as determined by more or less accurate dryings. In animal products used as food we have no crude fiber and the quantities of carbohydrates are generally so small, except in milk and its product, that we neglect them."

The report further stated that every kind of food and feed, whether seed, leaf, stalk, cereal or legume plant, tuber or root, was analyzed by the same procedure and equivalent nutritive values were assigned to corresponding groups of chemical substances irrespective of their origin. It is, therefore, clear that this principle was unsound on theoretical grounds, and accounts for the fact that their estimates of the nutritive values of feeding-stuffs often failed to agree with the results of feeding trials and with the teachings of experience.

The committee visualized that future research would lead to changes in the groupings of the official methods, and to special groupings and methods of analysis for different classes of vegetable and animal foods. "The first step toward reform must be research in analytical, organic, physical, and physiological chemistry. The needed improvement of methods will evidently come only as fast as does the chemical and physiological knowledge which must serve as the basis for changes. This means that the most abstract and profound study is necessary." This realization of the inadequacy of current analytical procedures, and the inability of the committee to make recommendations except in broad general terms, showed that an era in nutritional studies was nearing its end. But in the sixteen years that followed no significant progress was made.

Writing in 1906 H. P. Armsby, who had devoted many years to the study of animal nutrition, said (35), "We have come to question some of our standards. Some we have modified, and we hold them more flexibly than we once did, but protein, carbohydrates, and fats are still the nutritional trinity. Our theory of nutrition has become traditional, and has little pedagogic value and inspiration for the investigator. As a natural result it is more or less out of touch with practice, while our experiments, upon the theoretical side of the subject, have been marking time."

The Wiley Committee made no suggestion concerning the importance of studying the effects on animals of rations simplified as to their composition, and composed of known chemical substances, as a means to discovering what were the physiologically indispensable nutrients. The scientific literature contemporary with the committee did not lack experimental studies directed toward the solution of this problem, but none of these had yet had any influence on the teachings of practical men who were interested in animal production.

It seems that none of the men prominent before 1900 as investigators of the chemical analysis of food, or of human or animal nutrition, sensed the significance of the successive discoveries of new constituents in animal and vegetable substances which have been mentioned in earlier chapters. Nor did they comprehend that chemical analysis, even though it might be perfected to permit quantitative estimation of every known constituent of foods, could not be used as the basis for evaluating their nutritive values. It was not until 1914 that a new approach was devised; this method was based on a series of feeding experiments in which diets, simplified in the chemical sense and nutritionally inadequate, were supplemented stepwise with either known nutrients or with extracts of natural foods until optimal nutrition was secured. This type of experimentation brought to light new and surprising results.

A few chemists and physiologists after 1870 undertook to employ diets of isolated, purified, and recombined mixtures of protein, carbohydrate, fat, and inorganic salts for the specific purpose of inquiring into the physiological value of balance between acid and basic inorganic elements, the ability of the body to synthesize phosphoproteins, phosphorylated lipids, and nucleic acids, and the nutritive significance of individual amino acids. Such studies, although ignored by most nutrition investigators, were of capital importance in the advancement of knowledge. These studies will be described in a later chapter, but before they are discussed two other approaches to the solution of nutrition problems will be discussed, viz., inquiry into the significance of microorganisms in the alimentary tract and the interpretation of human experience with contrasting diets.

REFERENCES

1. Lavoisier, A. L.: Oeuvres de Lavoisier. Vol. 2, p. 586.
2. Gay-Lussac, J. L. and Thenard, L. J.: Recherches Physio-Chimique, ii, 265 (1811).

3. Prout, W.: Philos. Trans. 1827, p. 385.
4. Liebig, J. von: Pogg. Ann. *18*, 357 (1830); *21*, 1 (1831).
5. Dumas, J. B. A.: Traité de Chimie appliqués aux Arts. 1835, p. 3.
6. Varrentrapp, F. and Will, H.: Liebig's Ann. 39, 257 (1841).
7. Kjeldahl, J.: Zeitschr. f. analyt. Chem. 22, 366 (1883); 24, 199 (1884).
8. Ray, J.: Philos. Trans. 5, 2063 (1670).
9. Marggraf, A. S.: Opuscules Chymiques. *1*, 301 (1761–67).
10. Adet, P. A.: Ann. de Chim. 27, 299 (1797).
11. Thorpe, T. E.: Dictionary of Applied Chemistry (1926) vol. 6.
12. Thomson, T.: System of Chemistry (1804) vol. 4, p. 363.
13. Thomson, T.: System of Chemistry (1804) vol. 4, p. 358.
14. John, J. F.: Chemische Tabellen der Pflanzenanalysen, Nürnberg (1814).
15. Quoted from Elements of Agricultural Chemistry. Humphrey Davy. London (1813).
16. Vogel, H. A.: Annals of Philos. 2, 314 (1818).
17. Gorham, J.: Quarterly J. of Science, Literature and the Arts. *11*, 206–208 (1821).
18. Hermbstaedt, S. F.: Abhandlungen d. Akademie d. Wissenschaften in Berlin (1816–17) pp. 37–48.
19. Horsford, E. M.: Philos. Mag. 29, 268 (1846).
20. Thomson, R. D.: Philos. Mag. 26, 322–26 (1845).
21. Knapp, F.: Philos. Mag. 32, 456 (1848).
22. Fresenius, R.: Philos. Mag. 35, 137 (1849).
23. Bischoff, T. L. W. and Voit, C.: Die Gesetze der Ehrnährung des Fleischfressers. Leipzig (1860).
24. Pettenkofer, M.: Ueber die Respiration. Ann. d. Chem. u. Pharm. II Suppl. Bd. (1862) pp. 1–52.
25. Frankland, E.: Philos. Mag. (4th Ser.) 32, 182 (1866).
26. Stohmann, F.: Exper. Sta. Record. Washington, D.C. 6, 598 (1894–95).
27. Wagner, R.: Landwirthschaftl. Versuchsstationen *21*, 259 (1878).
28. Sestini, F.: Landwirthschaftl. Versuchsstationen 23, 305 (1878).
29. Kellner, O.: Landwirthschaftl. Jahrbücher von Thiel 8, 243 Suppl. (1879).
30. Dehmel, B.: Landwirthschaftl. Versuchsstationen 24, 214 (1879).

31. Schulze, E.: Landwirthschaftl. Versuchsstationen *24,* 358 (1879).
32. Weiske, H.: Zeitschr. f. Biol. *15,* 261 (1879).
33. Voit, C. v.: Bayr. acad. Sitzungsber. *14,* 401 (1883).
34. Report of the Wiley Committee: Exper. Sta. Record 2, 1850–1900 (1890).
35. Armsby, H. P.: Exper. Sta. Record (Washington, D.C.) *18,* 511 (1906–07).

12

The Physiological Significance of Microorganisms in the Alimentary Tract

IN 1878 L. BRIEGER (1) observed that after the ingestion of tyrosine, there was an increase in the excretion of phenol in the urine. In 1881 he estimated the quantities of phenol, indigo, paraoxyphenylproprionic acid, paraoxyphenlacetic acid, and ethereal sulfates which appeared in the urines of forty-seven patients suffering from various kinds of clinically distinguishable disorders. In most cases he found excessive amounts of these substances, which he believed to have their origin in putrefactive degradation of the protein residues in the colon. In 1885 (2) Brieger published an eighty-page paper on the chemical processes in putrefaction of proteins of flesh. In this study he isolated and identified a number of amines by purifying their double salts with platinum chloride. To the basic products which are formed in putrefaction he gave the name *ptomaines,* and expressed his belief that absorption of these bacterial products of protein brought about by anerobic microorganisms was harmful. His observations led to a widespread interest in the possibility of safeguarding human health by reducing the formation and absorption of these noxious products from the colon.

In 1886, Sucksdorff (3) studied the quantitative relations between the number of organisms of *Schizomycetes* in the large intestine, as influenced by the number in the food. He reported that these were reduced in numbers by taking sterilized food. This view was also supported by Brotzu (4) who, in 1895, reported that the numbers of colon bacteria could be reduced by the ingestion of sterile food. However, other investigations failed to confirm these findings, and, furthermore, established the fact that sterilization of food has little or no influence on the number of intestinal organisms.

Senator (5), in 1868, expressed the belief that in the putrefactive decomposition of proteins in the intestines there are produced, under ordinary conditions, substances which are toxic to the host. He was the originator of the theory of auto-intoxication. Brieger's chemical studies of putrefaction aroused great interest among clinicians, and resulted in many studies on the significance of toxic amines and their absorption on the health of the individual.

Bouchard (6–7), in 1884, published his studies on the toxicity of urine under experimental conditions. He introduced charcoal, naphthalene, and iodoform into the digestive tract and observed reduction of the toxicity of the stools and urine. Wassilieff (8) reduced the amount of putrefactive products in the feces of dogs by administration of calomel. Other investigators used quinine and naphthalene with similar results. In 1887, Müller (8a) noted that administration of calomel caused disappearance of ethereal sulfates from the urine. He also found that antiseptics reduced the hydrogen sulfide or soluble sulfides in the urine (8b), and in 1898 (8c) he discussed his belief that auto-intoxication may be of significance in impairing health.

In 1897 Lembke (9) discovered that the character of the intestinal flora could be changed to a striking degree by substituting bread for meat as the food. He did not attribute any significance to the aciduric types of organisms in the flora.

Morax (10), following Brieger, used the determination of the quantity of ethereal sulfates in the urine as a measure of the extent of protein putrefaction in the intestine.

In 1907 Combe published a book (11) in which he presented the evidence available in support of the view that a diet rich in protein will cause intoxication resulting from absorption of putrefactive products. In the same year Metchnikoff published *The Prolongation of Life* (12). He proposed to safeguard the body against premature aging due to poisoning by products of putrefaction by introducing into the alimentary tract organisms antagonistic to the proteolytic type. His choice for this purpose was *Bacillus bulgaricus,* one of the lactic acid bacilli. He found it could be made to replace putrefactive microorganisms when introduced in sufficient numbers in sour milk, and that its growth in the colon was favored by the presence of milk sugar. Combe's popular articles on deferring the process of aging ushered in a new field of inquiry, for they focused attention on the significance to health of the type of organisms which inhabit the alimentary tract, and on the application of a dietetic regimen for therapeutic purposes.

Metchnikoff advised that the desired replacement of an unwholesome by a wholesome type of flora in the colon could be secured by administering living cultures of lactic acid bacilli, either in milk soured by them or as cultures together with some fermentable carbohydrate. He assumed that the lactic acid bacilli fermented the carbohydrate in the intestines, thus producing lactic acid which is inimical to the growth of putrefactive bacteria. For this purpose he recommended sour milk, and, in particular, milk soured by *B. bulgaricus,* because his investigations of the geographic distribution of centenarians and other very old people among populations showed that the Bulgarian peasantry stood first in these respects. The name *B. bulgaricus* was given the lactic acid fermenting organism first isolated by Metchnikoff from sour milk found in Bulgaria.

Herter and Kendall (13), in 1909, described their studies on the effect that changing the character of the diet had on the nature of the bacteria which inhabit the alimentary tract. They restricted monkeys to a diet of eggs, and cats to a diet of meat for one or two weeks, then changed the animals to a diet of milk and glucose. Their previous studies had confirmed the observations of earlier observers that eggs, meat, or other protein-rich diets, encouraged the growth of putrefactive organisms in the colon, whereas milk and glucose favored the growth of fermentative, lactic acid-producing organisms. This is true also of a diet in which either dextrin or lactose is a prominent constituent. After one or two weeks on the milk and glucose diet the animals were returned to the egg or meat diet. Herter and Kendall found these time intervals were sufficient to change the character of the intestinal flora.

In the test with monkeys, as the proteolytic or putrefactive types of bacteria began to predominate, an occurrence which took place rapidly, the monkeys became sleepy and rested their heads on their hands in a bowed position. They were uninterested in their surroundings and responded slowly to external stimuli. They took their food very deliberately. Frequently after eating they would spend much time biting the woodwork of the cage. Their urine was of small volume, but with the increase in the protein-digesting organisms there resulted a marked increase in the quantities of the products of putrefaction in the urine.

When the animals were changed to the milk-glucose diet, both the psychical and physical attitudes underwent a great change. They no longer held their heads in their hands but assumed an erect posture, were alert and bright, and showed keen interest in their surroundings. Their appetites sharpened and food was consumed with avidity. The eyes, which were dull and lusterless while on the egg diet, became bright. They no longer chewed the woodwork. Moreover, the products of putrefaction disappeared from the urine. According to Herter and Kendall the evidence from human experience seemed to warrant the conclusion that similar changes in the diet of man induce modifications of the flora of the intestinal tract like those observed in monkeys. Thus, they based their interpretation of the effects of absorption of putrefaction products of protein on the belief that these substances are in some degree poisonous.

In 1921 Rettger and Cheplin (14) discussed their extensive studies on the effects of diets variously constituted with respect to carbohydrate and protein content, and source of the carbohydrate moiety on the ability of fermentative organisms, especially *Lactobacillus acidophilus,* to replace proteolytic types of microorganisms in the alimentary tract. They demonstrated that lactose and dextrin, when abundant in the diet, favored the flowering out of fermentative organisms, and in particular the lactic acid-producing forms. Cane sugar and starch were much less effective in this respect. This property of lactose and dextrin was attributed to their slow hydrolysis and consequent delay in absorption, so that when abundant in the food, they reached the colon in sufficient amounts to serve as pabulum for the acid-forming and aciduric bacteria.

Criticism of the Studies of Metchnikoff

Metchnikoff's essays on the prolongation of life aroused the interest of the public to a remarkable degree. The editorial comment of a British medical journal (15) applied to Americans as well as British and other Europeans: "Maccauley, in a famous passage, says: 'We know of no spectacle so ridiculous as the British public in one of its periodic fits of morality, the same public, in a fit of new-found panaceal therapy affords a spectacle only slightly less ridiculous.' Metchnikoff was the innocent cause of one of these. For several months one heard of nothing but the Bulgarian bacillus. The bacillus shared with Mr. Lloyd George's budget the honor of monopolizing the conversation at the dinner tables of the great. He dominated Belgravia, frolicked in Fulham, and bestrode Birmingham and the whole of the British Isles. Whether he did any good to anyone except the chemists and the purveyors of milk there is some reason to doubt. That he himself, or a colorable imitation of him, which was put upon the market by the unscrupulous, did a great deal of harm is quite certain. But the harm done was mostly to the self-prescribers, or to those introspective idiots who allow themselves to be treated by their lady friends. It was therefore not great."

The above quotation, reprinted by the Journal of the American Medical Association in 1916, obviously with approval, is a sad commentary on the attitude of many toward the views of the distinguished discoverer of the phenomena of phagocytic cells. Metchnikoff's attitude toward life and its physiological problems was essentially that of the sages of every age. His theme was old age and the prolongation of life. He did not offer a cure for old age, for he realized that old age is not a disease and cannot be cured. He clearly stated that it represents an accumulation of changes which begin in the earliest youth and continue throughout the life of the individual.

Brieger's "ptomaine" theory of poisoning from the colon met with skepticism by many because of the fact that the amines which were isolated from putrid flesh, when studied by pharmacologists, proved to be of low toxicity; and because of the discovery by Baumann (16) that phenols were conjugated with sulfuric acid to form "ethereal sulfates" which were held to be innocuous. But numerous clinical studies (14) led to the accumulation of abundant evidence that the use of sour milk, or of cultures of lactic acid-forming organisms in combination with lactose or dextrin, do change the character of the colon flora to the fermentative type, and reduce proteolytic organisms to a marked degree; and that such alteration of the flora is of physiologic advantage.

Investigations Regarding Meat Poisoning

In 1888 Gaertner discovered a microorganism, *Bacillus enteritidis,* in association with an outbreak of meat poisoning. This gave a great impetus to the study of bacterial food poisoning, and led to establishing the fact that many cases of supposed "ptomaine" poisoning were in reality due to infection with a specific organism, and that two kinds of organisms are primarily associated with meat poisoning, the Gaertner bacillus and *Bacillus botulinus,* which was discovered in 1896 by Van Ermengem. These discoveries marked the beginning of an understanding of the role which bacteria may play in contaminating food. Careless handling could convert wholesome food into a virulent culture of *B. enteritidis,* or lead to the synthesis of a highly poisonous toxin by *B. botulinus.*

Metchnikoff's observation that the regular ingestion of sour milk resulted in the virtual disappearance of proteolytic microorganisms from the alimentary tract and the flowering out of the lactic acid-forming organisms, which form wholesome rather than unwholesome products, was the basis of his recommendation of this method for maintaining a hygienic condition of the colon in the interest of health. The value of this principle was to be established in later years by the work of Herter and Kendall, Rettger, and others. Metchnikoff was, in his old age, one of the most optimistic men in all history. He devoted many years to seeking, through the biological sciences, new agencies for improving human health. His discoveries afforded for his own and future generations the hope that the chief evils that hang over the human race — disease, the degenerative changes accompanying the process of aging, and the sad spectacle of senility — might be prevented. These accomplishments mark him as one of the outstanding philosophers of all time. He sought for the solution of problems as old as the human race, inherent in growth, maturity, and decay of physical and mental qualities, and was successful to a notable degree in finding protection against these evils for which religions and philosophies had failed to discover efficient remedies or anodynes.

Folin and Denis (17) developed refined methods for quantitative determination of phenols and conjugated phenols. In 1915 they discovered that the total phenol products in the urine appeared to be much greater than is indicated either by the values for ethereal sulfate, or conjugated phenols. On the basis of their results and the observations of Herter and Kendall, they concluded that by no means can all of the phenols formed in the colon and absorbed into the blood be conjugated and detoxified. This conclusion was confirmed by Dubin (18), who showed that 30 to 70 per cent of the phenols originating in putrefaction in the colon fail to be esterified.

Using their improved technic for the quantitative determination of ammonia in body fluids, Folin and Denis (19) confirmed earlier observations that the blood of the portal vein contains a much higher content of ammonia than does systematic blood. By analyzing samples of blood drawn from various branches of the mesenteric vein, they found that ammonia was present in excessive amounts only in blood which had just passed through the walls of parts of the colon in which putrefaction of fecal residues was in progress. They proved that ammonia is absorbed in fairly large amounts from such fecal putrefaction. Even in very low concentration ammonia causes irritation and inflammation of mucous membranes.

It seems remarkable that in all the discussions concerning the absorption of toxic substances from the putrefaction of protein residues in the colon, no mention seems to have been made of the possible bad effects of absorption of hydrogen sulfide. It is an extremely toxic substance formed in considerable quantities during protein putrefaction, and is absorbable by the intestinal walls.

In 1919 Porter, Morris, and Meyer (20) discussed available information on the therapeutic value of changing the intestinal flora from the putrefactive to the fermentative type. They stated that "For years it has been the custom, in the management of infants suffering from putrid diarrhea, to furnish cereal decoctions or carbohydrates like lactose or maltose to them. The wisdom of such dietotherapy in suitable cases is being established on a scientific basis by some studies like those to which we have just referred (e.g., diarrhea)." An extensive bibliography of the publications relating to conflicting views of clinicians regarding the significance of different types of bacterial flora to human health is provided by Rettger and Cheplin (14).

Fermentation of milk is a means of preserving it against undesirable decomposition, and in a form which is wholesome and agreeable for human consumption. When a diet provides continuously a suitable amount of fermented milk, phenols, ammonia, amines, hydrogen sulfide, indol, and skatol, all of which are undesirable contaminants of the blood and tissues of the body, are either not formed in the colon by bacterial decomposition of protein residues, or are formed in very much smaller amounts than when the bacterial flora of the colon is of the proteolytic type.

Gastric Acidity as a Bactericidal Agent

In 1785 Lewis Brugnatelli (21a) published his studies on gastric juice from different animals. He noted the acid character of the juice from the stomachs of carnivorous animals. With Professor Carminuti (21b) he discovered that gastric juice from carnivores had great curative powers when applied to foul ulcers or wounds. The explanation for this property did not come to light until after the science of bacteriology was developed.

After the introduction in 1909 of the duodenal tube for aspirating contents of the intestine beyond the pylorus, numerous applications were made of this method of securing materials for study of enzyme activity in the upper part of the small intestine. The use of this tube made possible the study of the bacteriological condition of duodenal contents. In 1917 Sisson (2) reported that usually, under normal conditions of health, duodenal contents are practically sterile.

The earliest investigators to observe the bacteriacidal effects of gastric juice were McNeal and his associates (23) of the New York Post-Graduate Hospital. They found that bacteria in the fluids from the duodenum when counted under the microscope varied from 600 to 860,000 per cubic millimeter, and that almost all of them were dead. From such studies, gastro-enterologists concluded that the number of bacterial colonies developed in culture media seeded with duodenal fluid is significant as an indication of the state of the digestive function of the stomach. The acidity of the stomach came to be recognized as an agent for preventing the degradation of the products of normal digestion into more simple cleavage products which are of no value in nutrition.

Metchnikoff's views of what came to be known as auto-intoxication were given wide publicity by Combe's treatise (11) on the subject. Unfortunately, however, Combe overstated the danger to health from this source. The extreme of folly as respects this aspect of the health problem was reached by Sir Arbuthnot Lane, who referred to the colon as "a common sink," and in the interest of improving the health of patients diagnosed as suffering from auto-intoxication, he short-circuited the large intestine.

Other Explanations Offered for the Discomfort Attending Constipation

Donaldson (24) studied the response to delayed bowel evacuation in five young men, three of whom were accustomed to having one bowel movement each day and the others to two evacuations daily. Four were medical students and one a physician. All were of the opinion that the toxemia theory was correct. Each of the subjects voluntarily resisted the desire to defecate during a ninety-hour period. During this time they were studied while taking a liberal lacto-ovo-vegetarian diet. No drugs were employed. In each case the typical symptoms of "auto-intoxication" developed. All but one presented a coated tongue within sixty hours. The breath became foul, one had canker sores. The appetite was impaired in every subject, and all but one complained of some gas discomfort. No gastric distress was reported by four, while the other complained of some nausea after forty-eight hours. Mental sluggishness and increasing deficiency in the power of attention was a marked symptom in each subject. They were uniformly depressed, restless, and irritable; the night's rest was unrefreshing. A sense of heaviness in the pelvis and the dull "toxic" headache was noted in each case. In every way their symptoms compared favorably with the general malaise complained of by the constipated.

The sluggishness of the nervous system was also indicated by the increase in reaction time. This was true for sight, touch, and hearing, which changed from 0.184, 0.146, and 0.149 seconds respectively to 0.221, 0.165, and 0.162 seconds respectively (averages of four tests). These results showed an increase in reaction time (average) of 0.027 for sight, 0.019 for touch, and 0.013 seconds for hearing.

There was a pronounced increase in basal metabolic rate of each of four subjects, one showing a jump from a normal average of 2.09 plus to 18.1 plus per cent. This was in keeping with the blood sugar findings. The average blood sugar for the control was 97 mg. per hundred cubic centimeters, whereas examination of the blood made on the morning of the fourth day revealed an average sugar content of 124 mg. per hundred cubic centimeters, or 28 per cent above normal. Donaldson noted that from Cannon's studies it would appear that this glycemia pointed to suprarenal stimulation, and that the resulting increase in endocrine activity could be justly expected to account for the increased metabolic rate. Blood urea, non-protein nitrogen, and uric acid showed no alteration.

Ergographic determinations showed that there was more rapid onset of fatigue, an average of 64,000 gram-centimeters less work being done in the seventy-second interval than under the conditions of the control. The tests for indicanuria yielded indifferent results. The urine of three of the subjects contained traces of indican before the period of constipation, and two of them yielded no more at the end of the period than before.

At the close of the ninety-hour period of constipation, the men were instructed to take a cleansing enema and to report to the laboratory for further tests. Four of the subjects did so, but the fifth chose to relieve himself by a voluntary movement of the bowel. All were in the laboratory within one hour from the time relief operations for their condition were begun. Quizzed individually, they were unanimous in their opinion that they felt decidedly different, and their general attitude stamped their statements as true. In all cases the sense of oppression and marked mental depression were gone. Headaches were gone in the period of one hour in four subjects and within two hours in the fifth. Every man expressed himself as feeling a degree of mental alertness and physical fitness foreign to him for the days of the experiment. Retesting for reaction time for sight, touch, and hearing showed that the men promptly returned to normal upon relief from overloading of the colon with feces. In one hour retesting for neuromuscular fatigue showed that the subjects had regained their pre-experimental ability to perform work. The average content of blood sugar after the test period was 92 mg., a fall from 124 mg. during the experimental period.

Donaldson then packed the rectums of four of his subjects, using cotton pledgets saturated with petroleum and dusted with barium sulfate. This was done two days after the completion of the constipation study. The men asserted that within three hours during which the rectal packing was retained there was recurrence of the typical symptoms previously recited. Reaction time, blood sugar, and neuromuscular fatigue were all duplications of the data secured during the constipation period. Donaldson concluded that these symptoms could not be taken as evidence of the absorption of poisons. These observations on the symptoms following abnormal retention of fecal matter were in harmony with those of Alvarez (25) who, after much investigation of gastroenterological problems, concluded that the symptoms observed are not the results of absorption of poisonous substances but are referable to mechanical distention and irritation of the lower bowel by fecal masses. They are the results of alteration of the physiological activity of other organs and tissues brought about by the stimulation of sensory nerves in a distended, overacting bowel in a sensitive and often psychopathic person.

Adami (26) offered a different interpretation of the phenomena of chronic intestinal stasis, or "auto-intoxication." He set aside all arguments based on "indol, and phenols, amines of diverse varieties, and microbial toxins of uncertain origin (which) give opportunity for a play of words that still falls far short of conviction," and offered another hypothesis.

Adami pointed out that properly made blood cultures for bacteria were reported to show a high proportion of positive results in cases of continued intestinal stasis. He suggested that such symptoms as are observed result from sub-infection, not necessarily originating from the lower bowel, but due to the carriage of bacteria through the mucous membrane at any point from the mouth to the anus. He contended that not only the lymph nodes, but organs such as the liver and kidneys of healthy animals, constantly afford cultures of pathogenic and non-pathogenic bacteria; that through the agency of leukocytes bacteria are constantly being carried into the system and as constantly being destroyed in the healthy animal; that with inflammatory conditions in the alimentary tract and greater accumulation of leukocytes in its walls there must be greater passage of these from the surface and more extensive carriage of bacteria into the system. Foci of infection may thus be set up on the one hand, or on the other, a condition which he termed sub-infection. He reasoned that the bacteria here do not multiply and produce suppuration, but are destroyed, and their destruction liberates toxins which poison the cells immediately about them. The cumulative action of such poisons may bring about the death of certain cells and their replacement by fibrous tissue.

The results derived from studies by many investigators during the period from the discovery of *Bacillus enteritidis* (1888) and of *Bacillus botulinus* (1896) through the succeeding four decades established the fact that the bacteria found in the intestine deserve attention not only as causative agents of specific diseases, such as food poisoning by the Gaertner bacillus, botulism, typhoid, cholera or dysentery; but also as factors which determine the production of chemical products affecting in no small measure the sense of bodily and psychic well-being.

The fact was established by many clinical and other studies with different species of animals as well as human subjects, that the administration of *soured milk,* whether formed spontaneously and accidentally or from organisms purposely introduced, does serve to change the flora of the colon from the putrefactive to the lactic acid fermentative type. This status in the colon persists so long as cultured milk or naturally soured milk is taken in suitable amount. It would appear that the use of soured milk or buttermilk to combat the typhoid and cholera bacilli and other diarrheal infections has been demonstrated to have great clinical value. The longevity of people whose staple food is sour milk, such as the Berbers of the Northern

Sahara, the Bedouins of Arabia, the Kirghiz of the Caucasus, and the Tibetans and inhabitants of Mongolia, is sufficient evidence that its regular consumption is compatible with a high standard of health.

Goren and Ya (27) have reported favorable results from the administration to patients with colitis of one to one and a half liters of sour milk per day. Their observations are typical of other clinical studies in the control of intestinal infections by acidophilus or other sour milks. References to many clinical studies with acidophilus milk are given by Rettger and Cheplin (14). It is evident that cultures will not serve the useful purpose of the soured milk itself.

Thus far in this chapter we have given attention to the interest which investigators have shown in the types of bacteria which inhabit the alimentary tract (with the exception of the oral cavity) when the diet contains a liberal or preponderating amount of protein as contrasted with fermentable carbohydrate. The view generally held during the period of experimentation which has been considered was that a high protein diet favored the flowering out of proteolytic, and high carbohydrate of fermentative organisms. But milk sugar and dextrin do not behave like other food carbohydrates. They are both only slowly hydrolyzed in the small intestine and tend to reach the colon in considerable amounts when they are prominent constituents of the food. Much of the dextrin which is consumed by man is formed by heating cereal flour, as in the formation of the brown crust of bread or toast. This product of starch degradation by the heat of the oven or toaster is partially disorganized and less susceptible to enzyme hydrolysis than is starch which has been heated in the moist state with consequent swelling of the starch granules. Starch, maltose, cane sugar, glucose, and fructose behave differently, since all, with the exception of glucose which is ready for absorption, tend to be hydrolyzed and absorbed in the small intestine.

The Apple Diet in the Management of Diarrhea

In 1933 Birnberg (28) described the results of his experience in treatment of diarrhea, dysentery, colitis, and celiac disease in children by restricting them to a diet of raw apple. The idea was at once applied clinically by numerous pediatricians and there are a number of reports on the merits of the regimen (29). Schacter (30) refers to an English book published in 1775 in which a fruit diet, preferably apples, was described in the treatment of dysentery.

The mechanism of the beneficial action of apple in curtailing the diarrhea and effecting the return of the elaboration by the colon of the formed stool has been attributed to the astringent action of tannic acid present in the apple. This suggestion seems inadequate, however, for if tannic acid were the agent of value, other vegetable substances equally rich or richer in tannic acid should excel apple as a remedy for intestinal ills. Some have attributed the therapeutic effect to the presence of malic acid, and have pointed to clinical experience which indicates that juices of lemon, currant, et al., produce effects similar to those of the apple diet. Still other investigators have suggested that the pectin of fruits is responsible for the creation of a medium in the gastrointestinal tract which is unfavorable to the growth and functioning of the disease-producing organisms associated with the bowel infections in diarrheas, dysentery, mucous colitis, and celiac disease. The subject has been discussed by Heisler, Manville, and Hunt (31). It is mentioned here because of the practical significance of the possibility of changing at will, by simple dietary regimens, the flora of the alimentary tract.

The Relation of Bacteria to the Process of Aging

The views of Metchnikoff on the slow and progressive injury to tissue cells arising from the toxic effects of polluting their environing fluids with phenols, amines, and the like, resulting from degradation of proteins by proteolytic bacteria, initiated a long series of speculations and experimentation. J. Loeb remarked that the efforts to prolong life resulted merely in diminution of the chances of premature death. Indeed it is generally understood that the steady progress in life extension is in great measure the result of a succession of achievements in prevention of disease. Loeb and Northrup (32) were able to rear aseptically nearly a hundred successive generations of fruit flies, grown on sterilized food and themselves free from bacteria; yet these insects all progressed to senility during the normal span of life, and died. It is obvious from these and other studies, a discussion of which would be irrelevant, that factors other than bacterial poisons are prominent in the physiological processes of aging. However, it is equally well established that there are kinds of microorganisms which may inhabit the alimentary tract which are innocuous or beneficial, and others which are inimical to the physiological well-being of the host.

Synthesis of Vitamins in the Rumen and Large Intestine of the Ruminant

That ruminants can be maintained for long periods on food of very poor quality has been familiar knowledge to farmers throughout the history of animal industry. But the first to call attention to this fact were Theiler, Green, and Viljoen (69) in 1915. They seem to have been the first to discern that the nutritive needs of this class of animals differed greatly from that of omnivora and carnivora, and, as a result of this theory, they stated, "We . . . think it at least possible that the vitamin requirements of cattle are so low that they may even be covered indirectly by synthesis carried out by the extensive bacterial flora of the intestines." So far as water-soluble vitamins are concerned, studies by others have abundantly confirmed this view.

Discovery of Beneficial Effects Arising From Intestinal Bacteria

In 1885 Pasteur (33) said, in a talk before the French Academy, that he thought it unlikely that any animal could develop normally in the absence of an intestinal flora. The earliest definite evidence of the importance of alimentary flora was the discovery by Tappeiner (34) in 1882 that cellulose disappeared from the digestive tract of ruminants, and that this disappearance could not be ascribed to enzymes secreted by the animal. Up to this time it had been supposed by students of animal nutrition that cellulose was inert to all agencies to which it was exposed in the digestive processes, and that it passed into the feces unchanged.

Working in Liebig's laboratory at Giessen, Horsford (35) first attempted to estimate quantitatively the vegetable fiber in foods and feeding-stuffs. His method has been described in Chapter 11.

Tappeiner's discovery, made by applying Horsford's technic, stimulated Henneberg and Stohmann (36) to study the fate of cellulose in the food of herbivora. To the astonishment of agricultural chemists, they found it to possess a high nutritive value for ruminants. It was Tappeiner's belief that the several kinds of microorganisms inhabiting the rumen, including protozoa, could convert cellulose into organic acids, principally acetic and butyric, and to methane, and that the acids possessed nutritive value. Henneberg and Stohmann were convinced that in addition to these products, monoses (sugars) were liberated by microbial action on cellulose. Pringsheim (37) has published experimental evidence that monoses and possibly disaccharides are liberated by certain cellulose-digesting bacteria, but the evidence seems hardly conclusive and has not been substantiated by others.

As early as 1872 Weiske (38) studied the "digestibility" of cellulose of vetch and oats by swine. By digestibility he meant disappearance during the passage of the foods through the alimentary canal. He observed that between 41.06 and 48.87 per cent of the ingested cellulose from the sources studied could not be recovered in the feces. He did not distinguish between cellulose and lignin in analyses. Weiske and Mehlis (39) found that there was so little difference between the ingested and eliminated fiber from cereals when fed to geese, that they concluded that in this species there was no digestion of cellulose. However, Weiske did not give consideration to the possible role of microorganisms in the digestive tract in decomposing cellulose.

Lehmann (40), in 1889, made eleven experiments upon two wethers in which he attempted to determine the significance of "cellulose" in the nutrition of sheep. He used the term to include what actually consisted of cellulose, lignin, and pentosans. He compared the "cellulose" of beans, barley, and meadow hay, or oat straw, with the same feeds to which cane sugar had been added. From these studies, Lehmann concluded that the values of sugar and of "cellulose" for sheep stood as in the ratio of 100 to 75.7.

Weiske (41) fed a wether 500 grams of bean meal daily over a fourteen-day period. The sheep excreted 20.93 grams of nitrogen daily in the urine. He then gave it 490 grams of bean meal and 515 grams of oat straw; the output of nitrogen daily in the urine was 16.82 grams (average). He next fed it 500 grams of bean meal plus 200 grams of starch, and found the daily urinary nitrogen output to be 14.94 grams. Finally, he again fed the animal 500 grams of bean meal and 515 grams of oat straw, and found the daily urinary excretion of nitrogen to be 17.26 grams. From these data Weiske concluded that "cellulose" was not a protein-sparer. Weiske had no theory concerning the mechanism of utilization of "cellulose" in animal nutrition.

Little advance was made in the study of the significance of cellulose-fermenting and other microorganisms in the rumen of animals until Ferber (42) in 1928 introduced a counting technic for their approximate quantitative estimation. This method was used in extensive studies by Smith and Baker (43) and by Baker alone (44). By the use of histochemical and histophysical methods, they described various kinds of microorganisms which change cellulose to simple cleavage products and the manner in which some of these erode cellulose-rich feeds. They distinguished many types of such organisms in the rumen of cattle and sheep, and in the caeca of the horse, guinea pig, rabbit, and hen. These organisms included a wide range of readily identifiable morphological types. Each host species tended to harbor a characteristic microflora. The specificity persisted when guinea pigs and rabbits were kept in the same cage and were given identical diets.

In 1944, Thaysen (45) made approximately quantitative estimations of the microbial organisms which are formed daily in the rumen from 2 kg. of cellulose, which is approximately the amount which disappears in twenty-four hours from the rumen of an ox. By gentle centrifuging of rumen contents, he was able to separate most of the microbial growth from unattacked plant tissues, and also from the protozoa which grow in great profusion in the rumen where they ingest and digest bacteria. Assuming that the microorganisms produce one new generation of cells in twenty-four hours (most microbial cultures have shown a new generation in 1.5 to 2.0 hours), he calculated that (on an average of sixteen experiments) there are formed 404 grams of microbial substance in the 100 liters of rumen liquor which is estimated to pass from the rumen in twenty-four hours. This material contained 45 per cent of protein and about 20 per cent of carbohydrates, together with 2 per cent of ether-soluble material. These quantities of microbial substance represent approximately 180 grams of microbial protein, 80 grams of carbohydrates, and 8 grams of ether-soluble substance, containing a total of about 139 grams of carbon. This corresponds to about 15 per cent of the carbon of two kilograms of cellulose. Using Tappeiner's estimate (1884) that there was in one liter of rumen liquor 2.35 grams of organic acid estimated as acetic, Thaysen calculated that 335 grams of acetic acid would be formed each twenty-four hours from 2 kg. of cellulose.

According to Baker (44), the carbohydrates of the microflora consist of a starch-like polysaccharide which reacts with iodine and yields glucose on hydrolysis. He points out that this must be available for the nutrition of the host, since it is not found in the microflora of the lower intestine. This evidence supports the view expressed by Henneberg and Stohmann (1885) that glucose is produced as an intermediate product in the microbic decomposition of cellulose in the rumen. The possibility is not excluded that the bacteria which accumulate the starch-like carbohydrate may synthesize it from some intermediate simpler than glucose.

The Synthesis of Protein by Rumen Bacteria

The chemists who were pioneers in the study of "albuminous" or "animalized matter" of plants and animals, relied upon coagulation and precipitation with tannin and certain heavy metal salts as qualitative tests for what later became known as protein. Early in research on this subject, the fact emerged that in plant juices a considerable portion of the nitrogenous constituents did not show these properties. The isolation and characterization of asparagine by Vauquelin and Robiquet (1806) (46) was the beginning of a long series of investigations which brought to light that plant juices and extracts contain many nitrogenous substances of much simpler composition than proteins. The history of attempts to discover the nutritive significance of some of these is related in another chapter. In the consideration of whether rumen bacteria synthesize protein from nonprotein nitrogenous substances, the questions which presented themselves for decision included determining whether rumen bacteria appropriate protein from the feeds of the ruminant for their cell multiplication, or grow at the expense of partial or complete protein digestion products formed by enzyme digestion of proteins, or whether they synthesize protein from such substances as asparagine or other "amide" substances.

In 1937 Krebs (47) reviewed 126 papers devoted to investigation of this question. He pointed out that the conflicting conclusions were attributable to many poorly planned experiments, the results of which could not be interpreted. The subject did not command much attention in England and America until the beginning of the second world war, after which time many thorough studies were carried out. These have been discussed by Smith (44). Two of the best controlled experiments may be abstracted to illustrate the findings bearing on the formation of protein from urea through the agency of rumen bacteria. Such protein could be digested, absorbed and utilized in the nutrition of the ruminant as if derived from ingested food protein.

At the Hannah Dairy Research Institute, Kirkhill, Ayrshire, Owen,

Smith, and Wright (48) kept seven cows in metabolism stalls in which urine and feces were collected separately and weighed. In one case five cows were first given a balanced diet in which 25 per cent of the total nitrogen intake was provided as blood meal. After three or four weeks on this diet, the blood meal was replaced by its nitrogen equivalent of urea. This mixture was fed during five or six weeks, after which the urea was omitted from the feed. The urea diet was found to be palatable, and was readily eaten by the cows. The nitrogen balance studies showed that feeding urea led to some increase in nitrogen elimination over the values obtained in the blood meal periods, blood meal having been found to be a good source of protein for milk production. This rise in urinary nitrogen excretion, which amounted to about 24 per cent of that fed, was interpreted to mean that some urea was absorbed into the blood stream of the cows and was excreted without undergoing any metabolic change either by microorganisms or by the cows.

At the Wisconsin Agricultural Experiment Station, Rupel, Bohstedt, and Hart (49) fed 25 Holstein cows through three lactation periods on a basal ration poor in protein in certain periods, and with the same ration supplemented with urea to supply about forty-four per cent of the total nitrogen. They recorded weight changes, yield and composition of milk, and weights of calves produced by the cows. The results showed clearly that when a diet provides sufficient carbohydrates and other nutrients, except for inadequacy of the protein moiety, the nitrogen derived from urea can supplement the basal ration as effectively as linseed meal protein. For feeding dairy cows in areas comparable to Wisconsin as respects production of hay, silage, and home grown grains, Rupel and his associates recommend the supplementing of a suitable farm ration with 3 lbs. of urea to 97 lbs. of the cereal grain.

Bartlett and Cotton (50) employed heifers 7 to 17 months old; they compared the growth of groups fed a low protein ration with groups fed this diet supplemented with (a) urea, and (b) with peanut press cake. Urea furnished about 30 per cent of the nitrogen of a normal successful ration. The daily average gain in weight per animal over a period of 142 days was, on the low protein diet, 0.99 lb. as against 1.23 lbs. on the urea diet, and 1.39 lbs. on the diet supplemented with peanut cake. It was thus clearly established that the bacteria which grow in the rumen synthesize protein from the nitrogen of urea; and that this protein is liberated by the death and autolysis of the microorganisms, or by their digestion by protozoa together with digestion by the secretions of the digestive tract of the host, the ruminant, and so serve the same purposes as protein taken in the food of the animal.

From the accumulated information derived from researches on the digestion of ruminants, it emerges that when the animal is hungry and the rumen content is at its minimum, the bacterial population in the rumen falls because of their excessive ingestion by protozoa. When the animal grazes or otherwise fills its rumen with cellulose-rich plant materials, these unchewed vegetable substances are at once bathed in rumen liquid, covering all surfaces with a heavy seeding of bacteria. These begin at once to erode the plant tissues, decomposing the cellulose and liberating the contained nutrients for digestion further along the alimentary canal.

As the bacteria in the rumen feed upon the abundant food supply and multiply rapidly, they afford abundant food for the protozoa which are predatory upon them, and these, prospering nutritionally, also multiply rapidly, and becoming extremely numerous they ingest and digest vast numbers of bacteria. Soon the animal begins rumination, in which process, in the case of the ox, four to six ounces of rumen contents are regurgitated at one time. The mass, on returning to the oral cavity, is chewed forty to forty-five times, and is reduced to a soupy consistence by the abundant saliva. When the ruminated feed is swallowed, it by-passes the rumen and enters the third, and later the fourth stomach, where the bacteria and protozoa are inundated with acid gastric secretion. This catastrophic event causes their destruction. The protozoa and their ingested bacteria are digested from within by autolytic enzymes and from without by gastric juice.

It seems evident from the studies of Baker (1943) that this theory is true, since he found that protozoa and the larger forms of the bacterial population of the rumen are usually absent from the feces. Furthermore, Baker was unable to find in the fecal microflora those forms of bacteria which in the rumen flora contain polysaccharides detectable by the iodine reaction.

Ankersmit (51) has provided evidence that the smaller forms of bacteria of the rumen, in so far as they can be grown on artificial media, are destroyed in passing through the small intestine. The disintegration (autolytic and external digestion) products of bacteria and protozoa afford absorbable and utilizable nutrients for the ruminant. Ruminants are clearly in a favored position nutritionally as compared with non-ruminants when a diet of poor quality is all that is available, since the saprophytic microflora of the rumen perform many syntheses of organic substances which the mammalian body is incapable of producing.

Utilization of Ammonia by Rumen Microflora for the Formation of Protein

Millar (52) (1944) has shown by well-controlled feeding studies with calves, that ammonium salts can supplement a low protein diet and increase growth in a manner comparable with the utilization of the nitrogen of urea. There seems no longer any question that a net gain in the protein element in the nutrition of ruminants fed a low protein diet can, within certain limits, be realized from either a urea or an ammonia supplement.

The Nutritive Significance of Coprophagy in the Rat

Herter and Kendall (1909) published their study of the effects on monkeys of contrasting diets which favored either proteolytic (putrefactive) or fermentative microbial growth in the colon. Their results suggested to Osborne and Mendel (53) (1911) that the microflora in the lower alimentary tract of the rat might have significance. They noted that rats are addicted to feces-eating, a fact doubtless long known to others but not previously considered of any significance to the well-being of the animals. They found that young rats on "purified" diets fared better when permitted to practice coprophagy than when kept from access to their own or the feces of other rats. Furthermore, they found that a supplement of feces from well-fed rats, given with a diet of purified food substances, exerted much more pronounced beneficial influence on health and growth than did feces derived from animals fed inadequate diets. Thus, they suggested that synthetic powers possessed by colon bacteria might result in formation of adjuvants to an inadequate diet which were beneficial to the host.

The Phenomena of Refection

An entirely new outlook on the significance of the intestinal flora resulted from the publication in 1927 by Fridericia and his associates (54) of a study entitled "Refection, a Transmissible Change in the Intestinal Content, Enabling Rats to Grow and Thrive Without Vitamin B in the Food." The new concept arose from their observation that out of a number of young rats which were restricted to a diet devoid of what was at that time called "vitamin B," a few grew, thrived, and multiplied. They reported, "All symptoms of lack of vitamin B disappeared and simultaneously the feces became white and bulky. This phenomenon was named refection. The white feces fed to rats on a vitamin B-free diet produced refection; hence they must contain the active agent. It is not filterable, it remains active in the dry state for 5.5 months, it is not killed by one hour at 80° C., but it is destroyed in ten minutes at 100°. The organs of refected rats are normal. Tests for bile salts and urobilin in the white bulky feces are positive. The color is due to a high starch content, consisting of unchanged starch grains. It contains bacteria which stain blue with iodine. The white feces contain 2 to 4 per cent nitrogen, 5 to 6 per cent fat and soaps, and 49 per cent of dry matter, 60 per cent of which is starch."

The study continued, "The white feces contain more amylase than ordinary feces. This amylase will dissolve ordinary starch grains but not those of the white feces. The resistance of this starch seems to be due to an absorbed protective substance which is soluble in acid alcohol. Refected rats remain normal for two or more generations on a vitamin B-free diet. Refection cannot be produced in the adult rat. White feces contain more vitamin B than do ordinary feces. The bacterial flora in the cecum of refected rats differs from that of other rats. The white feces are acid whereas ordinary rat feces show an alkaline reaction. When refected rats receive vitamin B in the form of yeast the feces become normal." Fridericia and associates interpreted this change as indicating a defect in starch digestion in the refected animals.

They stated further that starch digestion was not influenced when white feces were fed to rats on an adequate diet. When refected rats were fed a diet free from starch as well as vitamin B, the body weight decreased rapidly but the animals lived for a longer time than if they had not been refected. Refection, the men found, could not be induced in young rats if both starch and vitamin B were absent from the diet. Dextrin, they stated, served as a partial substitute for starch. Mice could be refected for a short time, but the same condition could not be induced in pigeons.

Roscoe (55) studied refection and concluded that there is very little antineuritic vitamin in the white feces of refected rats. She found it impossible to induce the condition when the total carbohydrate ingested was soluble. She found the proportion of insoluble starch necessary to be variable. From her tests, Miss Roscoe concluded that the presence of unchanged starch grains in the intestine is essential for refection.

Fridericia's remarkable observation stimulated other investigators to study the problem in greater detail. Scheunert and associates (56) found that refection could be induced by keeping rats on saw dust as well as by starch feeding. They maintained that the age of the rats was of no significance in respect to their ability to become refected. They associated the synthesis of "vitamin B" with the presence of intestinal vibrios, which, they concluded, were able to synthesize the antineuritic substance.

J. Taylor and Thant (57) stated that pigeons become refected when they are fed autoclaved or cooked *dhal,* a legume of India, but not when restricted to cooked rice.

At the time here considered only three *water-soluble* vitamins were known. These were the antineuritic factor (thiamin), discovered by Eijkman and by Grijns; the antiscorbutic factor, whose existence was first clearly established by the classic experiments of Holst and Froehlich in 1912; and the so-called antipellagra factor, designated as P-P factor by Goldberger and by others as vitamin G.

In the experience of the investigators above named, rats fed a diet composed of isolated and purified food substances not only failed to develop symptoms of polyneuritis (the only deficiency state considered in the writings of Fridericia and subsequent students of refection), but were able to grow, and even to reproduce. It was suggested by Palmer and Kennedy (58) that synthesis of other factors of significance for the health of the animals must also be considered. At that time there was still confusion about distinguishing several kinds of pathological states resulting from faulty diet which constitute disease entities, and which were later shown to arise from deficiencies of nutrients not then clearly defined.

The Role of Fat in the Phenomena of Refection

Whipple and Church (59) observed that thiamin appeared in the feces of rats restricted to a thiamin-deficient diet containing 10 per cent of lard, and with sucrose as the only source of carbohydrate. When the diet was made fat-free, the feces were free from thiamin.

But little of this vitamin was formed when corn starch was substituted for sucrose. The symptoms of thiamin deficiency were produced more quickly on the fat-free diets than when fat was provided, and the larger the amount of fat fed, the longer were the symptoms delayed. The feeding of fat alleviated the symptoms of polyneuritis in rats which had developed the disorder on a fat-free diet, but they eventually succumbed to the avitaminosis. The amount of thiamin eliminated in the feces was, Whipple and Church stated, directly correlated with the content of fat in the diet which, it would seem, is essential for the formation of the vitamin by microorganisms in the alimentary tract.

Extent of Bacterial Growth in the Human Intestines

Strassberger (60) estimated the average content of bacterial cells in the daily output of feces in man to be about 8 grams of (dried) substance. Berger and Tsuchiya (61) estimated the amount at 3.023 grams; while Mattill and Hawk (62) placed the value at about 8.27 grams. Others have reported quantities within this range. That feces contain many if not all of the essential nutrients is shown by the studies of Richter and Rice (63), who used the self-selection method of feeding with rats. They provided in separate dishes, dextrose, olive oil, vitamin-free casein, dried brewers' yeast or liver powder, cod liver oil, salts, and tap water. Thus the yeast or liver were the only sources of the B-vitamins (by 1945 known to be numerous) in the diet. Having found that this free-choice method with the substances named supported satisfactory nutrition in the rats, they next offered as the vitamin supplements, fed in separate dishes, a choice of yeast, liver, and feces from rats on stock diet. It was observed that the rats ate the feces at once, that they preferred them to liver powder, and ate them as readily as yeast powder. The feces proved to be as rich a source of all vitamins needed by the rat as did liver or yeast.

Cow Manure as a Source of Nutrients

In 1943 Bohstedt and associates (64) carried out a noteworthy study which revealed that a supplement of cow manure is of considerable value nutritionally to young swine fed principally on grains. The author remembers the expression of opinion by Kansas farmers in the early 1880's that hogs grew better when following fattening cattle which were fed a liberal corn ration, than when the hogs were fed principally on corn thrown into the feed lot. No one attempted to put this matter to test until Bohstedt et al. proved that cow manure when fed to pigs has a supplemental effect which cannot be accounted for on the basis of the undigested corn kernels which it contains. Although they did not succeed in illuminating the mechanism of such benefit to hogs, their results seem to have set others thinking and experimenting in ways which yielded new and important discoveries.

Hammond (65) in 1943 conducted experiments to determine the usefulness of dried cow manure or dried rumen contents as sources of vitamins for chickens and turkeys. Owing to the high content of riboflavin in cow manure, it was at first believed that this was the factor to which the supplement owed its value; however, later it was concluded that other factors were involved. On a simple chick diet composed chiefly of wheat and soybean meal, supplementation with dried cow manure or rumen contents at an 8 per cent level was superior to alfalfa meal. Results just as satisfactory were obtained when the ration was supplemented with two per cent sardine meal.

It was well known that a combination of proteins of wheat and soybean has rather low biological value, owing to deficiency of certain essential amino acids. So long as a supplement as large as 8 per cent of cow manure was given, the possibility was not excluded that the value of the latter was due to its content of fecal bacteria, the disintegration of the proteins of which might yield highly important amino acids and so improve the utilization of the food proteins. The nature of the constituent or constituents of cow manure of such great nutritional significance to the birds could be identified only by experiments in which extracts of cow manure were used. These had to be so concentrated that very small daily allowances sufficed for marked improvement in the performance of chickens on the basal diet of wheat and soybean. This important step was taken by Bird and his associates.

Rubin and Bird's Studies on Egg Hatchability

Rubin and Bird (66) conducted studies to find the cause of low hatchability of eggs produced by hens fed diets largely composed of corn and soybean meal. Their experimental work was based on the observation of Whitson, Titus, and Bird (67) that when such a diet was supplemented with alfalfa meal, together with vitamin and mineral concentrates, hens laid eggs which showed a hatchability inversely proportional to the amount of soybean meal in the ration. They found that addition of 8 per cent of dried cow manure which had been dried at 80° C., to destroy an androgenic substance, induced improved hatchability in eggs produced from high soybean feed, and largely eliminated seasonal variations in hatchability which are characteristic of the basal soybean oil meal diet.

Rubin and Bird (68) extended their studies to the discovery that addition of as little as 0.075 per cent of the acid precipitate of water extract of dried cow manure to a 35 per cent soybean oil meal diet resulted in excellent growth stimulus in chicks. Bird and his co-workers had previously shown that supplementing such rations with dl-methionine exerted a beneficial effect on growth, but was not so effective as their extract of cow manure. This evidence supported the idea that there is in cow manure a substance which is required for normal chick growth and development to overcome the detrimental effects of something in heated soybean oil meal in the diet. Since a supplement of protein from animal sources had shown similar beneficial effects on hens and their eggs when the diet was high in soybean oil meal, the cow manure factor became known as the "animal protein factor," and still later was associated with the cobalt-containing vitamin B_{12}.

Biosynthesis of Vitamins in Man

The earliest decisive experiments which revealed the synthesis of significant amounts of thiamin in the gastrointestinal tract of man were made by Najjar and Holt (70), who attempted to produce thiamin deficiency in young men. They reported that diets low in thiamin content failed to produce signs of nutritional deficiency in certain individuals. Search for an explanation led to the discovery that thiamin was being formed by bacteria in the bowel. The subjects excreted thiamin in the urine although without a dietary source of it.

Najjar and his co-workers (71) reported similar studies which related to riboflavin. Observations were made on twelve adolescent males 10 to 16 years of age. After a control period, the youths were placed on a diet consisting of vitamin-free casein, Crisco, dextrimaltose, a mineral mixture, and a vitamin supplement which contained no riboflavin. It was estimated that the diet provided only 70 to 90 micrograms of flavin per day per man. The study was continued through three months, during which time the youths remained in excellent health. Urinary and fecal excretion of riboflavin fell during the first two weeks but remained about constant thereafter, ranging between 150 and 250 micrograms per day. Thus, the combined excreta contained five or six times as much riboflavin as was taken in the food. In their study of biosynthesis of thiamin in man Najjar and Holt found that administration of succinylsulfathiazole, an intestinal antiseptic, decreased the synthesis of thiamin. In their study on riboflavin the same drug administration had but little effect on the excretion of this vitamin. These remarkable results indicate that an inquiry into the dietary conditions in which deficiency of riboflavin occurs in man is much to be desired.

From the foregoing it is evident that the synthesis of vitamins as well as the full quota of amino acids which are necessary units in the formation of biologically complete proteins, is brought about by microorganisms which, by feeding the host suitable diets, may be induced to inhabit the rumen, cecum, or colon. It is also evident that presence or absence of certain individual carbohydrates (e.g., starch and sucrose), as well as fats from certain sources, not yet well defined, and probably other nutrients which influence the nature and abundance of alimentary bacteria, effect organic syntheses of substances both important and unimportant in the nutrition of man, mammals, and birds.

REFERENCES

1. Brieger, L.: Zeitschr. f. physiol. Chem. *2*, 241–258 (1878).
2. Brieger, L.: Ueber Ptomaine, Berlin (1885) 80 pp.
3. Sucksdorff, W.: Arch. f. Hygiene *4*, 355–396 (1886).
4. Brotzu, L.: Centralbl. f. Bakt. *17*, 726–27 (1895).
5. Senator, H.: Berlin Klin. Wochnschr. *5*, 254–55 (1888).
6. Bouchard, C. J.: Compt. Rend. Soc. Biol. *1*, 665–668 (1884).
7. Bouchard, C. J.: Leçons sur les autointoxicationes dans les Maladies. Paris (1887).
8. Wassilieff, N. P.: Zeitschr. f. physiol. Chem. *6*, 112–134 (1882).
8a. Müller, F.: Mittheil a. d. med. Klin zu Würzburg, *2*, 341 (1886).
8b. Müller, F.: Berlin Klin. Woch. 23, 405–408 (1887).

8c. Müller, F.: Verhandl. d. Kongress f. innere Med. *16,* 149–175 (1898).

9. Lembke, W.: Arch. f. Hyg. *26,* 293–328 (1897); *Idem, 29,* 304–353 (1897).

10. Morax, V.: Zeitschr. f. physiol. Chem. *10,* 318–325 (1886).

11. Combe, A.: L'autointoxication intestinale. Paris (1907).

12. Metchnikoff, E.: The Prolongation of Life. New York (1907).

13. Herter, C. A. and Kendall, A. I.: J. Biol. Chem. *7,* 203–23 (1909).

14. Rettger, L. F. and Cheplin, H. A.: Intestinal Flora, Yale Univ. Press (1921).

15. Medical Press and Circular. Cited from J. Amer. Med. Assoc. *67,* 939 (1916).

16. Baumann, E.: Zeit. f. physiol. Chem. *10,* 123–133 (1886).

17. Folin, O. and Denis, W.: J. Biol. Chem. *22,* 309 (1915).

18. Dubin, H.: J. Biol. Chem. *26,* 69 (1916).

19. Folin, O. and Denis, W.: J. Biol. Chem. *11,* 161 (1912).

20. Porter, L., Morris, G. B. and Meyer, K. F.: Am. J. Dis. Child *18,* 254 (1919).

21a. Brugnatelli, L.: Opusculi Scelti *8,* (1775): Cited from Phil. Mag. *53,* 321–326 (1819).

21b. Brugnatelli, L. and Carminuti: Phil. Mag. *53,* 321–326 (1819).

22. Sisson, W. R.: Am. J. Dis. Child. *13,* 117–127 (1917).

23. McNeal, W. J., Latzer, L. L. and Kerr, J. E.: J. Infect. Dis. *6,* 123, 571 (1909).

24. Donaldson, A. N.: J. Amer. Med. Assoc. *78,* 884–888 (1922).

25. Alvarez, W. C.: J. Amer. Med. Assoc. *72,* 8 (1919).

26. Adami, J. G.: Brit. Med. Journ. (1914) p. 177; J. Amer. Med. Assoc. *62,* 702 (1914).

27. Goren, M. G. and Ya, D.: Abstract in J. Amer. Med. Assoc. *110,* 1884 (1938).

28. Birnberg, T. L.: Amer. J. Dis. Child. *45,* 18 (1933).

29. Literature on the apple diet: J. Amer. Med. Assoc. *109,* 1634 (1937).

30. Schacter, M.: Med. inf. *41,* 38 (1934).

31. Heisler, A.: Verlag der Aerztl. Rundsch. (1928); J. Amer. Med. Assoc. *109,* 1634 (1937).
Ibid. Klin. Woch. *9,* 408 (1930).

32. Loeb, J.: Sci. Monthly *9*, 578 (1919).
33. Pasteur, L.: Compt. Rend. Acad. Sci. *100*, 66 (1885).
34. Tappeiner, H.: Ber. d. deutsch. chem. Ges. *15*, 999 (1882).
35. Horsford, E. M.: Phil. Mag. *29*, 268 (1946).
36. Henneberg, W. and Stohmann, F.: Zeits. f. Biol. *21*, 613 (1885).
37. Pringsheim, H.: Hoppe-Seyler's Zeitschr. *76*, 266 (1912).
38. Weiske, H.: Landw. Versuchs. Stationen *15*, 90 (1872).
39. Weiske, H. and Mehlis, Th.: *Ibid. 21*, 411 (1878).
40. Lehmann, F.: Journ. f. Landwirth. *37*, 251 (1889).
41. Weiske, H.: Chem. Centrlbl. *15*, 385–386 (1884).
42. Ferber, K. E.: Zeit. Tierz. Zucht. Biol. *12*, 31 (1928).
43. Smith, J. A. B. and Baker, F.: Biochem. J. *38*, 496 (1944).
44. Baker, F.: Ann. Applied Biol. *30*, 223 (1943); *31*, 121 (1944).
45. Thaysen, A. C.: Proc. Nut. Soc. *3*, 208 (1945).
46. Vauquelin and Robiquet: Ann. Chim. *57*, 88–93 (1806).
47. Krebs, K.: Tierernährung *9*, 394 (1937).
48. Owen, E. C., Smith, J. A. B. and Wright, N. C.: Biochem. J. *37*, 44 (1943).
49. Rupel, I. W., Bohstedt, G. and Hart, E. B.: J. Dairy Sci. *26*, 647 (1943).
50. Bartlett, S. and Cotton, A. G.: J. Dairy Res. *9*, 263 (1938).
51. Ankersmit, P.: Zbl. Bakt. Abt. I, *40*, 100 (1905–06).
52. Millar, H. C.: Indust. & Eng. Chem. *33*, 274 (1941).
Ibid. U.S. Patent No. 2, 293, 845 (1942).
Ibid. J. Dairy Sci. *27*, 225 (1944).
53. Osborne, T. B. and Mendel, L. B.: Bull. 156 Carnegie Institution of Washington (1911).
54. Fridericia, L. S., Freudenthal, P., Gudjonnson, S., Johansen, G. and Schmoye, N.: J. Hygiene *27*, 70–102 (1927).
55. Roscoe, M. H.: J. Hygiene *27*, 103–107 (1927).
56. Scheunert, A., Scheiblich, M. and Redenkirchen, J.: Biochem. Zeitschr. *213*, 226–233 (1929).
57. Taylor, J. and Thant, U.: Indian J. Med. Res. *16*, 747–765 (1929).
58. Palmer, L. S. and Kennedy, C.: J. Biol. Chem. *74*, 591 (1927).
59. Whipple, G. H. and Church, C. F.: J. Biol. Chem. *109*, cvii (1936).

60. Strassberger, J.: Zeitschr. f. Klin. Med. *46,* 413–44 (1902); *Idem 48,* 491–505 (1903).
61. Berger, F. and Tsuchiya, I.: Zeitschr. f. exper. Pathol. und Therap. 7, 437–454 (1910).
62. Mattill, H. A. and Hawk, P. B.: J. Exp. Med. *14,* 435–443 (1911).
63. Richter, C. P. and Rice, K. K.: Amer. J. Physiol. *143,* 344 (1945).
64. Bohstedt, G., Grummer, R. H. and Ross, O. B.: J. Animal Sci. 2, 373 (1943).
65. Hammond, J. C.: Poultry Sci. *21,* 554 (1942); 23, 36 (1943).
66. Rubin, M. and Bird, H. R.: J. Biol. Chem. *163,* 387, 393 (1946).
67. Whitson, D., Titus, H. W. and Bird, H. R.: Poultry Sci. *25,* 52 (1946).
68. Rubin, M. and Bird, H. R.: J. Nut. *34,* 233 (1947).
69. Theiler, A., Green, H. H. and Viljoen, P. R.: Rep. Vet. Res. S. Africa. 3 & *4,* 9 (1915).
70. Najjar, V. A. and Holt, L. E., Jr.: J. Amer. Med. Assoc. *123,* 683 (1943).
71. Najjar, V. A., Johns, G. A., Medairy, G. C., Fleischmann, G. and Holt, L. E., Jr.: J. Amer. Med. Assoc. *126,* 357 (1944).

13

Some Attempts to Learn About Diets from Human Experience

THE EXPERIENCE OF MANKIND with good and bad foods through many centuries led reflective men to conclude that the diet had much to do with health. Without understanding the chemical nature of foods, or the nature of the changes involved in their conversion to the uses of the body, observations by some philosophic minds on the personal experiences of individual people were made the basis for speculation concerning eating practices which best promoted health. A history of ideas in nutritional investigations would be incomplete without an account of the most notable attempts to interpret the results of human experience with diets and eating habits.

Cornaro's Observations on Diet and Health

Luigi Cornaro (1) (1467–1566), a Venetian gentleman, who lived to be over one hundred years old, attained lasting fame by writing an account of his personal experiences with eating and its effects on his health. He stated that he had been endowed with a feeble constitution, and "had fallen into different kinds of disorders, such as pains in my stomach, and often stiches, and spices of the gout, attended by what was still worse, an almost continual slow fever, a stomach generally out of order, and a perpetual thirst." He had practiced indulgence in eating and drinking, and at about the age of 40 he resolved to enter upon a new course and betake himself to a spare diet and be scrupulously regular in his habits, in order to "avoid those evils which we do not find it easy to remove. These are melancholy, hatred, and other violent passions, which appear to have the greatest power over our bodies."

Within a few days after he began the new diet, Cornaro perceived that such a course agreed with him very well. In less than a year he found himself entirely freed from all his complaints. Of his dietary practices he said, "I chose wine suited to my stomach, drinking of it but the quantity I knew I could digest. I did the same with meat, as well in regard to quantity as to quality, accustoming myself to contrive matters so as never to cloy my stomach with eating or drinking, but constantly to rise from the table with a disposition to eat and drink still more. In this I conformed to the proverb which says that a man, to consult his health, must check his appetite. What with bread, meat, the yolk of an egg, and soup, I ate as much as weighed in all 12 ounces, neither more nor less . . . I drank 14 ounces of wine."

Stark's Experiences With Dieting

Dr. William Stark (2) inquired assiduously into the effects of different foods upon himself. He subsisted two weeks on bread and water, and during this period he lost 3.5 pounds weight. During a month he ate only bread, sugar, and water, and lost another 3.5 pounds. He then ate only bread and olive oil for a few days but its severe purging forced him to give it up. Next he took bread and milk and felt better, but he still lost weight. Bread, water, and roasted goose seemed to agree well. Next he tried bread, water, and boiled beef; stewed lean beef with gravy and water; the same with addition of suet. Other combinations which he tried were flour, oil of suet, water, and salt; flour, fresh butter, water, and salt; bread with roasted fowl, and the same with tea and sugar; yolks of eggs, suet, figs, and water; oil of marrow, water, and salt; bread and stewed lean beef with gravy, tea and sugar; bread, beef fat and jelly, water, and salt; bread, fat of bacon or ham, and tea with sugar.

Stark continued his experiments for more than six months, when a fever speedily carried him off. While no conclusions were possible from his observations, they indicated that some combinations were better than others, and suggested the desirability of employing a greater variety of foods in the interest of health.

Sanctorius' Observations on "Insensible Perspiration"

Sanctorius (3) (1561–1636) was professor at Padua, a contemporary of van Helmont, and a friend of Galileo. Galileo invented an air thermometer, the first effective instrument for the measurement of degrees of heat. It consisted of a glass tube with an air bulb at the end. Expansion of air in the bulb drove water out of the tube. About 1610 Sanctorius used this type of thermometer to measure body heat. His fame rests principally on his sustained interest in determining, by weighing himself before and after eating, how much body weight was lost through "insensible perspiration."

King Charles II of England was strongly motivated in the same direction. At the session of March 9, 1661 of the Royal Society (London) the Secretary reported, "Sir Robert Moray mentioned that his Majesty had the curiosity of weighing himself very frequently, in order to observe the several emanations of his body before and after sleep, tennis, riding abroad, dinner, and supper; and that he had found that he weighed less after tennis by two pounds three ounces, but his Majesty drinking two draughts of liquor after play, made up his weight. After dinner (he weighed) more by four pounds and a half." (4)

Takaki's Prevention of Beriberi by Diet

With the exception of Lind's studies of scurvy among sailors, the most notable experimental studies of human nutrition before 1900 were those of Takaki (5), Director-General of the Japanese Navy. About the year 1878 beriberi became a devastating disease of sailors in the Japanese Navy. The average number of cases treated medically each year between 1878 and 1883 was 323.5 per 1000 men.

The principal components of the sailors' diet at that time were polished rice and fish, the remainder being derived from a number of vegetables. Takaki was greatly impressed with the superiority of the health of British sailors as compared with Japanese. On studying the composition of foods employed, he suggested that this superiority might be due to the greater quantity of protein in the diet supplied on British ships. The officers on Japanese ships were much better fed than were the common sailors, and they escaped the disease.

Takaki introduced changes in the naval dietary, replacing a part of the polished rice by barley, and introducing evaporated milk and meat. These changes resulted in eradicating beriberi from the Navy. Unfortunately, ignorance of the chemical composition of foods at that time, and of the existence and importance of many nutrients then unsuspected, prevented Takaki from correctly interpreting his observations. He thus attributed the beneficial effects of his dietary reform to the provision of a more liberal protein allowance.

Sylvester Graham's System of Vegetarianism

Before the Christian Era, pure-minded and pious people, notably the Jewish sect known as Essenes, some of whom followed the monastic life (6), practiced vegetarianism. So, too, did ascetics in India, China, and elsewhere. The earliest advocate of the vegetarian regimen for man was Sylvester Graham (1794–1851), who attempted vigorously to teach his system of dietetics in the interest of health. The seventeenth child of his parents, and a sufferer of chronic poor health, Graham devoted great energy to improving the happiness of the human race. A volume containing twenty-three of his lectures was published in 1892 (7).

In seeking to improve his own health Graham, in 1829, advocated moderation in eating and the use of a diet consisting of vegetables, Graham bread (made from unbolted flour), fruits, nuts, salt, and pure water. He excluded meats, sauces, salads, tea, coffee, alcohol, pepper, and mustard. He said that milk was wholesome when obtained from cows kept in clean pastures, but that most milk was obtained from cows kept under unsanitary conditions and was unwholesome. Eggs he placed in the same category with milk, recommending them only when fresh. But he maintained that a strictly vegetarian diet with water was most satisfactory for promoting health, strength, and longevity (8).

Graham possessed no knowledge of chemistry in its application to foods and to physiological phenomena, and drew his conclusions from observations, accounts given by travellers of dietary practices of peoples in different parts of the world, and from his personal experience with different dietary regimens. The subject required more critical inquiry than he was qualified to devote to it.

Atwater's Views on Human Foods and Nutrition

In other chapters an account has been given of the progress in the development of metabolism studies, especially of respiratory exchange, urine analysis, and the quantity and composition of food metabolized. These investigations were designed to reveal what was important in human and animal nutrition. Prout, Liebig, Voit, Pettenkofer, Rubner, Atwater, and Lusk were the outstanding investigators who experimented and taught in this field.

After a period of study with Voit and Pettenkofer at Munich, Atwater returned to America in 1892 with an ambitious plan for investigations of human nutrition. He proposed to analyze chemically, using the "official" method formulated by the Association of Agricultural Chemists, all important American foods, and to determine their energy values and digestibility. He further planned to study the energy requirements of human subjects doing various kinds of work, and to make dietary surveys, after the pattern set by Voit, to learn how much protein and how many calories Americans consumed daily. In his opinion, these were the only important data which were needed to establish a science of human nutrition, which he conceived to comprehend chemical composition of foods, their availability through digestion and absorption, their physiological effects, and the economics of food purchasing. At the end of the nineteenth century Atwater's teachings had great influence among teachers of nutrition. He carried on his work in the tradition of the Munich school.

The basic beliefs on man's nutritive needs that were generally accepted by authorities during the opening years of the present century were summarized by C. F. Langworthy (9), who was long associated with W. A. Atwater in nutrition investigations in the U. S. Department of Agriculture. He stated, "Foods have a dual purpose: Building and repair. Energy for heat and work. Foods consist of the nutrients protein, fat and carbohydrates, and various mineral salts." Langworthy's "Laws of Nutrition" were:

1. All nitrogen is supplied by food, i.e., none from atmosphere.
2. All nitrogen is excreted in urine and feces, none as gaseous nitrogen.
3. The animal adjusts itself to its nitrogen intake and comes into N-balance, in which state the intake and output are equal.
4. A certain amount of food material, i.e., protein, fat, and carbohydrate, is required for maintenance. Mineral matter is also essential, but very little is known regarding the kind and amount necessary.
5. A more abundant ration is required for muscular work, fattening, and milk production.
6. Food supplied in excess of all needs is stored, in part at least, as reserve material, principally as fat and glycogen.
7. The body comes into nitrogen equilibrium at different levels of protein intake.

8. Body fat may be formed from food fat (precipitated as such), or from carbohydrate, and doubtless from protein also.
9. As furnishers of energy the different nutrients may replace each other in approximately the following ratios: Protein: fat: carbohydrate as 1:2.5: 1. That is, having the requisite amount of nitrogen for repair of tissues or some vital process not understood, or both, it is, theoretically and within certain limits, unimportant which nutrient supplies the necessary energy.
10. The nutrients of the food combine within the body with oxygen of the air and undergo combustion, thus liberating energy for the body.

The views expressed by Langworthy were in accord with those of Atwater who in 1895 (10) published a table showing the amounts of nutrients which sold for twenty-five cents in Massachusetts in that year. Representative are the following:

Food	*Protein*	*Fat*	*Energy*
Beefsteak	2.5 oz.	5.33 oz.	1,120 calories
Oysters	1.0 oz.	2 oz. total nutrients	230 calories
Wheat flour	12.8 oz.	—	11,755 calories

Since the nutrients from all food sources were regarded as of equivalent values, the economics of food purchasing, as then understood, clearly pointed to the wisdom of deriving the diet from cereals, peas, and beans, and of omitting from the diet the water-rich fruits, meats, and garden vegetables.

The Period of Controversy Over the Protein Needs of Man

The results of extensive studies of Voit, in which he recorded the amounts and kinds of foods eaten by German people, convinced him that he had established the following facts: A man weighing 70 kg., doing light work, and in the fasting state, metabolized daily approximately 2,240 calories, or 32 calories per kilogram. The ingestion and metabolism of food stimulated heat production, a phenomenon known as "specific dynamic action," or heat-increasing power of the food-stuff. Accordingly, the individual required between 11 and 15 per cent above the starvation level for maintenance. This amounted to between 35 and 37 calories per kilogram of body weight for a 70 kg. man. The energy requirement was obviously influenced by such factors as efficiency of clothing for keeping the body at its normal temperature; by the breathing of cold air, which is warmed in the upper part of the respiratory tract; and especially by the amount of work performed.

From his studies on laborers, especially soldiers in a garrison, Voit (11) concluded that the daily requirement for nutrients would be provided by a diet containing 118 grams of protein, 500 grams of carbohydrates, and 56 grams of fat. This diet provided 3,055 calories.

The allowance of 118 grams of protein caused much discussion. Using Voit's method, Atwater (12) secured records of the diets eaten by people and found that American men of 70 kg. weight averaged 125 grams of protein consumption daily. Rubner made similar studies and concluded that 127 grams of protein were necessary per day. For a man at work Voit recommended 145 grams, while Rubner and Atwater recommended 150 grams of protein per day. At the end of the century it was generally believed that these recommended values, based upon observations of what people ate when guided by their appetites and money resources, represented the actual physiological needs of the body for the maintenance of health.

Siven's Study of the Minimum Protein Requirement of Man

In 1900 Siven (13), of Sweden, using himself as subject, published a study of the protein requirement of man. His results were in marked contrast to those of German and American investigators and started a controversy which lasted a decade.

Since protein was estimated on the basis of 6.25 x N, 125 and 150 grams of protein in the daily diet represented 20.3 and 24.37 grams of nitrogen respectively. Siven, who weighed 65 kg. (143 pounds), found that he could maintain himself in nitrogen equilibrium on 25 to 31 grams of protein daily. These amounts correspond to only 4.0 and 5.0 grams of nitrogen. He took a liberal amount of carbohydrate, and his diet supplied daily 2,717 calories, or 43 calories per kilogram of body weight.

Physiologists who had for years accepted the view of Voit, Rubner, and Atwater that a liberal protein regimen was essential for the maintenance of normal health, were not satisfied with Siven's evidence that maintenance of nitrogen equilibrium for short periods proved that adherence to a low-protein diet was consistent with safeguarding of health. In 1891 Munk (14) and Rosenheim (15) had restricted dogs to diets containing protein in amounts only sufficient to maintain nitrogen-equilibrium; they had found that the animals gradually lost strength, and were apparently afflicted with digestive disturbances. These findings were considered by advocates of a high protein regimen to be weighty evidence in favor of their contention that the portein consumed by people generally represented physiological need. At this juncture, Professor R. H. Chittenden of Yale University came forward with experimental evidence that a dietary which provided much less protein than the accepted standards was not only safe, but had the merit of being decidedly beneficial to health.

Chittenden's Investigations with Low-Protein Diets

Chittenden (1856–1943), when about 44 years of age, suffered from persistent discomfort in a knee-joint, which medical advisors diagnosed as "rheumatic" in nature. He was also troubled with "sick headaches" and bilious attacks. These persisting notwithstanding medical treatment, he resolved to test on himself the effects of reducing the protein and calorie intake. During the first eight months of dieting there was a loss of eight pounds weight. For nine months thereafter, the weight remained stationary. To Chittenden's surprise and satisfaction, his knee trouble and other attendant indispositions no longer recurred periodically as before. He stated that his appetite was keener, his sense of taste more acute, and that these resulted in greater appreciation of the food eaten. He also had a more thorough liking for simple foods. Toward the end of the period of his abstemious regimen, he spent two months at an inland fishing resort where, before breakfast, he often rowed a boat six to ten miles, sometimes against head winds. He felt much greater freedom from fatigue and muscular soreness under these conditions than in previous years when on a fuller dietary (16).

During the nine-months period of stationary weight, the nitrogen content of the urine was determined daily. The average was 5.69 grams. During the last 2.5 months the average was 5.4 grams. At this time Chittenden's body weight was 57.5 kg. (126.5 pounds).

The urinary nitrogen values corresponded to a diet containing 40 to 36.6 grams of protein. His protein intake was in striking contrast with the 118 to 125 grams being eaten daily by people in Europe and America, and with the beliefs based on habit and tradition. Chittenden's improvement in health seemed to leave no doubt of the superiority from the standpoint of physiological well-being of the low over the high-protein regimen.

Chittenden's Dietary Studies on Students and Teachers

Chittenden was convinced from his personal experience with abstemiousness in the consumption of protein and energy (calories), that he had made a discovery of great significance. He thereupon arranged an experiment with human subjects which lasted nine months, and was designed to furnish valuable educational data.

A group of Yale students, some athletes, others sedentary, volunteered to eat at a special table throughout the school year. Only protein-poor foods were served. The average nitrogen in the daily output of the urines of the men during a five-month period ranged between 7.03 and 8.91 grams. Voit's standard of 118 grams, and Atwater's standard of 125 grams of protein daily corresponded to 19.17, and 20.31 grams of nitrogen respectively. A group of faculty men also ate the low protein diet during the school year. Personal testimony, athletic record, reaction time, and photographs all supported the claim that the abstemious system of eating was sound, and could to advantage be adopted generally.

Chittenden did not recommend any special combinations or selections of food other than on the basis of their protein content. His contention was that the ideal diet was composed of the smallest amount of protein together with sufficient non-nitrogenous food that would suffice to keep the body in a state of continual vigor. He asserted that protein digestion products absorbed beyond the actual requirements of the body were injurious, because of the extra burden imposed upon the tissues involved in converting them into the normal waste products of metabolism and in their disposal by the kidneys. He also emphasized the possible danger to health of absorption of substances of bacterial origin. Bacterial decomposition products of protein formed by microorganisms associated with putrefactive processes in the colon were at that period being discussed as health hazards by a number of scientists, following the lead of Brieger, Combe,

Metchnikoff, and others, as has been related in some detail in Chapter 12.

Chittenden pointed out that the protein residues available for putrefaction in the large intestine would be greater when a liberal amount of protein was eaten than when the amount consumed corresponded closely with the actual body requirements. Notwithstanding the long-known investigations of Lind on scurvy, those of Takaki, who attributed beriberi to deficiency of protein in the diet, and also the then recent demonstration by Eijkman and Grijns that beriberi was due to deficiency of a minute amount of a hitherto unsuspected nutrient, Chittenden did not take into his philosophy the possibility of the danger of assessing quality in the diet solely on the basis of protein and energy requirements. Chittenden discussed in his book, *Physiological Economy in Nutrition,* the new principles of dietetics, in contrast with the traditional systems. The volume attracted wide attention (16).

"Parcimony" in Nutrition

Soon after the appearance of Chittenden's volume, Sir James Crichton-Browne, a distinguished physician in London, published a reply under the title *Parcimony In Nutrition* (17). In it he vigorously attacked the idea that a low-protein diet is favorable to physiological well-being. As proof of his belief, he cited opinions expressed by medical authorities and physiologists in favor of a generous protein regimen. His most emphatic criticism of Chittenden's system was that the nine-month experiments with men was too brief a period to produce conclusive results. He stated his opinion that human experience supported the view that meat-eating promoted physical vigor and the development of manly attributes in general. Like Chittenden, Sir James was not conscious of the need for considering any constituents other than protein and energy needs.

The Vogue of Fletcherism

Between 1903 and 1905 a book by Horace Fletcher passed through six editions (18). It was devoted to promoting the physiological benefits supposed to be derived from prolonged mastication of food. Fletcher was not the first to advocate this practice, but he made more extravagant claims for it than any of his predecessors. Accordingly, excessive chewing of food in the interest of health became known as "Fletcherism."

Kellogg (19) collected a list of advocates of thorough mastication of food as a health measure. Among them the most notable were Count Rumford, Brillat-Savarin, the French political economist, Sir Andrew Clark, physician to Queen Victoria, and Gladstone, Prime Minister of England. Sir Andrew said that every mouthful of food should be chewed thirty-two times, in order "to give every tooth a chance." However, he failed to note that the teeth work in pairs and that sixteen chews would have accomplished his objective. Gladstone is reported to have required his children to chew each morsel of food forty times.

Fletcher was a business man of means who for years had been a convivial banqueter. He reported that he was shocked when, at the age of forty, he was denied life insurance because of overweight and digestive troubles. It was then that he resolved to devote himself to the recovery of his health, and with this purpose he retired from business, lived a vigorous outdoor life, and practiced excessive mastication of his food. He claimed that he enjoyed greater satisfaction from food flavors; through psychic factors, recently made popular by the experimental studies of the Russian physiologist Pavlov, he believed that he induced more effective secretion of digestive fluids and greatly enhanced utilization of his food. Furthermore, by chewing each morsel as long as he could keep it in his mouth, Fletcher asserted that his appetite was satisfied with much less food than formerly, when he ate as people usually do. A further claim was that he preferred to eat little of protein-rich foods, and so automatically reduced his protein intake.

Fletcher lectured successfully to lay audiences on the way to achieve health and long life, and for some years he had a large following. At Battle Creek Sanitarium (Michigan), Dr. J. H. Kellogg recommended the practice advocated by Fletcher. He placed a sign bearing the word *Fletcherize,* covering a space of ten feet, where it could be seen frequently by his patients. Although Fletcher exhibited himself as a marvel of physical efficiency after the age of fifty, and according to the testimony of Dr. William G. Anderson, who then had supervision of the Yale gymnasium, was able successfully to compete with college athletes in strength and endurance tests, he proved to be as susceptible to aging processes as are common men. He died at 63 of chronic bronchitis. Almost all converts to "Fletcherism" as a way to restoration of health reverted to their old eating habits after disappointment with its results.

McCay's Studies of the Diets of Peoples of India

In 1912 Major David McCay, professor of physiology at the Medical school at Calcutta, published a notable book (20) in which he described the diets of racial population groups of India, and his observations on their physical status. He approached his problem without any preconceived opinion about diet, and stated that he was motivated solely by a desire to improve the prison dietaries of that country. His most important observations were that the pastoral peoples of India, whose food was largely derived from cereals, milk, and meat, were greatly superior in physical development, health, and strength to other racial groups who in great measure subsisted upon cereals. Especially inferior were those who, as in Bengal, employed polished rice as their staple food.

So inadequate was the state of knowledge concerning the essential components of an adequate diet at that period, that McCay could interpret his observations only by comparison of the amounts of protein in the different diets. At the time of publication of his studies he saw no reason for serious consideration of any constituents of the human diets other than protein and energy.

Physical Efficiency of Flesh-eaters, and Flesh-abstainers

Although the vegetarian diet was advocated by Daniel, at the court of Nebuchadnezzar, and by a few leaders of thought throughout subsequent history, no attempt was made to compare flesh-eaters with flesh-abstainers by physiological tests until about 1900, when personal testimony concerning the superiority of fleshless diets was presented by Graham (7) in his lectures.

In 1904 Schouteden (21) published the data secured by tests on twenty-five students at the University of Brussels, in Belgium. He used an ergograph, which recorded the mechanical work done by successive contractions of one hand, when it worked in unison with a metronome, lifting a weight attached to a string which passed over a pulley. The contractions of the muscles were continued while they passed through progressive fatigue to exhaustion.

His report showed that the mean number of contractions with the right hand was 69 for vegetarians and 38 for meat-eaters. The mean total height of the ergogram obtained with the strongest vegetarian was 1,457 kilogram-meters, whereas that for the strongest meat-eater was 1,049. It was also reported that fatigued hands of vegetarians, when rested for short periods and again subjected to test, recovered their ability to work far more rapidly than did the hands of meat-eaters.

Irving Fisher's Studies of Vegetarians

While undergoing treatment for tuberculosis, Irving Fisher, a noted economist at Yale University, became impressed with the reports from Belgium on the benefits to be derived from abstention from flesh-eating. On his return to his professional duties he conducted extensive tests, principally on students, to inquire into the reliability of published accounts of the Belgian studies. He wrote, "The experiment consisted of endurance tests made on forty-nine persons representing two contrasted types of dietetic habits. These fall into three groups: first, athletes accustomed to a high proteid-diet and full-length dietary; second, athletes accustomed to a low-proteid and non-flesh dietary; third, sedentary persons accustomed to a low-proteid and non-flesh dietary . . . The results of the comparisons given would indicate that the users of the low-proteid and non-flesh dietaries have far greater endurance than those who are accustomed to the ordinary American diet. . . . Three simple endurance tests were employed: first, holding the arms horizontally as long as possible; second, leg-raising with the subjects lying on the back; third, deep-knee bending. All these tests were made before witnesses."

His results showed that even the maximum record of the flesh-eaters was barely more than half the average of the flesh-abstainers. Only two of the fifteen flesh-eaters succeeded in holding their arms horizontally over a quarter of an hour; whereas twenty-two of the thirty-nine abstainers surpassed that limit. None of the flesh-eaters reached half an hour, but fifteen of the thirty-two abstainers exceeded that limit. Of the latter, nine exceeded an hour, four exceeded two hours, and one exceeded three hours. All deep-knee bending contests were won by vegetarians by wide margins (22).

Kellogg (23) at Battle Creek Sanitarium, who was a flesh-abstainer, conducted experiments similar to those of Fisher. His results were comparable to those of the Yale contests.

These experiments were widely publicized, and aroused much discussion concerning the cause for the reported superior endurance of the flesh-abstainers. Caspari (24) reviewed the evidence and concluded that the tests were reliable. He believed that the most probable cause of lack of endurance of meat-eaters was due to absorption from the colon of toxic substances which had their origin in bacterial decomposition of protein residues. He attributed the superior endurance record of the vegetarians to the driving passion of devotees to a cherished principle, a zeal not shared by the flesh-eaters.

It seems remarkable that so much experimental data on the contrasting endurance of vegetarians and meat-eaters should have been published within a few years after 1900, and that the three principal investigators in this field should have been in entire agreement. Considering the extravagant claims for the superiority of the vegetarian regimen, it is surprising that nothing further was ever done by nutrition investigators during the next fifty years to confirm or disprove these claims.

After 1900 new and highly important information concerning the differences in amino acid composition of proteins from both vegetable and animal sources gave physiologists and chemists a new viewpoint from which to judge quality in foods. The vitamin hypothesis followed within a few years. Rapid advance was made, too, in the understanding of the great importance of the inorganic moiety of the diet. These new concepts so changed the ideas regarding the nature of an adequate diet, that it was no longer logical to make sweeping statements about the superiority of a vegetable diet over one of mixed animal and vegetable foods. The important objectives now became inquiry into which of the recognized essential nutrients each food provided. Furthermore, emphasis was placed on the importance of combining foods of contrasting composition in meal-planning so that what was lacking in one would be supplied by another, thus making a diet which supplied all essential nutrients in favorable proportions and which could be made acceptable to varying tastes.

REFERENCES

1. Cornaro, L.: *Trattato della vita sobria.* Padua (1588).
2. The Works of William Stark. By J. G. Smith, London (1788) 89 pp.
3. Aphorisms of Sanctorius. By John Quincy, London (1712).

4. History of the Royal Society, London. James Birch, London (1746), Vol. I, p. 444.
5. Takaki, K.: Health of the Japanese Navy. Lancet, London *ii,* 86 (1887).
6. Encyclopedia Britannica. 14th ed. Vol. *8,* 717–720 (1939).
7. The Science of Human Life. Sylvester Graham, New York and London (1892).
8. Clapp, Charles: The Graham Journ. of Health and Longevity. Vol. *1,* 57 (1837).
9. Langworthy, C. F.: Exper. Sta. Record (Washington, D.C.) *9,* 1003–19 (1898).
10. Atwater, W. O.: Chemistry and Economy of Food. Bull. No. 21, U.S. Dept. Agric. (Washington, D.C.) (1895).
11. Voit, C.: Physiologie des Stoffwechsels. (1881) p. 519.
12. Atwater, W. A. and Bryant, M. S.: Bull. No. 28, U.S. Dept. Agric. (Washington, D.C.) (1902).
13. Siven, V. O.: Skand. Archiv. f. Physiol. *10,* 91–148 (1900); *11,* 308 (1901).
14. Munk, I.: Arch. f. Physiol. (1891) p. 338.
15. Rosenheim, O.: *Ibid.* p. 341.
16. Chittenden, R. H.: Physiological Economy in Nutrition. New York (1904).
17. Crichton-Browne, Sir J.: Parcimony in Nutrition, London and New York (1909).
18. Fletcher, H.: The A. B-Z of Our Own Nutrition. New York (1903).
19. Kellogg, J. H.: The New Dietetics, 2nd ed. pp. 82–85 (1923).
20. McCay, D.: The Protein Element in Nutrition. London (1912).
21. Schouteden, H.: Ann. de Soc. Roy. des Sciences med. et nat. de Bruxelles (Belgium), I (1904).
22. Fisher, I.: The Yale Medical Journal, March (1907).
23. Kellogg, J. H.: Modern Medicine *17,* No. 2 (1909), Battle Creek, Mich.
24. Caspari, W.: Physiological Studies With Vegetarians, Bonn (1905); Pflüger's Arch. *109,* 478–595 (1905).

14

The Discovery of the Vitamins

In Chapter 11 it was shown that food chemists and nutrition investigators who employed chemical data as the basis for assessing food values had, even as late as the year 1900, contributed very little to knowledge of the essential constituents of an adequate diet. Scientific curiosity had motivated organic chemists to separate from plant and animal materials many organic compounds whose existence was hitherto unsuspected, and to study their properties. There was no comparable wave of enthusiasm among nutrition investigators for the study of foods. The practical objectives of animal husbandry men and the economic aspect of human nutrition overshadowed the scientific viewpoint. Langworthy's summary of knowledge of human nutrition (p. 190) revealed unwarranted confidence in a greatly oversimplified theory concerning the nutritive constituents of foods and the nutritive needs of the body. Armsby's treatment of the same subject (p. 153) reflected disappointment with past nutrition studies and little optimism for future progress.

In 1906, however, there were hidden in scientific journals thirteen papers which contained accounts of nutrition experiments based upon diets which were simplified in the chemical sense. The food given to the animals consisted of mixtures of relatively pure protein, carbohydrate, fat, and the mineral substances thought to be of physiological significance. These were the nutrients which chemists believed to be of importance, and were the only constituents which they had attempted to estimate quantitatively in food analyses. Since in every such experiment the animals quickly declined, manifested malnutrition, and survived but for short periods, the conclusion was inevitable that some one or more unknown nutrients were necessary for the preservation of health and maintenance of life.

In several instances the investigators tested a known chemical substance prepared from natural foods as a supplement to the "purified" diets and observed the response of the failing animals to such a supplement. These experiments represented the pioneer efforts to discover in terms of known chemical compounds what represented the simplest diet on which an animal could maintain health. They were the only animal nutrition studies which differed in plan and objective from the animal husbandry type conducted by practical minded men. Feeding tests of the latter type showed only the comparative values of various combinations of farm crops for inducing growth, milk, egg or wool production in domestic animals; they did not reveal why such combinations succeeded or failed.

Between 1870 and 1920 some discoveries of great significance were made. Several investigators used diets made of isolated and recombined nutrients, or greatly simplified diets (polished rice). Because none of these was followed up by further inquiries, they did nothing more than prove that unknown nutrients existed, and that organic iron or phosphorus compounds were not the mysterious unknowns a lack of which was responsible for nutritive failure of animals on the diets. The more important experiments based on this procedure tell the story of progress which converted nutrition studies from empirical to sound scientific investigations. The use of simplified diets furnished the key to the discovery of what every physiologist and chemist wanted to know about foods and the nutrients they provided. This chapter is an account of the dawn of rewarding investigations in animal nutrition.

A Lesson from Nutrition Observations in a Besieged City

So far as the writer has learned, with the exception of earlier speculations on the efficacy of fresh vegetable food for the prevention of scurvy, J. B. A. Dumas (1800–1884) was the earliest man of science to question the adequacy of a diet composed only of protein, carbohydrate, fat and salts. In 1871 (1) he published in English a paper on "The Constitution of Blood and Milk," in which he described his observations on the effects of food on the infants of Paris during the siege by the Germans (1870–71). Here for the first time a competent observer and distinguished man of science observed human beings under conditions of dietary restrictions so severe that the results could be interpreted with the accuracy and reliability ordinarily obtainable only in well-controlled animal experiments.

Dumas told of the extremity of the people of Paris after they had exhausted their supplies of food and fuel. Inventories showed, he said, not only that the capitulation of the city was inevitable, but marked the precise day for it. Parents were in the greatest distress because of scarcity of milk and eggs, and attributed to it the high mortality among infants and young children. "Scientific men were asked urgently to find ways to obtain heat without combustibles; to reconstruct food with mineral materials, without the cooperation of life . . . to reproduce at least the essential food of man with non-alimentary materials."

Since, with few exceptions, chemists and physiologists believed that protein, carbohydrates, and fats were the only indispensable nutrients, it was thought possible to construct an artificial milk by emulsifying fat in a sweetened, albuminous solution. Dumas did not disclose the sources of the materials employed for this purpose. Although these mixtures were made in imitation of the composition of milk, their effects on infants were disastrous. From this sad experience Dumas drew the conclusion that something essential to life was lacking in the artificial milk.

Dumas's paper might have been expected to turn the thoughts of nutrition investigators toward search for the nature of the unknown dietary essential or essentials in milk and other foods, but for some reason his clear announcement of this new viewpoint in nutritional research remained unnoticed. A decade elapsed before the earliest experiment having a bearing on this subject was reported.

Lunin's Famous Experiments on Acid-Base Balance in Nutrition

After the noteworthy attempts by Magendie and the Gelatin Commission to study the effects of feeding single substances such as gelation, oil, sugar, egg-white, and wheat gluten (p. 76), all of which were carried out between 1816 and 1841, no effort was made until 1873 to test by animal experiments whether Liebig's view was correct. Liebig believed that albuminous substance together with fuel foods and certain mineral salts were all that an animal needed for nourishment. In that year, as has been described elsewhere, Forster reported the rapid nutritive decline and death of dogs and pigeons fed diets that were almost ash-free. It has been mentioned that von Bunge, Professor at the University in Dorpat, advanced the idea that Forster's animals perished sooner on the ash-free diets than did animals that were fasted. This von Bunge attributed to the accumulation of sulfuric acid in the body from oxidation of the sulfur in the proteins fed.

At von Bunge's request, his pupil, N. Lunin, attempted to test the validity of this theory. Lunin (2) used adult mice, and fed them a diet composed of casein, cane sugar, and water. The mice survived from 11 to 21 days, whereas the control animals given only water died within 3 to 4 days. He tried adding enough sodium carbonate to neutralize the sulfuric acid equivalent to the sulfur in the casein; this addition led to survival of mice for 12 to 30 days. When only sodium chloride, which has no neutralizing value, was added to the food, the mice survived for even shorter periods. Addition of potassium carbonate or chloride gave no better results.

Lunin then fed mice a diet consisting of casein, milk fat, and milk sugar, together with a salt mixture made in imitation of the ash of milk; this did not improve the health of the animals. In marked contrast to the early fatal results of restricting animals to his imitation milk, Lunin found that when he gave the mice milk to drink, and no other food, they remained in good health and were lively after sixty days. Accordingly, he wrote in his dissertation, "Mice can live well under these conditions when receiving suitable foods (e.g., milk), but as the experiments show, that they cannot subsist on proteins, fats, and carbohydrates, salts and water, it follows that other substances indispensable for nutrition must be present in milk besides casein, fat, lactose, and salts."

Voit's Comment on Experimenting with Isolated Food Substances

Voit contemplated the advantages which might be derived from studying the effects on animals of simplified diets of purified foodstuffs. In 1881 he wrote (3), "Unquestionably, it would be best for the purpose (experimental study) if one could feed only pure chemical compounds, for example, pure protein, fat, sugar, starch, and ash constituents, or mixtures of the same. However, inasmuch as men and animals only rarely tolerate continuously such tasteless mixtures, it is necessary in most cases to choose foods as they are provided by nature. Nevertheless, it would probably be possible and very desirable to repeat the tests with the natural food products by using the pure substances, although the results yielded thereby might not be essentially different." Voit's words seem to show that he had no doubt that if diets composed of the recognized nutrients in suitable proportions were fed, they would be adequate physiologically, and that the only reason why they might fail to nourish a man or animal would be unpalatability, and not a lack of essential nutrients.

Socin's Experiments with Simplified Diets

Ten years after Lunin's publication, Socin (4), another student of von Bunge, conducted experiments with simplified diets to determine the physiological values of different iron compounds. Von Bunge had prepared from fat-free egg yolk, by digestion with artificial gastric juice, a nitrogenous substance which he called hematogen. This differed widely in composition from proteins, and, in addition, contained phosphorus and iron. He believed hematogen to be of great physiological importance. Socin employed a diet consisting of blood serum, fat, sugar, starch, cellulose, and ash of milk. This basal diet lacked iron which was supplied in different experiments as hemoglobin, hematin, hematogen, or ferric chloride. On none of these iron supplements did the mice survive more than thirty-two days. Control mice fed egg yolk, starch, and cellulose were still alive after ninety-nine days. Socin concluded that there must be in egg yolk something of unknown nature which is essential. It seems incredible that von Bunge did not pursue further so important an observation and seek to discover the nature of the deficiencies in the diets of Lunin and Socin. Coppola (5) and Hall (6) confirmed the fact that the cause of failure of animals on the diets of these investigators was not due to a lack of a suitable source of iron.

In 1895 Pasqualis (7) restricted chickens to a diet composed of protein, starch, dextrin, sugar, olive oil, wood chips (2 per cent), common salt, and the ash of maize kernels. The birds lost weight rapidly. He then extracted natural foods with hot alcohol and recombined the extracted material and the extract. He found that the mixture had lost its power to support birds in health or to maintain life. Pasqualis thus asserted that any diet containing only the constituents listed in tables of food composition based on chemical analyses had no value whatever in animal nutrition.

Experiments to Determine the Nutritive Values of Inorganic and Organically Bound Phosphorus

The possibility that phosphorylated proteins and other organic compounds containing phosphorus (lecithin, cephalin, nucleic acid) might be indispensable constituents of an adequate diet was put to experimental test by Steinitz (8), Zadik (9), Leipziger (10), and

Ehrlich (11). All of these investigators used diets composed of isolated and recombined substances comparable to those of Lunin, but they extended their studies to compare phosphorus-containing with phosphorus-free proteins. Egg albumen, myosin (from muscle) blood, albumen, and edestin (from hemp-seed) were compared with casein (from cow's milk) and vitellin (from egg yolk), both of which contain organically bound phosphorus. The experimental animals included dogs, mice, pigeons, and hens. All the diets failed to prevent rapid decline and death of the animals. The experiments, therefore, afforded no information concerning the relative worth of organic and inorganic phosphorus in animal nutrition.

Influence of the Discovery of "Nuclein" and Nucleic Acid on Thought about Animal Nutrition

The discovery of nucleic acids and related substances called "nucleins" further broadened speculations concerning the nutritive needs of animals. In 1871 Miescher (12) prepared from egg yolk a material which was resistant to digestion with artificial gastric juice. This juice contained phosphorus and was called *nuclein.* Hoppe-Seyler (13) prepared a similar substance from pus obtained from an abscess. These were phosphorus-rich protein compounds and were called nucleoproteins. In 1881 Miescher (14) prepared nucleic acid from the nuclei of the heads of salmon sperm. This substance contained about 12 per cent phosphorus. In 1874 Piccard (15) discovered that the purines, guanine, and xanthine were liberated by hydrolysis of nucleoproteins.

Eventually, these new findings became of interest to students of nutrition. After the above mentioned experiments had shown that neither phosphorylated proteins nor organic iron compounds would adequately supplement diets composed of purified nutrients, Falta and Noeggerath (16), in 1905, tried adding nucleic acid, lecithin, and cholesterol to such diets. They found that either singly or collectively these substances did not provide all that was needed for the nourishment of an animal. It is surprising that these investigators failed to realize that their results offered unmistakable evidence of the existence of nutrients of unknown chemical nature.

Pekelharing's Demonstration of the Existence of Unidentified Nutrients

In 1905 Pekelharing (17), professor of hygiene in the University of Utrecht, made a highly important discovery. He fed mice a diet composed of a baked mixture of casein, egg albumen, rice flour, lard, and the salts which he believed to be of physiological importance. This mixture he called bread. When given this food along with water the animals eagerly nibbled it, but after a few days they lost their healthy appearance, grew thin, and lost their appetite. Within four weeks all of the mice were dead. When Pekelharing fed milk in addition to the baked mixture, the mice remained healthy. He said that the amount of protein, lactose, and fat which the mice obtained from the milk was "quite negligible in comparison with what the bread on which they were fed contains."

Pekelharing observed that if, instead of milk, a small addendum of whey, formed by removing the casein and fat from milk, was given the mice remained in health throughout the experimental period. This showed that a supplement of something in whey, effective in very small amount, was of great physiological importance. Thus, he wrote, "My intention is to point out that there is still an unknown substance in milk which even in very small quantities is of paramount importance to nourishment. If this substance is absent, the organism loses its power properly to assimilate the well-known principal parts of food, the appetite is lost and with apparent abundance the animals die of want. Undoubtedly this substance not only occurs in milk, but in all sorts of food stuffs, both of vegetable and animal origin."

Pekelharing's contribution lay in his finding that a small amount of whey, which contained very small proportions of protein and fat as compared with milk, was as effective as milk in promoting health in mice. He went beyond Lunin and Socin by demonstrating the minuteness of the effective dose of some unknown nutrient. His paper, published in Dutch, was not abstracted in Maly's *Jahresbericht,* and received so little publicity that, apparently, later workers did not know about it. This study was first announced in English in 1926 (18). Funk, in his book *The Vitamins,* published in 1922, did not mention Pekelharing.

Willcock and Hopkins's Experiments with a Purified Diet Containing Zein as Source of Protein

In Chapter 4 an account was given of the state of knowledge of the chemical nature of proteins about the beginning of the twentieth century. By 1905 the work of Nasse, Kossel, E. Fischer, Osborne, and others had shown that proteins from different sources had, in many instances, strongly contrasting chemical composition as shown by their yields of certain amino acids. By that time amino acids were replacing proteins in speculations about protein nutrition.

In 1900 Hopkins and Cole isolated and described a new amino acid, tryptophan, which gives a positive test with Adamkiewicz's reagent, first described in 1875. The alcohol-soluble protein zein, from maize, does not contain tryptophan. It was for the purpose of determining the importance of tryptophan in nutrition that Willcock and Hopkins (19) carried out a nutrition experiment using mice. In the light of what has been recorded in earlier pages, it appears that Hopkins, in 1906, was not acquainted with the series of consistent failures experienced by those investigators mentioned above who attempted to solve certain problems in nutrition by restricting animals to purified food substances with and without supplements of known nature.

Willcock and Hopkins employed a basal diet composed of finely ground zein with 2.5 times its weight of carbohydrate (2 starch to 1 sugar), and the ash of a mixture of oats and dog biscuits. They had previously tested oats with dog biscuit as food for mice and found the combination satisfactory for inducing growth. Paper, and later charcoal, was added to serve as indigestible material. With this diet different fats were tried: butter fat, ether extract of cheese, clarified bacon fat and olive oil, and in some cases a drop of cod liver oil added to the food. A little lecithin was added to supply additional phosphorus. The mice were not fully grown, but were well on toward maturity.

On this zein diet mice survived an average of fourteen days. When a supplement of tryptophan was given, the average survival period was twenty-eight days. This was the earliest animal experiment in which a decisive test proved the indispensability of a specific amino acid in nutrition, and yielded information concerning the mode of failure caused by "partial starvation" for a specific nutrient. Willcock and Hopkins described the symptoms of tryptophan deficiency in mice as torpor (no movement when touched or handled), coldness of tails and feet, eyes half closed and glary.

Notwithstanding the other factors influencing the nutritional failure of their mice, it is certain that the provision of tryptophan doubled their survival time. It seems probable that these investigators were not familiar with earlier recorded experiences with feeding isolated food substances, because they gave no references to any previous investigations of such diets. Their only reference to previous work was to a paper by Szumowski (20) who, in 1902 at Heidelberg, under the guidance of A. Kossel, carried out some experiments designed to show whether or not zein was absorbed without digestion and could be detected in the tissues of an animal. Szumowski ground zein to a fine powder and fed it to geese and pigeons. Afterwards he sought to recover it by extracting the bodies of the birds with alcohol, in which zein is soluble. He found no zein in the tissues after feeding it. No review of the literature relating to experiments with purified food mixtures was written until 1909 (20a).

In 1906 F. G. Hopkins was the most advanced thinker on the phenomena of animal nutrition. In a notable lecture in that year (21) he cited the most recent advances in protein and amino acid chemistry, which had transformed the outlook of physiologists and chemists on nutrition. Specifically he mentioned that the necessary precursor of adrenalin, a hormone which must be continuously formed, must be derived from the diet. He did not mention tyrosine, but apparently had this amino acid in mind as a precursor of some synthetic product important in metabolism. Hopkins introduced the idea that hormones are derived from digestion products of proteins. He emphasized the importance as a promising field of inquiry of chemists devoting their efforts to the isolation from animal and plant tissues of unknown substances with unknown properties.

Turning to the subject of dietetics, Hopkins said, "But further, no animal can live on a mixture of proteins, carbohydrates, and fats, and even when the necessary inorganic material is carefully supplied, the animal still cannot flourish. The animal body is adjusted to live either on plant tissues or on other animals, and these contain countless substances other than proteins, carbohydrates, and fats. Physiological evolution, I believe, has made some of these well nigh as essential as are the basal constituents of the diet. Lecithin, for instance, has repeatedly been shown to have a marked influence on nutrition, and this just happens to be something already familiar, and a substance that happens to have been tried. The field is almost unexplored; only it is certain that there are many minor factors in all diets, of which the body takes account. In diseases such as rickets, and particularly in scurvy, we have had for long years knowledge of a dietetic factor; but though we know how to benefit these conditions empirically, the real errors in the diet are to this day quite obscure."

Henriques and Hansen's Demonstration of Synthesis of Protein In the Body from Amino Acids

In an earlier chapter it was noted that over a period of half a century physiologists sought to determine whether "peptone" could be converted in the body into protein. Liebig's assumption, shared by Dumas, was that synthesis of complex organic substances could be accomplished only by plants, and that animals were limited in their metabolism (called metamorphosis of food) to degrading plant products to simple end products resulting from the chemical activity of the body. The conclusion was, however, gradually forced upon physiologists that the animal body was capable of complex syntheses. Ure's demonstration of synthesis of hippuric acid when benzoic acid is fed was the first definite example about which there could be no doubt.

An experimental study carried out in 1905 by Henriques and Hansen (22) provided more information about what constitutes an adequate diet than even its authors recognized. Their results, if thoughtfully considered, clearly indicated the need for unidentified substances in addition to the classical dietary components. It is appropriate, therefore, to describe it here. Apparently these investigators, like most others at that period, were unacquainted with recorded experiences with purified diets. Their objective was to determine whether protein could be synthesized from amino acids in the body.

They kept young rats in metabolism cages and fed them a diet of isolated food substances in which either casein or Witte's peptone (an enzyme digest of protein) provided the protein moiety. They found, as had all their predecessors, that the animals could neither grow nor long remain alive on such food. When they substituted acid-hydrolyzed casein, the results were the same. In marked contrast, however, were the results when they used as the source of amino acids, either autolyzed (self-digested) pancreas or autolyzed mucous membrane from intestines of dogs. On such a diet young rats grew and remained healthy. Henriques and Hansen stated that their experiments proved that enzyme-digested proteins of pancreas and mucosa, which were composed mainly of amino acids and simple complexes of these, could be synthesized into protein by the growing rat. Later knowledge showed that these experiments had clearly proven that the digested glandular substances supplied something of importance in addition to amino acids.

Röhmann's Experiments With Purified Diets Plus Additions of Natural Foods

In 1908 Röhmann (23) reported highly instructive results from restricting small animals to diets composed in great measure of purified food substances, but with small additions of natural foods. The purified diet without such additions appeared to lack nutritive value. With the additions some measure of success was realized.

These observations should have suggested to Röhmann's contemporaries that the small allowances of natural foods provided unidentified indispensable nutrients, but they were not meaningful at that time. His data were comparable to those of Lunin and of Pekelharing, in whose experiments the unknown nutrients were supplied by whey, and to those of Socin, in which the unknown nutrients were derived from egg yolk. As late as 1912, Hopkins (24) regarded as a discovery the fact that young animals in decline on a diet of purified ingredients resumed growth when a supplement of milk amounting to about four per cent of the diet or a small supplement of yeast was given. He interpreted the favorable effect of these adjuvants to their containing unidentified nutrients. Nevertheless, Hopkins's experiments did not advance knowledge beyond what had been proven by the studies of Lunin, Socin, Pekelharing, and Röhmann.

Stepp's Studies with "Lipoid-Free" Diets

In 1909 Stepp (25), while a student of Hofmeister in Strassburg, carried out experiments designed to show whether fats and related substances were essential in animal nutrition. At that time it was well known that the cellular components from both plant and animal sources contain a number of substances resembling fats in their physical properties, especially in solubility in solvents such as ether and alcohol. Stepp prepared a bread from milk and wheat flour, and another from milk and "protomol," a protein-rich preparation from rice. These he extracted thoroughly with ether and alcohol. Some mice were fed the unextracted and others the extracted breads. Those fed the unextracted food remained in health during the six to eight weeks they were observed, whereas those fed the extracted foods all died within thirty days. Stepp interpreted his results to mean that certain lipids (fat-like substances), were essential in the diet.

Next Stepp sought to discover whether any one of the best known substances of this class was indispensable as a nutrient. For this purpose he restricted mice to his extracted foods and tested successively the effect of adding lecithin, cholesterol, cephalin, and cerebrosides. In no case were the mice benefited. After preparing from egg yolk an extract made by shaking it with cold alcohol, he divided the solution into two portions. One portion was heated for two days in a water-bath with ninety-five per cent alcohol, the other was subjected to the minimum amount of heat necessary to evaporate the alcohol. Each of these preparations he added to his extracted bread, and tested their values as food for mice. The group fed the heated preparation all died within thirty days, while the group fed the unheated preparation remained in health. Thus Stepp discovered that whatever it was that dissolved out of the breads with alcohol and was of physiological value to mice, was easily destroyed by heating with alcohol. His observations were reminiscent of those which Pasqualis (7) had reported fourteen years earlier. Since many organic substances present in plant and animal materials other than "lipids" are soluble in alcohol, Stepp was not warranted in concluding it was some fat-like substances that benefited his mice.

Birds Synthesize Complex Lipids in Egg Formation

In 1912 Fingerling (26) in Germany, using ducks, and McCollum, Drescher, and Halpin (27), using pullets, proved that birds can subsist on very low-fat diets and produce eggs of normal lecithin content. Fingerling used a diet consisting of cooked potatoes and cooked blood albumen, with inorganic salts; McCollum, Drescher, and Halpin used a diet consisting of polished rice and ether-extracted skim milk. In each experiment the birds incorporated into their eggs several times as much lecithin as was contained in their bodies. Thus, these results suggested that in interpreting his experimental results, Stepp was dealing with substances other than complex lipids.

McCollum and Davis' Efforts to Make Purified Diets Palatable

It would seem, from what has been related of the efforts made over a period of forty years to nourish animals on simple mixtures containing an abundance of everything shown by chemical analyses to be present in foods, that by 1909 when Stepp reported his studies, further efforts in this direction were futile and doomed to failure. Experiments up to that time indicated that only when some natural food was included in the diet could animals survive. Yet in 1907 McCollum (28), because he had not fully comprehended the evidence afforded by recorded experimental studies, again attacked the problem of securing well-being in animals restricted to purified food substances. As a step in this direction, he increased the palatability of the insipid mixtures.

Many years earlier Voit had suggested that unpalatability and monotony would interfere with the success of such experiments should they be attempted. In 1897 Pavlow published his extensive observations on the influence of appetite on the secretory function of the digestive glands. Pavlow suggested that flavor is a strong incentive in the selection of foods. His work in this field aroused great interest among physiologists.

For a time McCollum believed that improving the flavor of the unpalatable mixtures of purified proteins, carbohydrates, fats, and mineral salts could turn failure into success. He sought to prove this in a number of ways. He used a greater variety of sugars, two proteins instead of one, and added flavor by moistening the diet with an aqueous distillate from highly flavored cheese, or by adding freshly rendered bacon fat. But all such efforts proved futile. It emerged that whenever some degree of improvement in growth and health of the animals was secured, it was due to two factors: impurities in the food materials, especially milk sugar; and feces-eating, the significance of which McCollum had not considered.

Osborne and Mendel's Experiments with Purified Diets

In 1909 Osborne and Mendel (29) began investigations with purified foodstuffs. Since chemical studies had clearly shown great differences in the yields of certain amino acids by proteins from various sources, it seemed obvious that their nutritive values would differ markedly. Earlier efforts by these men to compare individual purified proteins by feeding them in purified mixtures of nutrients had resulted in failure, which the experience of others had shown to be inevitable.

Nevertheless, Osborne and Mendel made an extremely important observation which had hitherto escaped the notice of experimenters with purified diets. They noted that young rats confined to such diets and allowed to eat their feces were in better nutritive condition than when coprophagy was prevented. Furthermore, they found that if rats on nutritionally inadequate diets of this type were permitted to eat the feces of rats fed natural foods, they were far better off than when the feces were derived from animals fed the purified diet. Announcement of this fact led later investigators to avoid this source of error by keeping their experimental rats on screens, thus depriving them of their own droppings.

Osborne and Mendel's second discovery was "protein-free milk." Use of this material enabled them to realize their objective of comparing the nutritive values of different proteins in Osborne's collection. "Protein-free milk" was prepared by acidifying separator skim milk to cause coagulation of the casein, and heating the whey thus secured to coagulate the lactalbumen. The latter was filtered off, and the resulting essentially protein-free whey was evaporated to dryness. This material contained the sugar and salts of milk, together with yellow-green pigments and small amounts of a considerable number of unidentified substances of unknown nutritive significance.

Using young rats and feeding diets containing 28.3 per cent of this deproteinated whey powder along with a single protein in amounts varying from 9 to 20 per cent, the remainder of the food consisting of starch and fat, such as lard, Osborne and Mendel secured reproduction and also growth at the normal rate. With this technic they were able to show that proteins from different sources differed as widely in their nutritional values as chemical data already available suggested they should.

Certain proteins (e.g., casein or lactalbumen, egg albumen, edestin from hempseed) were complete proteins, a single one sufficing to support growth and well-being in young animals. In marked contrast were zein from maize and gliadin from wheat. These were incomplete because of absence or deficiency of one or more amino acids. Thus lysine, histidine, and tryptophan, since they supplemented these incomplete proteins and made them complete nutritionally, were shown to be indispensable nutrients. Feeding at a high level a protein containing little of some essential amino acid supported growth, whereas a lower level of a protein intake sufficed if it yielded favorable percentages of all the essential amino acids. The comprehensive program which Osborne and Mendel carried out, in which many proteins were compared, resulted in establishing their approximate quantitative biological values and aroused great interest.

Osborne and Mendel's Interpretation of Their Early Achievement

These investigators were not receptive to the view of Grijns and Funk (then receiving strong support from clinical studies on human beriberi and its analog experimental polyneuritis in animals) that a substance called *vitamine* was essential for normal nutrition. They were at first inclined to believe that in protein-depleted whey, "protein-free milk," a favorable balance existed among the inorganic elements and ions and that this was a factor of great importance. That certain quantitative relations between ions was of great significance in physiological processes had recently been shown by the dramatic experiments of J. Loeb (see Chapter 21).

Accordingly, Osborne and Mendel sought to make an artificial "protein-free milk" by combining milk sugar with a salt mixture prepared in imitation of the ash constituents of natural "protein-free milk." As late as September 1912, after three years of experimenting, they were convinced that they had succeeded in nourishing young rats with this mixture, every constituent of which was believed to be a substance of known chemical composition. In a paper which he presented before the Fifteenth International Congress on Hygiene and Demography, Mendel (30) stated, "Latterly, Osborne and I have further succeeded in imitating the inorganic make-up of the natural protein-free milk by uniting the various ions shown by analysis to be therein, into an artificial salt mixture. This too has proved to be a reasonably successful diet adjuvant; and the results furnish, so far as we are aware, the first published records of successful feeding experiments in which prolonged growth has been induced by carefully purified isolated foodstuffs and an artificial salt mixture. By prolonged growth we refer to the capacity of the animals to triple or quadruple their weight." In the same paper (p. 6) he said, "The simplest food mixtures with which characteristic growth curves have been obtained have been made up of only one protein, starch, and sugar, and the artificial salt mixture, i.e., they have been fat- and presumably lipoid-free." Later every claim made in the above quotations had to be abandoned in the light of a few months of further experience with this simplified diet of known constituents.

The Emergence of the Vitamin Hypothesis

It is an old belief that certain foods possessed special properties as remedies for disease. Thus, Hippocrates advocated liver for the treatment of night-blindness. The people of Newfoundland, at some unknown time, discovered that eating liver was a prompt and certain cure for night-blindness caused by overexposure of the eyes of fishermen to light. In 1720 Kramer, a surgeon in the Austrian Army, observed that fresh vegetable food cured scurvy in soldiers, whereas dried vegetables did not. Darby, in 1789, employed cod liver oil therapeutically. These and other recorded experiences with the therapeutic use of foods either by physicians or laymen supplied evidence which should have stimulated experimental inquiry long ago, but the time was not ripe for this type of investigation until the beginning of the twentieth century.

About the year 1896 C. Eijkman (1858–1930), a military doctor in the Dutch Indies who later became professor of Hygiene in Utrecht, made a momentous discovery in nutritional research. "Eijkman's original research in connection with beriberi began in a curiously accidental way. He wished to carry out certain investigations on fowls, and in order to economize on their food he fed them on scraps from the wards of the military hospital to which he was attached. On these scraps, which consisted chiefly of cooked, polished rice, the fowls developed paralysis, the nature of which was at first obscure. A clue thereto was unintentionally given by a newly appointed director of the hospital, who refused to let Eijkman feed his fowls any longer on scraps from the wards. Henceforth they were fed on *gaba* (rice still in the husk) and on this diet they recovered. Eijkman's identification of this *polyneuritis gallinarum* with beriberi of human beings was at first generally scorned and ignored, but about 1896, after much painstaking research in cooperation with Grijns and Vordermann, he came to the conclusion that a diet of overmilled rice was the chief cause of polyneuritis in fowls, and of beriberi of human beings. The term partial hunger was given to this condition." (31)

Eijkman proposed to explain the observed phenomena by postulating the presence in the endosperm of rice of a nerve poison for which there was, in the outer layers of the whole rice a substance which neutralized or antagonized this in the pharmacological sense. He also suggested that a poisonous substance might be formed from excessive starch in the intestine. Grijns (32) was the first to interpret correctly the connection between excessive consumption of polished rice and the etiology of beriberi. He concluded that rice contained an essential nutrient found chiefly in the outer layers of the grain which are removed in polishing. This, he said, could be extracted from these layers by means of water or alcohol. Vordermann (33) eradicated beriberi from prisons by substituting whole rice for polished rice. Fraser, Director of the Institute for Medical Research, and Stanton, Director of Government Laboratories of Federated Malay States (34) conducted many experiments on humans and animals, and from these confirmed the deficiency theory of the cause of beriberi.

Holst and Froelich's description in 1907 (36) of the experimental production of scurvy in guinea pigs fed dry or cooked diets, and its cure by feeding fresh vegetables or fruits, was a highly important contribution. It not only confirmed the vitamin hypothesis, but made available experimentally-induced scurvy in animals for study of the nature of the anti-scorbutic vitamin.

In 1912 Funk (35) propounded the theory that beriberi, scurvy, pellagra, and possibly rickets were caused by deficiency or lack in the diet of "special substances which are of the nature of organic bases, which we will call vitamines." This paper was widely read, and many accepted the new concept of dietary deficiency diseases.

It will be recalled that, in 1906, Hopkins had expressed his belief that scurvy and rickets were disorders caused by diets deficient in unidentified nutrients. The same idea had been repeatedly recorded by others concerning scurvy (Chapter 17), and the therapeutic use of cod liver oil implied the view that in rickets the oil supplied something which was lacking. The important fact was that these observations were unknown to medical men and chemists of that period. Hopkins, therefore, rendered an important service by again recording his views in such memorable terms that they received wide recognition.

Like that of Hopkins, Funk's prediction was a shrewd one. It opened the eyes of physiologists and biochemists to new vistas of exploration and techniques.

The Discovery of the First Fat-Soluble Vitamin

A new viewpoint concerning the essential nutrients which the diet must provide originated with the discovery that some fats contain a substance which is indispensable for the maintenance of life. Surprisingly enough, this observation was the result of two errors in judgment. McCollum and Davis (37), in their experiments with purified diets, used milk sugar which was contaminated to a significant degree with whey constituents. They also permitted their experimental rats to have access to their feces. The other constituents of the diets fed the rats were relatively pure proteins, starch, sucrose, and a mixture of inorganic salts. Certain diets happened to contain just sufficient impurities of nutritional value to permit young rats to grow fairly well and maintain a reasonable standard of well-being when either butter fat (ether-soluble matter only), or the ether-soluble matter from egg-yolk, was included in the diet. The animals failed rapidly on the same basal diets when the fats provided were lard or olive oil. This was a surprising discovery, since up to this time it was believed that all fats were useful in nutrition only as fuel foods. In the light of the experiments by McCollum and Davis it became evident that a hitherto unsuspected nutrient existed, and that it was carried by certain fats. These results were published in 1913.

McCollum and Davis Separate the Fat-Soluble Factor from Butter Fat

Next, McCollum and Davis (38) transferred the new fat-soluble factor from butter fat to olive oil by the following procedure: Butter-fat was saponified with potassium hydroxide in alcohol. The resulting soap was dissolved in water, and olive oil was thoroughly emulsified in the soap solution. The olive oil was of the same sample which had been tested on rats and found to be of no value in protecting them against decline on the basal diet. The emulsion was then broken with ether, and the olive oil was recovered in that solvent. After evaporating the ether, the olive oil was found by a feeding test to have acquired the nutritive quality of the butter fat.

A short time thereafter, McCollum and Davis found by experiments that the new nutrient, at first called fat-soluble A but later renamed vitamin A, was present in kidney and other glandular organs, and accompanied the ether-soluble fats from these sources. Ether extracts from the dried leaves of plants also contained it. This nutrient was not found, however, in adipose tissue fats and certain vegetable oils. Five months after the publication of the first announcement of this discovery, Osborne and Mendel (39) confirmed the observations of McCollum and Davis, and added cod liver oil to the list of animal fats which contained vitamin A, and almond oil to the list of vegetable fats which did not.

Osborne and Mendel's earliest experiments (40) which led them to conclude that butter fat was the carrier of some unknown nutrient, were made by adding unsalted *butter* to the basal diets and noting resumption of growth in rats in decline. Since butter contains a considerable amount of whey constituents, no conclusion was warranted that the fat moiety alone was responsible for the benefit to the animals. In subsequent experiments comparable responses by young rats were secured with ether-soluble fats from melted butter.

The observation that a fat-soluble as well as a water-soluble unidentified dietary essential (the anti-beriberi substance) existed aroused great interest among nutrition investigators and brought new recruits to this field of study.

Confusion Arising From Different Species' Requirements for Nutrients

Even in 1915 investigators who had experience in observing the effects of experimental diets with rats, dogs, fowls, or other common domestic animals, were confused as to recorded statements about the cause and prevention of the hemorrhagic condition known as scurvy. The history of clinical and experimental studies of scurvy in man and animals is considered in Chapter 27. There it is shown that the prevention and cure of scurvy in man had fully established the fact that fresh fruits and vegetables were effective prophylactic and remedial foods, whereas heated or dried foods possessed no antiscorbutic value. But experience with rats did not reveal any distinction in nutritive value between fresh and dried or heated foods. Osborne and Mendel's rats thrived when all unknown dietary factors were derived from whey which had been heated during evaporation to dryness. McCollum and Davis had made cereal grains complete nutritionally by adding inorganic salts, dried protein, and certain fats, none of which were reputed to possess antiscorbutic value. Hence, even with their limited experience, they saw no reason for believing that a special dietary factor which functioned as an antiscorbutic agent existed. The use of guinea pigs by Holst and his associates for experimental testing of foods for their power to prevent hemorrhagic disease, showed that this species required a nutrient which could be dispensed with by rats and several other species. This is mentioned here because when McCollum and Davis distinguished between fat-soluble and water-soluble vitamins, they were quite unaware of the existence of a second water-soluble dietary essential for species susceptible to scurvy.

The Biological Method for Analysis of Foods

The biological method for determining the nutritive value of a food was developed for the purpose of discovering the nature of the deficiencies of the cereal grains. About the beginning of the twentieth century the results of pig-feeding experiments in the United States and Canada showed that pigs fed corn (maize) alone did not make satisfactory gains (41). The practice recommended by experiment stations for profitable pork production was to supplement corn with protein-rich concentrates such as meat-meal, cottonseed oil-meal, linseed oil-meal, and others, together with ashes or bone meal. It was believed that such supplements increased the available bone-forming elements. In explaining the value of such concentrates, animal husbandrymen mentioned only their protein and mineral content.

McCollum and Davis found by many feeding trials that young rats failed to grow when restricted to any cereal grain or mixtures of several of them. This they interpreted to mean that cereal grains have certain nutritive deficiencies in common, since when fed together they do not make good each other's nutritional inadequacies. These considerations led them to test the possibility of identifying the dietary principles which were lacking or not sufficiently abundant in cereal grains, by supplementing them progressively in a series of experiments, with increasing numbers of known individual nutrients, and observing the response of young rats to such additions. The following newly-established facts were taken into consideration by McCollum and Davis:

1. Corn alone as food resulted in nutritional disaster to young rats and swine.
2. Willcock and Hopkins had shown that zein, the principal protein of maize, was inadequate nutritionally as a source of tryptophan, which they had proved to be indispensable. Osborne and Mendel had demonstrated the indispensability of tryptophan, and lysine.
3. A great number of analyses of the ashes of farm crops showed that all cereal grains are low in their content of calcium. Supplements of calcium salts had repeatedly been reported to be beneficial for promoting skeletal development of animals fed principally on cereals.
4. The newly-discovered, fat-soluble, unidentified nutrient was not present in certain vegetable fats and oils.

5. McCollum had demonstrated that inorganic phosphates could serve all the purposes of physiology as respects organic phosphorus compounds, and that the latter could be synthesized by the body.
6. Water extracts of cereal grains contained the antineuritic substance which prevented and cured beriberi in man. Polyneuritis in birds had been experimentally produced by feeding them a diet of polished rice.

The Biological Method of Analysis Applied to Wheat

In order to investigate the nature of the nutritive deficiencies of wheat which, like corn, does not support growth or sustain health in young rats or swine, McCollum and Davis (42) conducted the following experiments with young rats, with the results as noted:

1. Wheat alone: no growth, short life.
2. Wheat plus casein (purified protein), to supply amino acids in which wheat proteins are deficient: no growth, short life.
3. Wheat plus a salt mixture which gave it a mineral content similar to that of milk: very little growth.
4. Wheat plus the new fat-soluble vitamin (supplied by butter fat): no growth, nutritional decline.

From these observations it was apparent that wheat was deficient in more than a single dietary essential. Accordingly, wheat was fed with two supplements of known substances. The results:

1. Wheat plus casein, plus the salt mixture: good growth for a time, few or no young, short life.
2. Wheat plus casein, plus the fat-soluble vitamin (butter fat): no growth, short life.
3. Wheat plus the salt mixture plus the fat-soluble vitamin (butter fat): fair growth for a time, few or no young, short life.

The nutritional response of young rats fed wheat with two known supplements was distinctly better than those which were fed wheat with but a single supplement of the kinds mentioned. But the results showed that more than two kinds of deficiency were involved. This was proven to be the case by the results of the following experiment:

Wheat, plus the salt mixture, plus butter fat, plus casein induced good growth, approximately normal fertility, and success in rearing young. The life-span was long in comparison with any other groups in the series of experiments described above. The nature of the three deficiencies in wheat were thus demonstrated. Other experiments revealed that calcium was the first limiting element in the mineral constituents of wheat.

McCollum and Davis called this system of feeding an incomplete food with single and multiple purified supplements the *biological method of analysis.* It was based upon setting up nutritional situations in which the animal, by its physiological response to supplements of known substances, yielded information about its nutritional requirements.

The Biological Analysis of Maize (Corn) Kernel, and Oat Kernel

When ground maize (corn meal) was fed alone and in combinations with casein, butter-fat, and salt mixture, the results were closely comparable to similar experiments with wheat. The three supplements were necessary in order to enable young rats to grow, reproduce, and rear young (43).

When rolled oats was tested by the biological method, the responses of young rats were qualitatively the same as with wheat and corn, but the response to the mixture of oats with the three purified supplements was less satisfactory than with the other cereals named. The reason for this difference was not at once apparent; however, it came to light in 1926, in a study by Smith and Hendrick (44) which is described in Chapter 20. These men proved that oat grain is deficient in a water-soluble, heat-stable vitamin, distinct from the antineuritic vitamin which cures pigeons suffering from polished-rice disease (polyneuritis, or berberi).

McCollum and Davis found flax-seed meal and also millet to be deficient in the same nutrients as wheat and other cereals.

The Biological Analysis of Polished Rice

McCollum and Davis (42) applied the new method to the examination of the nutritive properties of rice. They found that when unpolished rice was supplemented with the single and multiple additions employed in the wheat study, the response of the animals was similar in every respect to those with wheat. Rice, like the other cereal grains, requires supplements supplying certain amino acids, inorganic elements, and the fat-soluble vitamin contained in butter-fat. But these three types of supplements did not suffice to make polished rice complete nutritionally for young rats. For this species, it was necessary to add the supplements in which wheat is deficient, together with a water or alcohol extract of some natural food. Wheat germ was found to be a rich source of the additional factor required.

That remarkably small amounts of the dietary factor which such extracts contained were sufficient to meet the needs of young rats was shown by the observation that animals in decline on a diet of polished rice, casein, butter-fat and a salt mixture resumed growth when given the amount of water-soluble substance from eight grams of wheat germs in 100 grams of food. The extract supplied only 0.0368 grams of nitrogen. In another experiment the water-soluble factor was supplied by extracting 200 grams of hard-boiled egg-yolk with water, evaporating the extract to dryness, and extracting the trace of fatty constituents with ether. The total weight of material in the ether-insoluble fraction was 4.5 grams; this was found to consist principally of inorganic salts, yet the addition of this preparation to 3.12 kg. of the basal ration enabled young rats in decline to recover and resume growth.

At the time of their study of the deficiencies of rice, McCollum and Davis learned through Vedder's Cartwright Prize Essay, *Beriberi* (1913) (45), and Funk's *Die Vitamine* (1914) (46), of the investigations on beriberi by Eijkman, Grijns, Vordermann, Fraser and Stanton, Holst, and others. These studies identified the nutritive value of the substance in their water extracts of wheat germ and egg-yolk with the anti-beriberi factor. Available evidence seemed to them to warrant the assumption that the effective extracts contained but a single nutrient of importance to the animals in their experiments. Notwithstanding that in his prize essay Vedder had given a good digest of the studies of Holst on "ship beriberi," which afforded convincing evidence of the existence of two water-soluble vitamins, McCollum and Davis proposed, as a working hypothesis, that the minimum adequate diet for the rat must provide, in addition to the long known nutrients, two unidentified factors which they designated "fat-soluble A" and "water-soluble B." These terms referred to the fat-soluble nutrient present in butterfat, egg yolk, green leaves and cod liver oil and the anti-beriberi substance.

The Opportunity for Pathologists to Contribute to Nutritional Investigations

Although clinicians were the first to suggest that unidentified nutrients were involved in the etiology of scurvy, rickets, and beriberi, almost all of the systematic efforts to investigate the problems of human and animal nutrition were carried out by chemists. These experiments spanned more than one hundred years, from Fourcroy, Vauquelin, and Boussingault, to Hopkins, Osborne, Mendel, and McCollum. These and other chemists laid the foundation for effective inquiry into many specific studies of both normal and diseased conditions as related to diet. This was to be expected, since nutrition is a chemical process of great complexity. Thus, only chemists could think constructively about how to experiment with the chemical examination of plant or animal substances, or how to formulate ideas and investigate the utilization of foods by animals. As knowledge advanced the problems grew more complex, because the processes of metabolism, which involve the stepwise utilization of the digestion products of foods, form an extremely complex system of concatenated catalytic actions which are in many ways interdependent.

Malnutrition is the result of many factors. Deficiency in the food of an essential chemical unit and the time of its availability, and in removing from the tissues the end products of the metabolic scheme, all serve to disturb and pervert the chemical interactions and spoil the integrity of tissue elements. Every specific dietary error, when considered by chemical philosophy, might justifiably be conceived to cause a unique mode of metabolic disturbance — a unique deficiency syndrome. Although this concept did not develop in pace with knowledge of the number and nature of essential nutrients, it was inherent from the beginning in the thinking of chemists concerned with nutrition studies. However, they were not competent to observe deviations from the normal in the eyes, skin, hair, bones, nervous system, and other individual tissues as indicators of the types of damage being done to these structures in response to chemical errors in the food supply.

Only slowly and with halting steps were chemists able to extend their thinking to correlate pathological changes with specific kinds of malnutrition. The earliest indications of such progress were the conception that scurvy, a hemorrhagic condition, was due to lack of something present in fresh but absent from dried vegetable foods (Bachstrom and Lind); that beriberi, a type of paralysis arising from nerve injury (Grijns and Eijkman), was due to lack of an unidentified element contained in rice polishings; and that xerophthalmia was associated with deprivation of something present in certain fats (McCollum). Once these facts had been established, the philosophic concepts of nutrition assumed a new aspect. Nutrition investigations, hitherto blocked by confusion and an attitude of hopelessness as to discovery, now seemed to offer a field of great promise. Pathologists became interested in contributing their knowledge to that of chemists in the study of specific states of malnutrition.

Throughout the nineteenth century a few chemists devoted much thought and laboratory work to isolating the constituents of organic products of plant and animal origin. After 1870 interest in such work steadily intensified, and greater numbers occupied themselves with study of the nature and distribution of substances of physiological interest. But the difficulties involved in devising quantitative technics for their determination (with the exception of urea and ammonia) prevented workers in this field from achieving much in understanding of the processes of animal physiology. At midcentury, fallacy was general in clinical chemistry, as is apparent from the thorough efforts of Simon (47) and of Lehmann (48) to compile, interpret, and apply existing chemical knowledge on the nature of blood, urine, bile, bone, and so on, to diagnosis of diseased conditions.

Liebig's optimism about progress of animal and plant chemistry, which was reflected in his book published in 1842 (49), exerted a tremendous influence in many countries, and aroused strong opposition among some medical men. The most notable antagonist was Dr. Charles Caldwell (1772–1853) who held the chairs of the institutes of medicine, medical jurisprudence, and clinical medicine in Louisville Medical Institute (Kentucky). In 1843 he published a pamphlet of ninety-five pages (50) in which he savagely denounced Liebig and declared his own conviction that chemistry had nothing to contribute to medical science. However, Liebig's optimism triumphed, and between 1870 and 1900 there were abstracted 13,769 papers devoted to animal chemistry (51).

Even as late as 1915 pathologists manifested little interest in malnutrition. This is not surprising when one considers the rich harvest of new knowledge on the nature of bacterial diseases brought to light by the studies of Pasteur, Koch, and their successors. However, great interest was aroused by Behring's discovery of biological products known as antibodies. The application by Ehrlich of the use of dyes in the study of sections of normal and diseased tissues, as well as the blood in anemias, and the advances in the study of the relation of parasites to disease, fired the imagination of pathologists.

Improved microscopes and the staining and other technics applicable to the study of the problems of pathology so monopolized the attention of investigators that they had little incentive to consider any aspect of malnutrition as a cause of disease. Moreover, with very few exceptions, medical men were so innocent of knowledge of chemistry that they were unable to think of the metabolic processes in terms of chemical systems. Accordingly, they did not comprehend the idea that deficiency of some specific chemical substance could cause derangement of physiological processes and result in pathological states.

It was not until the syndromes of beriberi, scurvy, and the type of malnutrition arising from deficiency of vitamin A, a prominent symptom of which was xerosis of the conjunctivae were demonstrated, that pathologists turned to the study of the lesions characteristic of deficiency states. S. Mori (1922) and S. B. Wolbach (1926) were the first workers in this field to go beyond clinical description and reports of autopsies. They reported detailed and precise studies of the histological abnormalities of the tissues involved. Their studies are described in the chapters on vitamin A deficiency and on the scorbutic state, respectively.

In 1915 new criteria were adopted for the purpose of assessing quality in human and animal foods. Slow in coming, these developments occurred only after many years during which diets were evaluated solely on the basis of their protein and energy values. This progress was the result of many individual studies: the discoveries of vitamins, as described in this chapter; the demonstration of the specific kinds of nutritive deficiencies of individual natural foods; the recognition of the superiority of the leaf as compared with the seed of the plant as the source of certain nutrients; and the proven effectiveness of milk, egg yolk, leafy vegetables, or crude extracts of these as supplements to a diet of purified nutrients.

Information was now available which made it possible to so combine foods that what was lacking in one would be supplied by another. The recognition of supplementary values among foods overshadowed the importance of the results of chemical analysis as the basis for making combinations of foods in practical dietetics.

REFERENCES

1. Dumas, J. B. A.: Philos. Mag. *42*, 129 (1871).
2. Lunin, N.: Ueber die Bedeutung der anorganischen Salze für die Ernährung des Thieres. (Inauguarl-Dissertation, Dorpat, 1880.)
3. Voit, C.: Ueber die Ernährung des Menschen in Verschiedenen Klimaten. Munich, 1881, p. 19.

4. Socin, C. A.: Hoppe-Seyler's Zeitschr. *15,* 93 (1891).
5. Coppola, F.: Rendiconti della R. Accademia del Lincei. 6, 362 (1890); Maly's Jahresber. d. Thierchemie *20,* 116 (1890).
6. Hall, W. S.: Du Bois-Reymond's Archiv. physiol. Abth. (1896), pp. 142–153 (1896); Maly's Jahresber. d. Thierchemie *26,* 787 (1896).
7. Pasqualis, G.: Atti d. Inst. Venet. d. scienze, etc. 3, 535–554 (1895).
8. Steinitz, F.: Pflüger's Archiv. *77,* 75 (1898).
9. Zadik, H.: Pflüger's Archiv. *76,* 1 (1899); *77,* 1–21 (1899).
10. Leipziger, R.: Pflüger's Archiv. *78,* 402 (1900).
11. Ehrlich, P.: Inaug. Diss. Breslau. (1900).
12. Miescher, F.: Hoppe-Seyler's med., chem. Untersuchungen *4,* Heft 502–509 (1871).
13. Hoppe-Seyler, F.: *Ibid. 4,* Heft 441–460 (1871).
14. Miescher, F.: Arch. f. Anat. u. Physiol. anat. Abth. 193–218 (1881).
15. Piccard, J.: Ber. d. deutsch. chem. Gesellschaft 7, 1714–19 (1874).
16. Falta, W. and Noeggerath, C. T.: Beiträge z. chem. Physiol. u. Pathol. 7, 313 (1906).
17. Pekelharing, C. A.: Nederlandsch. Tijdschr. N. Geneesk. 2, 3 (1905).
18. Van Leersum, E. C.: Science *64,* 357 (Oct. 8, 1926).
19. Willcock, E. G. and Hopkins, F. G.: Journ. of Physiol. (London) *35,* 88–102 (1906).
20. Szumowski, W.: Zeitschr. f. physiol. Chem. *36,* 198–218 (1902).
21. Hopkins, F. G.: The Analyst and the Medical Man. The Analyst *31,* 385 (1906).
22. Henriques, V. and Hansen, C.: Zeitschr. f. physiol. Chem. *42,* 417 (1905).
23. Röhmann, F.: Allgemeine med. Centr. — Ztg. *9* (1908); Maly's Jahresber. d. Thierchemie *38,* 659 (1908).
24. Hopkins, F. G.: Journ. of Physiol. London *44,* 425–460 (1912).
25. Stepp, W.: Biochem. Zeitschr. *22,* 452 (1909); Zeitschr. f. Biol. *57,* 135 (1911); *59,* 366 (1912).
26. Fingerling, G. L.: Biochem. Zeitschr. *38,* 448 (1912).
27. McCollum, E. V., Drescher, A. H. and Halpin, J. G.: J. Biol. Chem. *13,* 219 (1912).

28. McCollum, E. V.: Amer. J. Physiol. *25*, 120 (1909).
29. Osborne, T. B. and Mendel, L. B.: Bull. No. 156, Parts I and II, The Carnegie Institution of Washington (1911).
30. Mendel, L. B.: Trans. XVth. Internat. Congress on Hygiene and Demography. Washington, D.C. (September 1912).
31. Lancet (London), *219* (Vol. 2 for 1930), p. 1097.
32. Grijns, G.: Geneesk. Tijdschr. v. Ned. Ind. 1, (1901).
33. Vordermann, A. G.: Geneesk. Tjidschr. v. Ned. Ind. (1898).
34. Fraser, H. and Stanton, A. T.: Collected Papers on Beriberi No. 17, Studies from the Inst. for Med. Res. Fed. Malay States. London (1924).
35. Funk, C.: Journ. of State Medicine *20*, 341 (1912).
36. Holst, A. and Froelich, T.: J. Hygiene 7, 634 (1907).
37. McCollum, E. V. and Davis, M.: J. Biol. Chem. *15*, 167–75 (1913).
38. McCollum, E. V. and Davis, M.: J. Biol. Chem. *19*, 245 (1914).
39. Osborne, T. B. and Mendel, L. B.: J. Biol. Chem. *16*, 423 (1913–14).
40. Osborne, T. B. and Mendel, L. B.: J. Biol. Chem. *15*, 311 (1913).
41. Experiment Station Record (Washington, D.C.) *19*, 803 (1907–08).
42. McCollum, E. V. and Davis, M.: J. Biol. Chem. *23*, 231 (1915). McCollum, E. V.: The Newer Knowledge of Nutrition, 2nd ed. (1925) pp. 32–33.
43. Harvey Lecture Series 12, January 17 (1917), pp. 151–180.
44. Smith, M. E. and Hendrick, E. G.: U.S. Pub. Health Reports *41*, 767 (1927).
45. Vedder, E. B.: Beriberi. Wm. Wood & Co. New York 1913, pp. 427.
46. Funk, C.: Die Vitamine. Wiesbaden (1914).
47. Simon, J. F.: Animal Chemistry, with Reference to the Physiology and Pathology of Man. 2 vols. 1845. Trans. by Geo. E. Day, for the Sydenham Society. London.
48. Lehmann, C. G.: Physiological Chemistry, 2 vols. Trans. by Geo. E. Day. Philadelphia (1855).
49. Liebig, J. v.: Animal Chemistry (1842).
50. Caldwell, C. C.: Physiology Vindicated, in a Critique of Liebig's Animal Chemistry. See Klickstein, H.: Chymia *4*, 129–157 (1953).
51. Maly's Jahresbericht der Thierchemie. Vols. 1–30 (1871–1900).

15

Pioneer Studies of Vitamin A

When McCollum and Davis discovered that the provision of something in butter-fat or egg-yolk fat made the difference between moderate success in the nutrition of young rats on certain diets, and prompt nutritive failure in its absence, they did not observe the specific eye lesions which later were shown to characterize this deficiency. Decline versus growth defined the limit of their interpretation of the pathology of vitamin A deficiency — it was a chemist's diagnosis. Osborne and Mendel (1913) described the condition as a "type of nutritive deficiency exemplified in the form of an infectious eye disease prevalent in animals inappropriately fed," and stated that it was speedily alleviated by the addition of butter-fat to the diet. The eye symptoms here considered were not new. They had been observed repeatedly in malnourished animals, although they had attracted little attention.

In 1816 Magendie (1) had restricted dogs to wheat gluten, starch, sugar, or olive oil as their sole food. In describing the symptoms of inanition which developed, he mentioned that ulcers formed on the corneas when animals were so fed. In 1857 David Livingstone, a medical missionary in Africa, described the effects on his native carriers when they were forced by circumstances to subsist for a time on sugarless coffee, manioc, and meal (2). He stated, "the eyes became affected as in the case of animals fed on experiment on pure gluten or starch." It is probable that he referred to the experiments of Magendie.

Early Recognition of Association of Eye Disorders with Malnutrition

In 1863 Biot (3) described xerosis of the conjunctivae in twenty-nine patients who suffered from night-blindness. In 1883 De

Gouvea (4) described night-blindness in poorly nourished slaves in Brazil. He noted that although it was darker in the morning than in the evening, the slaves were unable to see when returning from work after sunset, but could see well when starting for work before sunrise. Their food was beans, pork fat, and maize meal. De Gouvea observed further that slaves on other plantations who were better fed did not develop night-blindness. Exposure to sunlight was suspected of inducing night-blindness, and resting the eyes at night was believed to result in recovery.

There is a long history of clinical association of eye disorders with malnutrition. Eusterman and Wilbur (5) have given a historical account of the principal papers published on the subject. Of special importance was the report in 1904 by M. Mori (6) of 1400 cases of xerophthalmia among Japanese children aged 2 to 5 years. These children exhibited keratomalacia as well as xerosis of the conjunctiva. The syndrome was known in Japan as *hikan*. Mori stated that *hikan* was common among people who subsisted in great measure on rice, barley and other cereals, beans and other vegetables, whereas it did not occur among fisher folk. Administration of cod liver oil, he said, was followed by speedy relief from the disorder, and chicken livers and eel fat were effective remedies also. He concluded that deficiency of fat in the diet was the cause of the disease.

Histological Studies of the Eyes and Related Structures in Vitamin A Deficiency

The earliest histological study of the eyes and related structures of experimental animals subjected to vitamin A depletion was made in 1916 by Freise, Goldschmidt, and Frank (7). They restricted young rats to a diet of purified foodstuffs, and noted that about three weeks after the start of the experiment the eyelashes began to fall out. After about thirty-five days the sclerotic coat became dry; the corneas clouded and finally ulcerated, but without marked inflammation. The animals developed rough coats and succumbed to malnutrition. Histological examination of the sclerotic coat revealed keratomalacia as it is seen in man. The process of ulceration could be arrested by giving the affected animal 2 ml. of skim milk per day. This treatment did not permit interpretation of the nature of the nutrient responsible for the recovery of the animals. The pathological manifestations described were attributed to lack of "accessory" substances in the diet. Thus, Freise, Goldschmidt, and Frank produced and described the lesions of vitamin A deficiency without recognizing their cause.

In 1922 S. Mori (8), while working in McCollum's laboratory, made histological studies of young rats in several stages of vitamin A deficiency. He found that the primary change occurred in the lacrymal glands. Describing the changes in these glands which resulted in their failure to secrete tears, he referred all other changes in the eyes and related structures to lack of tears to wash the conjunctival sac. There was cornification of surface cells of the cornea, with piling of the flattened cells into what he called a pseudostratified arrangement resembling the horny layer of the skin. Ulcers formed on the cornea owing to death of the tissue. These later perforated and the lens was extruded. Mori regarded the ophthalmia due to vitamin A deficiency as analogous to *hikan,* which had been described in 1904 by M. Mori.

The ducts of the Meibomian glands (in the eyelids) were dilated with accumulations of desquamated cornified epithelial cells, and cysts formed. The glands of Harder (in the lachrymal caruncle) and the mucous cells of the conjunctiva were mostly destroyed by the keratinizing process. The submaxillary and sublingual salivary glands were also damaged by keratinization, and were obviously secreting little or no saliva. Mori ascribed the overgrowth of the conjunctiva and cornea by microorganisms to stagnation resulting from failure of the tear glands to secrete tears to bathe the eyes.

Xerophthalmia in Danish Children

In 1917 Bloch (9) described fifty cases of xerophthalmia in children living in the vicinity of Copenhagen during the years 1912–1916. Most cases were infants under one year of age. Their skin was dry, shriveled, and scaly, and the children were in severe states of malnutrition. Their diet consisted of separator skimmed milk, which was practically free from fat, and which was pasteurized and heated again in the home before being fed. The other important constituents in the diet were oatmeal gruel and barley soup. Since the condition was relieved by administration of cod liver oil, whole milk, or cream, Bloch attributed the malnutrition to a deficiency of fat in the diet. He made a clinical test of a vegetable fat, which the McCollum-Davis and Osborne-Mendel experiments had shown to be valueless as sources of the fat-soluble vitamin A (10). Bloch, too, found it without remedial value.

In 1919 Bloch divided into two groups thirty-two healthy children, one to four years of age, who lived in an institution for child care. Their diets were the same except for breakfasts. The diet of Group 1 consisted of oatmeal porridge and rusks, whereas Group 2 received beer soup and some milk. Apart from the whole milk allowance of Group 2, the only fat provided was margarine made from vegetable fat. In Group 1, during May and June, eight cases of xerosis occurred. The children in Group 2 remained free from the disorder. Apparently the small amount of milk fat was sufficient to protect the children from xerophthalmia. All cases of xerophthalmia were promptly cured by giving cod liver oil (11).

McCollum and Simmonds (12) gave special attention to the occurrence of ophthalmia among the experimental animals in their large rat colony. Many groups of young rats in the colony were fed special diets for experimental purposes. Over a period of four years they observed groups fed diets which led to severe malnutrition from various causes. They noted that only the animals deprived of vitamin A developed ophthalmia. In 1917 McCollum and Simmonds correlated their observations on rats with those of M. Mori (1904) and of Bloch on children; they expressed the belief that xerophthalmia or keratomalacia in animals was the analogue of the similar condition in humans, and that the disease was caused by deficiency of vitamin A.

Wolbach's Studies of the Pathology of Vitamin A Deficiency

Wolbach and Howe (13), Goldblatt and Benischek (14), and others made detailed investigations of the tissue changes in various species of animals brought about by deficiency of vitamin A. These studies established the fact that the earliest observable consequence of this type of malnutrition relates to changes in the epithelial structures. These are replaced in many locations, especially in glands and mucous membranes, by stratified, keratinizing epithelium, identical in appearance in all locations, and arising from local proliferation of basal cells. Where keratinization occurs, atrophic changes progress to extinction of physiological function. But regardless of the previous function and morphology, new cells continue to grow and undermine the original epithelium, and form stratified, keratinizing epithelium.

In 1917 Osborne and Mendel (15) pointed out the high incidence of urinary calculi in their experimental rats which were deprived of vitamin A. In the light of the investigations of Wolbach and of Goldblatt, it appeared that a probable explanation for this was invasion of the urethra and bladder by urea-fermenting organisms as the result of keratinization of urethral epithelium. The resulting alkalinity of the urine favored precipitation of calcium salts.

It is unnecessary in this discussion to extend references to studies which revealed atrophic changes in the endocrine and other glands, since these might well be secondary to keratinization of epithelia.

Experimental Night-Blindness in Vitamin A Deficiency

An important contribution to knowledge of the functions of vitamin A was made by Fridericia and Holm in 1925 (16). In 1907 Hess (17) had studied the effect of previous illumination on visual acuity in hens by watching them pick up grains in light regulated as to intensity. He found that after a stay in the dark they would eat in light less intense than that in which they had stopped eating previous to exposure to darkness.

Holm (18) devised a test based on a somewhat different principle. His test was based on a rat's aversion to remaining exposed on a plane surface, and its desire to hide under shelter. Holm's animals were placed on a table. On a shelf, which was about ten centimeters from the edge of the table, he placed a cage which afforded shelter. The cage was marked with a piece of white paper to make it clearly visible. The table was frequently turned to a new position to require the rats to depend on sight. It was found that rats placed on the table explored its edges, and when they could see the cage immediately jumped over to it. The degree of illumination could be controlled.

Vitamin A-deficient rats were compared with normal ones. In dim light the difference between the two groups was easily apparent. The normal rats would immediately see the cage and jump across the gap to it. The depleted animals would show the impulse to leap, but would give up after several unsuccessful efforts. At last they would jump, miss their aim, and fall to the floor. Their attitude when preparing to jump, and in the act of jumping, was different from normal rats. When the intensity of light was increased sufficiently, the A-depleted rats acted as did normal animals. Provision of vitamin A improved their vision.

Holm's studies were extended by examination of the content of visual purple in the retinas of normal and depleted rats, and of rats whose eyes had been exposed to strong light. Already at that period ophthalmologists believed that night-blindness might arise from an abnormality in the rod cells of the retina. These are the only cells which contain visual purple. Vision in daylight, with perception of color, was believed to be the function of the cones, whereas vision in twilight, in which colors are not distinguished, was the function of the rods, and was dependent on the presence of visual purple. These views have been fully established. Fridericia and Holm found that both the retinas of A-deficient rats and of rats whose eyes had been strongly illuminated were depleted of visual purple.

Steenbock's Correlation of Vitamin A Values in Foods with Yellowness

In 1919 Steenbock and Gross (19), using animal feeding experiments, studied various foods as sources of vitamin A. They made the highly important observation that yellow foods (e.g., carrots, sweet potatoes) were good sources of the vitamin, whereas white foods (e.g., parsnip, potato) and red foods (red beet) appeared to contain practically none of this nutrient.

Previous to the Steenbock-Gross studies, Palmer (20) had found that cottonseed oil freed from resins, which still possessed a golden yellow color and was rich in carotenoid pigments, was devoid of vitamin A activity. He could not detect carotene or closely related pigments in the blood of sheep, swine, rabbit, dog, cat or guinea pig. This he interpreted to mean that carotene cannot be absorbed from the intestinal tracts of these species.

In order to test further the nutritive significance of yellow plant pigments, Palmer and Kempster (21) studied the possibility of rearing birds on a diet free from such pigments. They raised newly-hatched white leghorn chicks for six weeks on a mixture of white maize and maize meal, white maize bran, skim milk, and bone meal. At the end of this period the birds began to fail, but responded well to a supplement of pork liver. Pork liver had been carefully examined for the presence of carotenoid and other yellow pigments, and these were found to be absent. After three months on a diet with the liver supplement, the birds were normal in size. They were then given the white diet described, together with an occasional feeding of white summer squash and white Spanish onions. At the age of six months the pullets, which were essentially free from yellow pigments, as shown by the bleached appearance of the (normally yellow) shanks and earlobes, began to lay eggs. Seventeen hens produced 893 eggs in 233 days. One hen laid 88 eggs during the experimental period. The yolks of these eggs were free from yellow pigment. Many such eggs were incubated, and from them viable chicks were hatched, which appeared normal in every way except for the absence of yellow pigment in the shanks, skin, and earlobes. On the basis of his findings, Palmer criticized Steenbock's view that only foods containing yellow pigments were sources of vitamin A.

In 1920 Stevenson (22) dissolved yellow butter fat in petroleum ether and shook the solution with finely ground birch charcoal. This removed the yellow pigments from the butter-fat, which became as white as lard; feeding tests showed that it was still a good source of Vitamin A.

Steenbock and Boutwell (23), in 1920, definitely stated their belief that carotene was not vitamin A but was associated with it. They prepared from plants pigments consisting of a mixture of carotenes and xanthophyll, and found that when these were separated, the vitamin A property accompanied the carotene fraction while the remaining fraction was devoid of it. They studied butter samples having different degrees of yellowness and found that the vitamin A values did not correspond to intensity of color. Palmer (24), in 1922, provided convincing evidence that the yellow pigment in cod liver oil is not carotene. It thus became evident that the vitamin A property could not be attributed to carotene, nor to any other yellow pigment, notwithstanding the convincing evidence that the two were in many cases associated in natural foods.

Carotene Proved to Be Provitamin A

In the experiments made by Steenbock and by others who tested the vitamin A value of carotene, it was the general experience that the animals became stunted within a few weeks. The reason for this was made clear in 1928 by von Euler, Euler, and Hellstrom (25). Using carotene as a source of vitamin A, they confirmed in principle the experiments of Steenbock. In 1922 McCollum and his co-workers demonstrated the existence of the anti-ricketic vitamin D, and noted that young rats kept indoors, away from direct sunlight, and deprived of this vitamin, developed abnormal bones and were stunted. Von Euler and his associates conducted experiments with young rats in which they provided both carotene and vitamin D. By doing this, they clearly demonstrated that carotene was, indeed, a source of vitamin A. Previously, many investigators of carotene had failed to get satisfactory results when they did not include vitamin D in their rations.

In 1929 Moore (26) provided proof that carotene is provitamin A. It is converted in the body into the vitamin, which is almost colorless. Moore fed highly purified carotene to A-depleted young rats, and demonstrated that their livers became rich in vitamin A. This explained why Palmer and Kempster succeeded with their chickens when pig liver free from yellow pigments was the sole source of vitamin A. The pigs had eaten carotene and converted it into the nearly colorless vitamin.

Since Palmer and Kempster kept their chickens in sunlight, the birds secured vitamin D from the irradiation of their feathers, which birds eat to some extent ordinarily. The food of their birds was also exposed to sunlight and, because of this, acquired vitamin D potency. The conflicting results of the several investigators were thus explained.

The Effects of Vitamin A Deficiency on Bone Growth

In 1926 E. Mellanby (27) reported the first of his studies on the cause of the widespread degenerative nerve changes. The report was based on his observation of abnormalities in young animals restricted to diets deficient in vitamin A. At first he attributed these changes to deprivation of the vitamin, but further study led him to conclude that they were secondary to overgrowth of the bones in the vicinity of the affected nerves and brain cells. He ascribed the nerve damage to pressure from decrease in the size of foramina through which they pass, and brain injury to overgrowth of the cranial bones, especially of the posterior fossa of the skull, so that the medulla oblongata, pons, and cerebellum, and the nerves close to these parts were particularly affected. Bone abnormalities were also found in the vertebral column in which the spinal canal was reduced, crowded the cord, and squeezed the posterior root ganglia and the anterior root nerves. Intracranial pressure was found to be considerably increased over normal.

From his histological studies of the long bones of A-deficient puppies, Mellanby concluded that osteoblastic activity was greater than normal on the endosteal side of the trabeculae, and the osteoclastic activity greater than normal on the outer side, thus reducing the area of the marrow spaces. He postulated that one function of vitamin A was to control the number and activity of osteoblasts and osteoclasts. In the absence of sufficient vitamin A these cells retain their normal functions but become abnormally active.

Wolbach and Bessey's Interpretation of the Cause of Nerve Injury in Vitamin A Deficiency

In 1941 Wolbach and Bessey (28) made a careful study of the bones of young rats kept on vitamin A deficient diets. Their conclusions concerning the cause of nerve and brain injury differed from those of Mellanby. They found that nerve injury occurs only when the animals are able to grow on the deficient diet, which consisted of casein 18, a salt mixture 3, brewers' yeast 10, peanut oil 8, corn starch 60.9, and viosterol (vitamin D) 0.1 per cent. If growth was retarded (as by underfeeding) the paralysis due to nerve injury did not develop. It was shown that age was not important, since young rats were protected during the fourteen weeks by restriction of their food intake. This prevented growth, but the rats developed nerve injury when given food enough to induce growth.

Dissections of the rats revealed overcrowding of the cranial cavity, resulting in distortion of the brain, dislocation of parts of it, and herniation of the cerebellum into the foramen magnum. There were multiple herniations of the cerebrum and cerebellum into the venous sinuses of the dura at the sites of arachnoidal drainage structures. Overcrowding of the spinal cord and its distortion by pressure were also noted.

Wolbach and Bessey (29) stated that they could not confirm Mellanby's observations on overactivity of osteoblasts and osteoclasts. They attributed injury to the nervous system in A-deficiency to depression of bone growth, while the nervous system continued to increase in size and outgrow the bony cavities and foramina with resulting pressure and deformation. Mellanby had noted deafness in puppies with vitamin A deficiency of the degree he described. This finding was confirmed by Wolbach and Bessey, and they regarded it as another example of retardation of the growth of the skeleton in relation to the growth of the central nervous system.

Evidence of Direct Nerve Injury in Vitamin A Deficiency

Evidence has been presented by several investigators that pressure on nervous tissues from arrest of bone growth is not the sole cause of injury. Sutton and his associates (30) stressed their belief that deficiency of vitamin A alone, without other factors being involved, caused nerve degeneration. In his studies of the livers of young calves on vitamin A deficient diets, Dann (31) described nuclear condensation, degeneration, and necrosis accompanied by lymphocytic infiltration. He suggests that from these pathological effects it is to be expected that diverse symptoms may appear and many functions may be stimulated or depressed, depending on the severity of the deficiency. Phillips (32) has discussed the experimental work in this field.

Function of Vitamin A in Tooth Development

Wolbach and Howe (13) concluded from their studies that in no other dietary deficiency state are there such pronounced lesions in the teeth as in deprivation of vitamin A. The ameloblasts, or enamel-forming organs, are of epithelial origin, and they share with other epithelial structures a high degree of sensitivity to deficiency of this vitamin. In avitaminosis A they undergo atrophy and metaplasia, with consequent formation of hypoplastic enamel. This is in accord with the observation of M. Mellanby (32a). She showed that the incisors of rats, which normally continue to grow through life, have no enamel on the areas of growth which form after the animals have been brought into severe avitaminosis A, and that they consist of dentin without enamel covering. When the animals were somewhat depleted, the persistently growing incisors exhibited hypoplastic enamel.

Wolbach and Howe (13) described the disturbance of function of the odontoblasts, or dentin-forming organs, in avitaminosis A. These structures remain morphologically normal and functionally active on the labial side of the tooth in apposition to the enamel organ long after their complete disappearance from other surfaces. With complete atrophy of the ameloblasts in the rat, the odontoblasts also disappear on the labial side. While they survive in this deficiency state, the odontoblasts lose their columnar shape and continue to deposit dentin, but in a centrifugal pattern like that of osteoblasts, or bone-forming cells, instead of at the outer pole only as in the normal cells.

Deficiency of Vitamin A Reserves in New-Born Animals

In 1918 Osborne and Mendel (33) discovered that the liver is the principal storage organ for vitamin A. Hart and Guilbert (34), in 1933, pointed out that the liver stores of vitamin A in animals at birth are relatively low. This fact has been confirmed by many investigations. Dann (31) and Wolff (35) have reviewed the literature on this subject, and all investigators are agreed that vitamin A does not easily pass the placenta, so that fetal blood at term contains about half as much of this nutrient as does average adult blood.

The Importance of Colostrum in the Nutrition of the New-Born Calf

In 1922 T. Smith and R. B. Little (36) demonstrated the great value of ingestion of colostrum as a factor in the development of passive immunity against the infectious diarrhea, a malady which invariably causes death in young calves fed milk instead of colostrum during the first days of post-natal life. They attributed the specific role of colostrum to its contribution of immune bodies to the calf. Later studies by E. Jameson and his associates (37) demonstrated that the serum of the new-born calf does not contain an appreciable amount of gamma globulin, but that it appears promptly in the blood after feeding colostrum. Although this observation accounted in considerable measure for the immunity against diarrhea, further investigations showed that colostrum has another extremely important function in the nutrition of calves. This is attributable to its content of vitamin A which is 10 to 100 times that of milk. Since at birth the store of this vitamin in the liver is very low, it is extremely important that an abundant supply be provided promptly.

Hansen, Phillips and Rupel (38) showed that the needs of the new-born calf were in excess of 10,000 I.U. per 100 lbs. of body weight per day when severe diarrhea and survival served as the criteria of the minimum requirement. They found that the daily requirement, on a similar weight basis at 3 to 8 weeks of age was, in contrast, only 3,000 to 5,000 I.U. per day.

Isolation of Vitamin A

Steenbock's demonstration of the association of vitamin A value with carotene, and von Euler's proof that carotene is provitamin A were the starting points of all later investigations on the chemical nature of this nutrient. In 1937 Holmes and Corbet (39) reported the isolation and crystallization of vitamin A from the liver oil of mackerel and other fishes. They saponified the oil in isopropanol, and from the nonsaponifiable matter crystallized the vitamin from anhydrous methanol chilled with solid carbon dioxide. Biological analysis of this material was made by Guerrant and Dutcher, who found it to possess vitamin A activity between 2,265,000 and 3,400,000 International Units per gram.

Also in 1937, Hickman (40), using a molecular distillation technic, was able to show by study of distillation curves that vitamin A was present in cod liver oil mainly as a mixture of esters, but that a small proportion was present as the unesterified alcohol.

Synthesis of Vitamin A

In 1936 two groups of chemists reported the chemical synthesis of vitamin A. Fuson and Christ (41) accomplished this by condensing β-cyclocitral with dimethyl acrolein to form an aldehyde, which upon reduction yielded vitamin A. Kuhn and Morris (42) synthesized the vitamin by condensing β-ionylidene acetaldehyde with β-methyl crotonaldehyde in the presence of pipiridine, and reducing the resulting aldehyde.

The Function of Vitamin A in Vision
Its Relation to Visual Purple

Night-blindness and xerophthalmia are two of the oldest afflictions of man. As early as 1900 B.C. Egyptians recognized diet as an etiologic factor. Egyptian and early Greek physicians recommended raw liver in the treatment of these disorders.

One of the greatest achievements of modern biochemical investigators was the discovery of the chemical processes by which light entering the eye initiates a nerve impulse. Mention has already been made of the discovery by Fridericia and Holm (16) that rats in vitamin A deficiency, and after exposure of the eyes to light, were unable to see well in light of low intensity. The provision of vitaman A restored the vision to normal. Fridericia and Holm, discovered that this was attributable to a more rapid rate of regeneration of visual purple in the retinas of animals with normal vitamin A reserves, than in those depleted of the vitamin.

Tansley (43), in 1931, made observations on the course of the regeneration of visual purple in normal and vitamin A-deficient rats. Her method of study consisted of extraction of visual purple from the retinas by means of a dilute solution of digitonin, and estimation of the pigment by a photographic method. The retinas of A-deficient rats contained subnormal amounts of visual purple.

Wald (44) in 1935, and Wald and Clark (45) in 1936 presented evidence that visual purple is a conjugated protein in which vitamin A is a prosthetic group. Tansley (46) discussed the distribution of visual purple in the retina. It is confined to the outer ends of the rods. Hecht (47) explained the process of retinal depletion of visual purple when the eyes are exposed to light. Visual purple (rhodopsin), when acted on by light, is converted into products which produce the nerve impulse and visual yellow (retinene). When vitamin A is available in the blood stream, new molecules of visual purple are synthesized. In vitamin A depletion this restoration of the pigment is abnormally slow, and so results in defective vision in light of low intensity.

Wald (48) demonstrated that the visual purple in the eyes of fresh water fish differs from that of mammals, birds, amphibia, and marine fish. He named this form porphyropsin. Gillam and Heilbron (49), and Lederer and Rathmann (50) discovered that the vitamin A in the retinas of fresh water fishes differs from that found in other animals. This form has been called vitamin A_2.

REFERENCES

1. Magendie, F.: Ann. de chim. et de phys. 3, 66 (1816).
2. Livingstone, D.: Travels and Researches in South Africa. London (1905) p. 470.
3. Biot: Cited by Blegvad. Brit. Med. J. (1924), i, p. 122.
4. De Gouvea: von Graefe's Arch. f. Opthal. 29, 167 (1883).
5. Eusterman, G. B. and Wilbur, D. L.: J. Amer. Med. Assoc. 98, (June 4, 1932).

6. Mori, M.: Jahrbuch f. Kinderheilk. 59, 175 (1904).
7. Freise, E., Goldschmidt, M. and Frank, A.: Monatschrift f. Kinderheilk *13*, 424 (1916).
8. Mori, S.: J. Amer. Med. Assoc. 79, 197 (1922); Johns Hopkins Hosp. Bull. 33, 357 (1922); Amer. J. Hyg. 3, 99 (1923).
9. Bloch, C. E.: Ugeskrift f. Laeger *79*, 349 (1917); cited from J. Amer. Med. Assoc. *68*, 1516 (1917).
10. Bloch, C. E.: Jahrbuch f. Kinderheilk. *89*, 405 (1919).
11. Bloch, C. E.: Journ. of Hygiene *19*, 283 (1921); Amer. J. Dis. Child. 27, 139 (1924).
12. McCollum, E. V. and Simmonds, N.: J. Biol. Chem. 29, 341 (1917).
13. Wolbach, S. B. and Howe, P. R.: Exper. Med. *42*, 753 (1925); Arch. Pathol. *5*, 239 (1928); Amer. J. Pathol. *9*, 275 (1933); J. Exper. Med. 57, 511 (1933).
14. Goldblatt, H. and Benischek, M.: J. Exper. Med. *46*, 699 (1927).
15. Osborne, T. B. and Mendel, L. B.: J. Amer. Med. Assoc. *69*, 32 (1917).
16. Fridericia, L. S. and Holm, E.: Amer. J. Physiol. 73, 63 (1925).
17. Hess, C.: Arch. f. Augenheilk. 57, 298 (1907); 59, 143 (1907).
18. Holm, E.: Amer. J. Physiol. 73, 79 (1925).
19. Steenbock, H. and Gross, E. G.: J. Biol. Chem. *40*, 501 (1919); *41*, 149 (1920).
20. Palmer, L. S.: J. Biol. Chem. 23, 261 (1915).
21. Palmer, L. S. and Kempster, H. L.: J. Biol. Chem. 39, 299, 313, 331 (1919).
22. Stevenson, M.: Biochem. J. *14*, 715 (1920).
23. Steenbock, H. and Boutwell, P. W.: J. Biol. Chem. *41*, 81, 163 (1920); *42*, 131 (1920).
24. Palmer, L. S. and Kennedy, C.: Proc. Soc. Exper. Biol. and Med. *20*, 506 (1922–23).
25. Von Euler, B., Euler, H. and Hellström, H.: Biochem. Zeitschr. *203*, 370 (1928).
26. Moore, T.: Lancet, London (1929) i, 499; ii, 380; Biochem. J. 23, 803 (1929); *24*, 692 (1930).
27. Mellanby, E.: J. Pathol. and Bact. 38, 391 (1934); J. Physiol. London *94*, 380 (1938); *96*, 36P (1939); *99*, 467 (1941).
28. Wolbach, S. B. and Bessey, O. A.: Arch. Pathol. 32, 689 (1941).

29. Wolbach, S. B. and Bessey, O. A.: Physiol. Reviews 22, 233 (1942).

30. Sutton, T. S., Setterfield, H. E. and Krauss, W. E.: Ohio Agr. Exp. Sta. Bull. 545 (1934); Sutton, *et al.,* J. Dairy Sci. 23, 574 (1940).

31. Dann, W. J.: Biochem. J. *26,* 1072–80 (1932).

32. Phillips, P. H.: Symposium on Nutrition (Ed. by R. M. Herriott), The John Hopkins Press (1953) p. 4.

32a. Mellanby, M.: Brit. Dent. J. *44,* 1031 (1923).

33. Osborne, T. B. and Mendel, L. B.: J. Biol. Chem. *34,* 17 (1918).

34. Hart, H. H. and Guilbert, H. R.: Univ. of Calif. Coll. of Agric. Exper. Sta. Bull. 560 (October, 1933).

35. Wolff, L. K.: Lancet, London 2, 617 (1932).

36. Smith, T. and Little, R. B.: J. Exper. Med. 36, 181 (1922).

37. Jameson, E., Alvarez-Tostado C. and Sorter, H. H.: Proc. Soc. Exper. Biol. and Med. *51,* 163 (1942).

38. Hansen, R. G., Phillips, P. H. and Rupel, I. W.: J. Dairy Science *29,* 761–66 (1946).

39. Holmes, H. N. and Corbet, R. E.: J. Amer. Chem. Soc. *59,* 2042–47 (1937).

40. Hickman, K. C. D.: Indust. and Eng. Chem. *29,* 1107–11 (1937).

41. Fuson, R. E. and Christ, R. E.: Science *84,* 294 (1936).

42. Kuhn, R. and Morris, C. J. O. R.: Ber. d. deutsch. chem. Ges. *70,* 853 (1937).

43. Tansley, K.: Journ. of Physiol. London *71,* 442 (1931).

44. Wald, G.: J. Gen. Physiol. *18,* 905 (1935).

45. Wald, G. and Clark, Anna-Betty: Amer. J. Physiol. *116,* 157 (1936).

46. Tansley, K.: Proc. Roy. Soc. London (Ser. B.) *114,* 79 (1933).

47. Hecht, S.: Physiol. Rev. *17,* 239 (1937).

48. Wald, G.: Nature *139,* 1017 (1937).

49. Gillam, A. E. and Heilbron, I. M.: Biochem. J. 32, 405 (1938).

50. Lederer, E. and Rathmann, F. H.: Compt. Rend. Acad. Sc. *206,* 781 (1938).

16

Pioneer Studies on the Antineuritic Vitamin

In Chapter 14 an account was given of the successful use of various experimental diets in establishing the existence of two classes of nutrients of unknown nature. These classes were characterized by pronounced differences in solubility. One was soluble in fats and fat solvents; the other was entirely insoluble in these solvents, readily soluble in water, and appreciably soluble in alcohol. The water and alcohol-soluble substance was known only by its preventive or curative action in human beriberi and in the analogous disease produced in birds by restricting them to a diet of polished rice. Polished rice was the basic food for millions of people. Therefore, its lack of the newly-recognized antineuritic nutrient aroused great interest, and several investigators sought to isolate it from natural foods and to learn its chemical nature. The pioneering studies of this problem form the subject of this chapter.

Progress in Isolating the Beriberi-Curative Substance

In 1906, Eijkman and Grijns (1) described the properties of the dietary factor which cured pigeons of the neuritis produced by feeding them only polished rice. It was soluble in water and in dilute alcohol, and diffused through a semi-permeable membrane.

In 1909 Fraser and Stanton (2) reported that the substance could be precipitated from its solutions by reagents which precipitate alkaloids. They said that mercuric chloride was a good precipitant, and also showed that the substance was labile and easily destroyed in alkaline solution.

In 1912 Suzuki, Shimamura, and Ohdake (3) isolated from rice bran the antineuritic component in the form of its crystalline picrate. Five to 10 mgm. doses introduced orally or subcutaneously cured pigeons suffering from the polished rice sickness. They found the substance curative for experimental beriberi in chickens, mice, and dogs. They also precipitated it by phosphotungstic acid from solution of the alcohol-soluble matter of rice bran. They called it *oryzanine* and secured it by removing the phosphotungstic acid with barium hydroxide. They noted that when prepared by this method, the antineuritic substance, *oryzanine,* was accompanied by nicotinic acid. This was the earliest observation of the occurrence of nicotinic acid in a plant material. Nicotinic acid was isolated as the picrate.

In the same year Funk (4) found the curative substance for pigeons in experimental polyneuritis to be stable even in hot concentrated mineral acids. This was shown by the effectiveness of preparations made from acid-hydrolyzed rice polishings and yeast. Using the precipitating reagents described by others, Funk succeeded in preparing a crude crystalline mixture from yeast, which was highly potent. The methods of concentrating and precipitating this substance indicated that it was an organic base, with properties similar to pyrimidines. In 1912 Vedder and Williams (5) began to study the problem of isolating the antineuritic substance. They verified the experimental work of earlier investigators described above and discovered that it could be adsorbed on charcoal.

The next step in progress in isolating the substance was taken by Seidell (6) who, in 1917 and 1926, described several modifications of the procedures mentioned, and succeeded in concentrating the vitamin from yeast. He obtained a preparation which was 100 times as potent as the yeast itself. By a modification of Seidell's long and troublesome method, Jansen and Donath in Holland (7) succeeded, in 1926, in obtaining from rice polishings extremely small yields of the hydrochloride of a base which crystallized in rosettes, melted at 250° C., and yielded analytical results corresponding to the empirical formula $C_6H_{10}N_2O$.

In 1932 Ohdake (8), using a method similar to that of Jansen and Donath, isolated what was presumably the identical substance described by the former workers, but which he found to contain sulfur. Analysis showed it to have the empirical formula $C_{12}H_{16}N_4O_2S$. In the same year Windaus and his associates (9), at the University of Göttingen, used the procedures of Jansen and Ohdake, and obtained crystals which corresponded to the composition $C_{12}H_{17}N_2OS$. Later studies confirmed the presence of sulfur in its composition. But there was evidence, from spectroscopic examination, that none of the preparations which had been obtained up to that time were pure.

After extensive studies, Williams and his co-workers (10) perfected a method in which the vitamin was adsorbed on fuller's earth and eluted with a solution of quinine. In 1934 they succeeded in consistently getting yields of the vitamin hydrochloride of about 5 grams per ton of rice polishings. With such success they soon accumulated sufficient of the vitamin to enable them to determine its molecular structure, with the ultimate objective of synthesis. The large scale undertaking was participated in by Merck and Co., Inc.

Synthesis of Vitamin B_1, or Thiamin Hydrochloride

In 1932 Windaus, Tschesche, and Grewe (11) secured, by oxidation of thiamin with nitric acid, two well characterized compounds, one of which contained sulfur. The following year Williams and his associates (12) discovered that by treatment with sulfurous acid at room temperature the vitamin was cleaved quantitatively into two products. These were obtained in the crystalline state. One was a sparingly soluble acid product, the other a base which was soluble in chloroform. The latter was isolated as the hydrochloride. The former proved to be a thiazole derivative and the latter a pyrimidine derivative. The molecular structures of these compounds were determined, and the synthesis of the vitamin was achieved by Cline, Williams, and Finkelstein (13) in 1937. The synthetic substance was shown to be identical with the naturally occurring vitamin (14).

Attempts to Discover the Function of Thiamin

In 1914 Funk (15) became the first to observe that polyneuritis in pigeons occurred sooner when the carbohydrate content of the diet was high. This fact was confirmed in the same year by Braddon and Cooper (16). Collazo (17), in 1923, noted an apparent toxicity from introducing carbohydrates into the crops of pigeons depleted of the antineuritic vitamin. From this he concluded that in this vitamin deficiency, carbohydrate metabolism is deranged. This view was supported by the work of others, and directed attention to investigation of the manner in which such a perversion of metabolism was brought about.

In 1929 Kinnersley and Peters (18) made the important discovery that lactic acid accumulates in the brain of a pigeon maintained on a thiamin-deficient diet. Reduction in the oxygen uptake of thiamin-deficient pigeon brain occurred *in vitro* when the tissues were treated with glucose, lactate, or pyruvate in Ringer-phosphate solution, and it was observed that the addition of thiamin produced large increases in oxygen uptake. With normal pigeon brain this was not the case. These observations set a number of chemists studying various aspects of carbohydrate metabolism (hyper- and hypoglycemia, defect in storage of glycogen, and carbohydrate tolerance, to name a few), with the result that a controversial literature accumulated. This was inevitable, since there was no knowledge of the individual nutrients that constituted an adequate diet.

Inanition, deficiencies of other vitamins, and perhaps other nutrients as well gave conflicting results in studies of metabolism. It was clear, however, that a high carbohydrate diet was much more effective in producing the symptoms of thiamin deficiency than was one high in fat. A number of studies to determine whether oxidative processes were disturbed in thiamin deficiency resulted in contradictory and inconclusive results. The publications concerned with the vitamin as an oxidative catalyst were reviewed in 1932 by Westenbrink (19). He concluded that no essential difference was manifest between the respiratory function in normal and vitamin deficient tissues.

The Discovery by Lohmann and Schuster

In 1937 Lohmann and Schuster (20) made the capital discovery that in yeast a diphosphate ester of vitamin B_1 functions as the co-enzyme, co-carboxylase, for the enzyme carboxylase. Carboxylase functions in the conversion of pyruvic acid, $CH_3 \cdot CO \cdot COOH$, into carbon dioxide and acetaldehyde. Co-carboxylase is thiamin pyrophosphate chloride, and the key substance in biochemical de-carboxylation. It catalyzes the decarboxylation of many alpha-keto acids.

In 1937 Stern and Hofer (21) synthesized co-carboxylase by the action of phosphorus oxychloride on crystalline thiamine in the cold. Then, two years later, Peters and his associates (22) presented evidence that vitamin B_1, in the form of its pyrophosphate, is indispensable for the removal of pyruvic acid, and indirectly of lactic acid, in the normal metabolic scheme.

Assay Methods for Vitamin B_1

The advancement of knowledge concerning the physiologic, pharmacologic, and pathologic significance of thiamin necessitated the development of accurate methods for its assay in foods, tissues, etc. Many studies were directed toward this objective. Biological methods based upon the response of a living organism to varying degrees of starvation for the vitamin have been devised. In general, they have been preferred to chemical methods because of the relative certainty of their specificity. The animals which have been most used for biological testing are the pigeon and other birds, and the rat. It would be beyond the scope of this work to describe these methods further than to state the principles on which they rest.

The basis for quantitative assays for the vitamin involves the use of a diet which is adequate except that it is devoid of vitamin B_1. Animals are fed this diet with graded dosages of the vitamin, or of a food containing it, and sufficient experiments are conducted to reveal the minimum *protective* daily allowance which will prevent the appearance of any symptoms of deficiency.

Modifications of this type of test depend on the minimum amount of the vitamin which permits a stipulated rate of growth, or which enables the animal to maintain its weight. Still others depend on producing incipient polyneuritis in the experimental animal and then finding the minimum amount of the substance to be analyzed which will effect cures. Curative tests usually depend upon the development of a specific symptom, such as head retraction in the pigeon, and its relief when the vitamin is given in suitable dosage. Neuromuscular symptoms in young rats have been found a reliable basis for the test.

One test, devised by Birch and Harris, is based on the fact that as Vitamin B_1 starvation progresses, the rate of heart beat decreases. Normally, in the young rat the rate is 500–550 beats per minute. After two weeks of withholding the vitamin, the rate falls to about 350. A single dose of the substance to be assayed is given and the animal is again tested for heart-rate after 24 hours. This is known as the *bradycardia* method.

There is a fermentation test which depends on the fact that in the presence of a sugar-salt buffer mixture, yeast cannot induce alcoholic fermentation. The addition of minute amounts of vitamin B_1 initiates fermentation. Within certain limits the fermentation rate depends on the amount of the vitamin added. Fungus growth and cocci growth methods have also been devised.

Chemical Tests for Vitamin B_1

The first observation which gave promise of devising a chemical test for vitamin B_1 was made by Jendrassik (23) in 1923. He found that every one of a long list of substances which were known to contain the vitamin reduced a solution of ferric ferricyanide. Hence, he concluded that the test was specific. In 1925 Levine (24) discovered that this reagent is also reduced by ortho and polyphenols. In 1935 Barger (25) and Peters (26) produced by oxidation of B_1 a yellow substance with intense blue fluorescence. In the same year Kuhn (27) suggested for this substance the name thiochrome. Following the work of these investigators, Jansen (28), in 1936, devised a procedure for the quantitative estimation of the vitamin based on thiochrome. This was later modified by others for specific purposes, and has had wide application ever since in biochemical and nutritional studies.

Some Fields of Investigation Relating to Vitamin B_1

With the perspective opened by the studies described above, and the opportunities made possible by quantitative investigations, many lines of inquiry were developed. Prominent among these were studies to determine the distribution of the vitamin in nature; the effects of its excessive ingestion; its storage and excretion; its stability under conditions to which commercially handled foods are exposed; and its synthesis by microorganisms. Extensive studies of the pathology of various organs and tissues in B_1 deficiency, and the associated perversion of physiological function have shed light upon many phases of metabolism. By 1941, 1,489 scientific workers had contributed 1,617 papers dealing with subjects in this field.

From the chance observation in 1896 by Eijkman of the occurrence of multiple neuritis in chickens fed only polished rice, there resulted a series of investigations, physiological and chemical, which, over a period of about forty-five years, brought to light the nature of a disease in man resulting from a lack in the diet of a specific substance. The disease afflicted great numbers of people and was a principal cause of disability and death in several geographic areas. Thus, isolation, identification, and synthesis of the antineuritic vitamin represent one of the great achievements of chemical science. The perfection of quantitative analytical methods for the determination of its presence in foods and animal tissues led to fundamental discoveries of great importance concerning certain chemical processes which are integral steps in the metabolic scheme of living creatures. Collectively, these investigations represent one of the greatest achievements in the history of science.

REFERENCES

1. Eijkman, C. and Grijns, G.: Arch. Hygiene *58*, 150 (1896).
2. Fraser, H. and Stanton, A. T.: Lancet (London) (1909), i, p. 451.
3. Suzuki, U., Shimamura, T. and Ohdake, S.: Biochem. Zeitschr. *43*, 89–153 (1912).
4. Funk, C.: J. State Med. *20*, 341–68 (1912).
5. Vedder, E. B. and Williams, R. R.: Philippine J. of Sci. *8*, 75–95 (1913).
6. Seidell, A.: J. Biol. Chem. *29*, 145–54 (1917); *67*, 593–600 (1926).
7. Jansen, B. C. P. and Donath, W. P.: Proc. Koninkl. Akad. Wettenschappen. Amsterdam, *29*, 1390–1400 (1926).
8. Ohdake, S.: Bull. Agr. Chem. Soc. Japan *8*, 179 (1932).
9. Windaus, A., Tschesche, R. and Ruhkopf, H.: Nachr. v. d. ges. Wissensch. zu Gottingen III, 334 (1932).
10. Williams, R. R., Waterman, R. E. and Keresztesy, J. C.: J. Amer. Chem. Soc. *56*, 1187–91 (1934).
11. Windaus, A., Tschesche, R., Ruhkopf, H., Laquer, F. and Schultz, F.: Zeitschr. f. physiol. Chem. *204*, 123–28 (1932).
12. Williams, R. R., Waterman, R. E., Keresztesy, J. C. and Buchman, E. R.: J. Amer. Chem. Soc. *57*, 517–20 (1935).
13. Cline, J. K., Williams, R. R. and Finkelstein, J.: J. Amer. Chem. Soc. *59*, 1052–59 (1937).
14. Williams, R. R. and Cline, J. K.: J. Amer. Chem. Soc. *58*, 1504–5 (1936).
15. Funk, C.: J. Physiol. *47*, xxv (1914).
16. Braddon, W. G. and Cooper, E. A.: J. Hygiene *14*, 331 (1914).
17. Collazo, J. A.: Biochem. Zeitschr. *136*, 278 (1923).
18. Kinnersley, H. W. and Peters, R. A.: Biochem. J. 23, 1126 (1919).
19. Westenbrink, H. G. K.: Arch. Neerland Physiol. *17*, 549 (1932).
20. Lohmann, K. and Schuster, P.: Naturwissenschaften *25*, 26 (1937).
21. Stern, K. G. and Hofer, J. W.: Science *85*, 483 (1937); Enzymologia 3, 82–95 (1937).
22. Peters, R. A. and others: Biochem. J. 33, 1109 (1939).

23. Jendrassik, A.: J. Biol. Chem. *57*, 129 (1923).
24. Levine, V. E.: J. Biol. Chem. *64*, 591 (1925).
25. Barger, G., Bergell, F. and Todd, A. R.: Nature *136*, 259 (1935).
26. Peters, R. A.: Nature *135*, 107 (1935).
27. Kuhn, R. and Vetter, H.: Ber. d. deutsch. chem. Ges. *68*, 2375 (1935).
28. Jansen, B. C. P.: Rec. trav. chim. *55*, 1046–52 (1938).

17

The Nature of the Antiscorbutic Substance (Ascorbic Acid)

THE EARLY WRITINGS on the nature and cause of scurvy are voluminous, but they contain little of interest in the way of accurate observations or constructive thought. A. Hirsch, in his *Handbook of Geographical and Historical Pathology,* Vol. II, p. 507 (1885), devoted sixty-one pages to the discussion of scurvy. He appended a bibliography of 178 papers of men who had written on the disease. Among these was a study by James Lind (1716–94), the outstanding investigator of the history, prevention, and cure of this disorder.

In 1753 Lind published the first edition of *A Treatise on the Scurvy,* in which he related the story of men in the command of Jacques Cartier during the winter of 1536. One hundred and ten men were disabled by scurvy, and seemingly miraculous cures were effected with an Indian remedy. The Indians, apparently familiar with this type of disorder, cured those afflicted by giving them an infusion of the needles of some evergreen tree. It was their belief that the specific remedial virtue existed only in the needles of this one kind of tree. Biggar (1) gives a full account of the history of Cartier's voyages.

Lind also cited a pamphlet by Bachstrom (2) (Lind, pp. 409, 411) which was published in 1734. Bachstrom gave an account of the epidemic of scurvy which he had witnessed at the siege of the Polish city Torun in 1703. It was his opinion that the disease was caused by lack of fresh vegetable food and greens, "which is alone the primary cause of the disease" (Lind's translation).

In 1737 Kramer (3) described his experiences with epidemic scurvy in the Hungarian army three years before. He noticed that the disease was almost always seen in common soldiers, whereas it seldom attacked the officers. This he ascribed to the fact that the former had nothing but farinaceous substances and legumes to eat, while the latter often had green vegetables. He asserted that when an officer neglected to eat these foods, he became scorbutic. Kramer observed the failure of dried vegetables to prevent scurvy in soldiers. Like Bachstrom, Kramer made a generalized statement that it was succulent fruits and vegetables of various kinds, as distinguished from ordinary dried seeds, which possessed antiscorbutic value. Other observers cited by Lind confirmed but did not extend knowledge of the cause of scurvy.

Lind himself was first to study experimentally the value of different substances in the treatment of scurvy. In the second edition of his *Treatise* (1757, p. 56) he stated that in May, 1747, he had treated twelve patients with scurvy on board the "Salisbury." The cases were similar in many aspects: all the men suffered from putrid gums, spots caused by hemorrhages in the skin, lassitude, and weakness of their knees. All were housed alike, and all ate a diet of water gruel sweetened with sugar in the morning, fresh muttonbroth, light puddings, boiled biscuit with sugar, barley and raisins, rice and currants, sago and wine, and the like.

Dividing the twelve men into pairs, Lind experimented with six different diets. To each of the first two men he gave a quart of cider daily. Two others were given twenty-five drops of *elixir vitriol*[1] three times a day, in addition to a gargle strongly acidulated with this liquid for their mouths. Both remedies were administered to the men before they had eaten. A third pair took two spoonfuls of vinegar three times a day, and their gruel was strongly acidulated with vinegar. They were also given an acid gargle for their mouths. The fourth pair, consisting of men in worst condition, received daily a half pint of sea water, which acted as a gentle physic. Another pair had each two oranges and one lemon daily; this treatment ended after six days, however, because the supply was no longer adequate. The remaining two patients received three times a day an electuary made of garlic, mustard seed, *rad. raphan,* Balsam of Peru, and gum myrrh. In addition, they drank barley-water well acidulated with tamarinds, by a decoction of which, with the addition of *cremor-tartar,* they were gently purged three or four times during the course of treatment.

[1] Sulfuric acid, alcohol, extract of ginger, and cinnamon.

The best effects were derived, Lind observed, from the diet supplemented with oranges and lemons. One man in the pair was fit for duty after six days, while the other returned to health more slowly. The next best results were secured from cider, those who had taken it being well on the way to recovery at the end of fourteen days. The other methods of treatment afforded no appreciable benefit to the patients, although Lind produced convincing evidence that scurvy-grass was a valuable antiscorbutic remedy.

A laudable contribution to constructive thinking was that of a certain "Mr. Young of the Navy," of whom nothing more appears to be known. In 1782 Charles Curtis (4), formerly surgeon of the Medea Frigate, wrote of Mr. Young's plan, "It proceeds upon the well known fact that nothing more is necessary for the cure of this disease in any situation where there is tolerably pure air, than not dead and dried, but a fresh vegetable diet, of greens or roots, in sufficient quantity. To be sure, we cannot have a kitchen garden at sea, and a short and scanty crop of greens can only be raised on board ship; *but beans and pease and barley and other seeds brought under the malting or vegetating process, are converted into the state of a growing plant, with the vital principle in full activity throughout the germ and pulp,* and if eaten in this state without any sort of preparation, except that of separating or rejecting the husks, cannot fail to supply precisely what is wanted for the cure of scurvy, viz., fresh vegetable chyle."

Garrod (5) was the earliest investigator to make inquiry into the chemical nature of the antiscorbutic substance. Led by a consideration of the great outbreak of scurvy in the United Kingdom during the potato famine of 1846–47, he analyzed the most common articles of diet to determine their relative richness in potassium, which he knew to be abundant in the ash of the potato. He determined the amount of this element in potatoes, lime juice, lemon juice, unripe oranges, mutton, beef, peas, onions, wheat bread, Dutch cheese, wheat flour, oatmeal, and rice. Garrod observed that those foods, the exclusive use of which was believed to favor the development of scurvy, contained much less potassium than did those whose consumption is never followed by the disease, and which had been proved by experience to possess antiscorbutic potency. He thus concluded that the cause of the malady was the use of a diet poor in carbonate of potash.

Diets derived from cereal grains and meats were long recognized as scurvy-producing. These foods, on incineration, leave strongly acid ashes, whereas fruits, tuber, root, and leafy vegetables, which were known to prevent or cure scurvy, leave alkaline ashes when burned. This suggested to Wright (6) that scurvy was caused by a state of acidosis due to deficiency of sodium or potassium in the diet. Later, however, this view proved untenable in the light of the demonstration by Lepper and Zilva (7) that sodium citrate failed to benefit guinea pigs with experimentally-induced scurvy. They showed further that scurvy in these animals could be cured by small amounts of lemon juice which contained one milligram of inorganic matter.

The scorbutic state was first induced in an animal in 1895 by Theobald Smith (8). Interested mainly in the study of the bacilli of swine disease, he used guinea pigs in his experiments, restricting them to a diet of oats and bran. Smith described the development in these animals of a peculiar disease, characterized chiefly by subcutaneous extravasations of blood, which caused death in four to eight weeks. He noted that a diet of oats and bran with a supplement of grass, clover, or succulent vegetable such as cabbage prevented the disease. Apparently Smith did not recognize the condition as experimentally induced scurvy, and he did not pursue the subject further.

Between 1907 and 1912 Holst and Fröhlich (9), in Oslo, ushered in a new era in the study of scurvy. They made extensive investigations of the effect of the diet in inducing or curing scurvy in guinea pigs. The guinea pigs remained healthy on a diet of several ordinary cereal grains and cabbage; however, when restricted to grains alone, they developed scorbutic lesions and died after twenty to forty days. Holst and Frölich also tested maize, oats, barley, rice, wheat, and rye, the last two in the form of bread. They found that supplements of fruits, fresh vegetables, or their juices to a diet of grain protected the animals against scurvy.

Holst and Frölich noted that daily allowances of thirty grams of fresh raw cabbage, cranberries, dandelion leaves, sorrel, or carrot prevented the appearance of scorbutic symptoms in guinea pigs restricted to a grain diet. These antiscorbutic foods lost their effectiveness when heated to 100° C. for a half to one hour. Dried, unheated carrot, dandelion leaves, or cabbage leaves, or dried potato were of no value as antiscorbutic foods. Most fruit or vegetable juices, it was found, lost their antiscorbutic value upon keeping, but strongly acid juices such as lemon or sorrel preserved this property for a considerable time. They observed further that dry seeds such as oats, barley, peas, beans, or lentils, which have no protective potency against scurvy, acquire this property to an astonishing degree when soaked in water and kept moist for a few days until they germinate.

Although every important fact which Holst and Fröhlich observed had been previously mentioned by others, as noted in the accounts of the early commentators on human scurvy, none of these facts was universally accepted. However, these two investigators are entitled to full credit for their pioneer studies which were so carefully and critically conducted and described as to reveal the methods which made possible rapid advances in knowledge of the etiology, pathology, prevention, and cure of human scurvy. Their observations opened the way for studies on the isolation, identification, and eventual synthesis of the antiscorbutic substance. Thus, these contributions form one of the monuments of achievement in the science of nutrition.

The profound significance of the discovery of a method of producing in an animal a syndrome directly attributable to a deficiency of a specific nutrient, is nowhere better illustrated than in the case of the production of experimental scurvy in the guinea pig. Of human experience with scurvy there was a long and sad history. The observations and clinical experiences of the great pioneers, Bachstrom, Kramer, and Lind, extended and confirmed by the recommendations of "Mr. Young of the Navy," led to the prevention of scurvy to a great extent on land and sea during a period of one hundred and fifty years. However, these studies failed to teach pediatricians and physicians generally how to prevent or treat scurvy in infants. This fact is well illustrated by the report of the American Pediatric Society on its Collective Investigation of Infantile Scurvy in North America, which appeared 1898 (10). The opening paragraph of this report reads, "The subject of infantile scurvy has so recently come into prominence, and still presents so many mooted questions, especially regarding its etiology, that it was the decision of the American Pediatric Society, a year ago, to undertake a collective investigation of the matter, based upon the cases occurring in America. This seemed particularly needed, as no other such study upon a large number of cases has yet been made in any country."

The committee studied 372 cases of scurvy in infants. Of 356 cases where the food of the child was specified, ten had breast milk alone, one had raw milk (cow) with carbohydrate, one had sterilized milk with carbohydrate. The remaining 344 cases were more complicated as to food provided. In general, heated milk formulas gave unfavorable results.

In 399 interviews with doctors, 275 stated their belief that diet was the cause of infantile scurvy; 24 were of opinion that the disease was attributable to other causes.

In most cases treatment could not be evaluated because where dietetic measures were employed, these were combined with other treatment. No patients were cured solely by drugs. Of the 356 cases where the diet was specified, only three were given fruit juice without other change in the diet. Two recoveries were reported from administration of beef juice. Two hundred and fifty-seven infants were reported to have been cured by administration of beef juice and fruit juice, with or without drugs. Thirty-eight cases of recovery were reported where some change in diet was made other than the inclusion of fruit juice.

The majority report stated that dietetic error was the cause of scurvy in infants, and that the same type of dietetic errors likely to induce scurvy in adults, caused scurvy in infants. The minority report, by Dr. Augustus Caille, set forth the following points: that scurvy seemed to be caused by absorption of ptomaines; and that prolonged use of improper food, and the resulting abnormal intestinal fermentation, was the predisposing cause. He said that sterilization, pasteurization, or cooking of milk were not responsible for scurvy *per se.* Caille stated, "Change of food and administration of fruit juice, and treatment of the underlying cause is the rational therapeutic procedure for scurvy."

The discussion following the reading of the report showed that wide differences of opinion prevailed in the medical profession at that time regarding the cause of infantile scurvy. It should be mentioned that until the 1890's scurvy in infants had not been frequently observed.

The upswing in incidence of scurvy, mentioned in the introductory paragraph of the report, was due to the adoption of milk pasteurization as a public health measure. Newly-acquired statistics derived from epidemiologic studies had clearly revealed that the spread of epidemics of scarlet fever, typhoid fever, and septic sore throat was traceable around milk routes. This fact, interpreted in the light of the recent discoveries by Pasteur, Koch, and their followers, led municipal health officials to conclude that the bacteria in raw milk were a menace to human health. Pasteur had found that a certain heat treatment could be depended upon to kill pathogenic microorganisms, and medical opinion quickly turned in favor of pasteurization of city milk supplies as a health measure. Ordinances requiring pasteurization were adopted in many cities. For this reason alone there was a great increase in the number of bottle-fed babies who were given milk which had been heated, but many physicians went further in attempts to safeguard the health of infants by prescribing milk sterilized by boiling.

In discussing the report made by the American Pediatric Society, Dr. Booker said, "When the sterilization of milk was introduced it was heralded by the medical profession as one of the most important advances in medicine. After ten years of experience in this method I am still of the same opinion that it is one of the greatest advances that had been made in infant feeding. The improved digestibility of milk after sterilization had attracted so much attention that the most important point had been lost sight of, viz., the prevention of digestive disorders in infants during summertime." He said further that infant mortality had been greatly reduced by sterilization of milk, and he ended with the assertion that he did not believe that sterilization of milk caused scurvy.

Fifteen years after the publication of the Collective Investigation of 1898, there was still a high rate of incidence of scurvy among bottle-fed infants. Alfred F. Hess, writing in 1914 (11), stated that numerous cases of scurvy had developed in the preceding few years at the Hebrew Infant Asylum (New York), over which he exercised medical supervision. He said that a number of these cases developed when an attempt was made to eliminate orange juice from the diet. This attempt was made on the basis of the recommendation of many, including the Commission on Milk Standards, that milk which was heated to a temperature of only 145° F. still retained its chemical constituents. On the basis of this assumption it seemed that infants should thrive on such milk and thus not require fruit juices in their diet. Experience proved that such confidence was unwarranted.

Most of the infants in the Asylum were fed "Grade A Pasteurized" milk (heated 30 minutes at 145° F.), together with barley-water, or malt soup. The important element in the situation was that all constituents of the infants' diets were heated sufficiently to reduce or destroy their antiscorbutic property. Hess was the first pediatrician to conduct thorough tests such as replacing heated milk by raw milk, and comparing the efficacy of fresh fruit juices and potato lightly boiled in the skin as scurvy-preventives. He demonstrated beyond doubt that pasteurization greatly reduces the antiscorbutic value of milk. In addition, he showed that when barley-water was replaced in a feeding formula based on pasteurized milk by lightly boiled and mashed potato, infants with scurvy were speedily cured.

Hess was, of course, familiar with the publications of Holst and Fröhlich, and their investigations were responsible for his systematic inquiries. Having convinced himself by many such comparative tests that heated milk formulas for infants must be amply supplemented with fruit or vegetable juices in order to prevent the development of scurvy, he began a vigorous campaign to educate the medical profession and mothers. As a result he accomplished his objective of practically eradicating scurvy among infants.

The fact that fresh and raw vegetable food, raw milk, and numerous other substances contain an antiscorbutic substance labile to heat, drying and exposure to oxidation, excited great interest among biochemists. Because of this knowledge, many investigators began to study specific problems relating to experimentally-induced scurvy in animals. Among the points studied were the lability of the antiscorbutic factor under diverse conditions; pathological lesions in blood, bone, skin, teeth and other tissues; and the distribution of the substance in natural and processed foods.

Barnes and Hume (12), and Harden and Zilva (13) concluded that monkeys were the most suitable animals for assaying foods. They fed them a scurvy-producing diet consisting of 100 g. dry weight of rice (boiled), 30 g. wheat germ and autoclaved milk 200 ml. By replacing graded amounts of the heated milk by the food to be tested, relative antiscorbutic values could be obtained. It was found that guinea pigs were not suitable for assaying milk samples because the protective dose of raw milk was just above their receptive capacity.

Cohen and Mendel (14) were the first to produce scurvy in guinea pigs on a diet which was complete from the nutritive standpoint except for the antiscorbutic vitamin, and which was suitable in its physical properties for that species. The guinea pig has a very large and delicate stomach and cecum; because of this fact, it cannot be satisfactorily nourished on a diet which fails to provide sufficient water-rich indigestible residue of proper physical quality. Cohen and Mendel used a diet composed of cooked soya flour, 3 per cent each of NaCl and calcium lactate, 5 per cent of dried brewer's yeast, and sufficient raw Jersey milk to furnish 5 per cent of butter fat.

Concentration, Isolation, and Identification of the Antiscorbutic Substance

In 1920 Drummond (15) proposed to call the antiscorbutic substance vitamin C, a name which was widely adopted until 1933 when Szent-Györgyi and Haworth (16) suggested that it be renamed ascorbic acid.

The first successful efforts to make highly potent concentrates of vitamin C were reported by Harden and Zilva (17) in 1918, and later by Zilva (18) and Bezssonoff (19). These were based on precipitating the vitamin as its lead salt by adding alcohol to the aqueous solution. Zilva introduced precipitation with basic lead acetate, after having first removed the bulk of the organic acids as calcium salts. Lepkovsky (20) and Grettie and King (21) improved the method by first removing sugars from the juices by fermentation with yeast. Employing these principles, Zilva, King, and their associates were able by 1929 to prepare concentrates which contained in 0.5 to 1.0 mg. of solid matter enough of the vitamin to protect a guinea pig against scurvy. This was equivalent to 1.5 ml. of lemon juice. The early studies were made with lemon juice, but the technics employed were found to work well with cabbage juice, turnip juice, and other fresh plant juices.

That vitamin C is very easily destroyed by oxidizing agents and air was first shown independently in 1920 by Delf (22) and Hess (23). Holst and Fröhlich (1912) had shown that inactivation proceeds rapidly in alkaline solutions in presence of air. Zilva (24) found that after vitamin C had been oxidized by atmospheric oxygen it could not be restored to biological activity by reduction with hydrogen and platinum black. Sherman and others (25) studied the stability of the vitamin at different pH values. Hess and his associates (26) discovered that the presence of copper in milk greatly accelerated the rate of destruction of the vitamin.

McKinnis and King (27) found that the vitamin rapidly diffuses through a collodion membrane. They also showed by electrical transference studies at different pH values that the vitamin was not a salt-forming nitrogen compound, such as an organic base or amino acid, and that it possessed distinct acidic properties. Sipple, Grettie, and Svirbely, in collaboration with King (28), showed that vitamin C is soluble in acetone, ethyl acetate, and propyl alcohol, but insoluble in ethyl ether and petroleum ether. The reducing value, solubility, syrupy nature, and acidity of their concentrates corresponded with the properties of an active hexuronic acid. Hexuronic acid is a term used to designate tetrahydroxy aldehyde acids obtained by oxidation of hexose sugars.

The earlier attempts to assay foods to determine their vitamin C values were based on animal experiments of the types already mentioned (12, 13, 14) which showed the relative values of different antiscorbutic foods. A chemical method was introduced in 1932 by Tillmans and associates (29), who discovered a striking correlation between the reducing values of foods and their vitamin C content. They introduced for this purpose 2, 6-dichlorophenol-indophenol, a reagent first employed by Mansfield Clark in his series of indicators for oxidation-reduction potentials. This reagent proved to be fairly accurate for quantitative estimation of vitamin C in foods except when some other strong reducing substances (e.g., cysteine) are present.

Three types of animal assay technics were perfected. Sherman and associates (30) developed one method. This was based on the determination of the minimum amount of the food or concentrate sufficient to protect guinea pigs on a standard diet from developing hemorrhages, bone changes, and tooth changes over a six to ten week period. A curative method was devised by Harris and his associates (31) to find the minimum amount of an antiscorbutic source which would enable guinea pigs in incipient scurvy to recover and increase in weight at a certain rate. Höjer (32) developed a third plan designed to note incipient damage to the odontoblasts observed in sections through the pulp cavity of a tooth. He used guinea pigs as his test subjects. All three methods of assay have been critically discussed by Coward (33).

In 1928 Szent-Györgyi (34), while studying oxidation-reduction factors in the laboratory of F. G. Hopkins, isolated from adrenal glands, cabbage and orange, a very active reducing substance which he named hexuronic acid. This substance was found to act as a hydrogen carrier in the cell respiration of certain plants and animals. In the autumn of 1931, after several years' study of fractionation and assay of antiscorbutic materials, King and his associates (35) succeeded in obtaining Szent-Györgyi's "hexuronic acid" in crystalline form, and found that the protective daily dose for a guinea pig was about 0.5 mg. They purified the lead salt of this acid by recrystallization from several kinds of solvents, without changing its activity in the cure of scurvy in guinea pigs.

This evidence that the antiscorbutic property resided in the crystals rather than in an impurity seemed to establish fully that the crystals were the antiscorbutic vitamin C. However, King and Waugh were deterred from publishing their observations because of a report by Rygh (36) and associates that they had identified vitamin C with methyl nornarcotine (a derivative of one of the opium alkaloids). Rygh asserted that his preparation had antiscorbutic activity about ten thousand times that of an equal weight of King and Waugh's crystals. Waugh and King reserved publicizing their findings until March 1932. Two weeks later Szent-Györgyi and Svirbely (37), the latter having been on an International Exchange Fellowship working in King's Pittsburgh laboratory, reported that guinea pigs kept on a standard scurvy-producing diet were protected from developing scorbutic symptoms by a daily dosage of 1 mg. of hexuronic acid. This was twice the minimum dose which King and Waugh had found effective. Hence, Szent-Györgyi and Svirbely had determined the biological effectiveness of their crystals, but not the minimum effective dose.

E. C. Kendall prepared crystalline vitamin C from adrenal glands, and Waugh and King (38), in testing the preparation, found it to produce the same quantitative physiological response as was found for preparations from lemon juice. This afforded conclusive evidence that the antiscorbutic property resided in the crystalline acid, not in an accompanying impurity.

Studies on the chemistry of vitamin C were greatly facilitated by the discovery by Szent-Györgyi and Svirbely (39) that Hungarian red peppers are extraordinarily rich in vitamin C. In their research these two were able to prepare nearly a pound of the pure substance from the peppers.

As soon as the pure vitamin became available in sufficient amounts for chemical investigation it was subjected to searching study by a number of able chemists. Waugh and King (40) were the first to show that the first stage oxidation product, though unstable and reversible, still possessed antiscorbutic activity.

The molecular structure of vitamin C was discovered through organic chemical investigations in several laboratories. Haworth

(41) ascribed to it the constitution of a 6-carboxylic acid of a keto-hexose. L. von Vargha (42) found that the substance was capable of forming a crystalline mono-isopropylidine derivative, which proved the presence of two vicinal hydroxyl groups. This was important in deciding on the details of structure of the molecule. Further investigations by Cox, Hirst, and Reynolds (43) led them to suggest the following tautomeric structures:

$$CO_2H \cdot CO \cdot C(OH){:}\ CH \cdot CH(OH) \cdot CH_2 \cdot OH \rightleftharpoons CO_2H \cdot CO \cdot CO \cdot CH_2 \cdot CH(OH) \cdot CH_2 \cdot OH$$

It was eventually established that ascorbic acid is the levo modification of 2, 3-dienol-gulonic acid lactone, which is represented by the following formula:

$$\begin{array}{cccccc} & OH & H & OH & OH & \\ & | & | & | & | & \\ H_2C - & C - & C - & C - & C - & C{=}O \\ | & | & \llcorner & - & O - & \lrcorner \\ OH & H & & & & \end{array}$$

Synthesis of ascorbic acid was first accomplished in 1933 by Reichstein, Grussner, and Oppenheimer (44). This they accomplished before the molecular structure was known. Other methods were soon discovered, and synthetic ascorbic acid became available in large amounts at low cost.

The primary effects of ascorbic acid deficiency occur in the intercellular substances. These changes have been especially well described by Wolbach and Howe (45). It is to deficiency of formation of intercellular cement substance that the fragility of blood capillaries is attributable.

The strongly-reducing properties of ascorbic acid suggested to investigators that this substance functions in cellular respiration as a component of perhaps several oxidase enzyme systems. It also appears to play a role in immunological reactions as well as in endocrine functioning. Outstanding is its significance in wound healing and in maintaining integrity of scar tissue.

Progress in the study of experimentally-induced scurvy in guinea pigs and monkeys led naturally to the study of ascorbic acid by organic chemists, and its eventual synthesis. Such developments opened the way for study of the distribution of ascorbic acid, its functions in metabolism, the pathology of its deficiency, minimum requirements, and method of preservation. These fields have been explored extensively; however, an account of the results achieved is outside the scope of this volume.

REFERENCES

1. Biggar, H. P.: Pub. Arch. of Canada, No. 11, p. 204 (1924).
2. Bachstrom, J. F.: *Observations circa Scorbutum;* etc. Leyden. (1734).
3. Kramer, J. G. H.: *De Scorbuto,* Dissertatio Epistolica, Nuernburg (1737).
4. Curtis, C.: An account of the diseases of India as they appeared in the English Fleet. Edinburgh, 1782 and 1783.
5. Garrod, A. B.: *Med. Times and Gaz.* March (1867) p. 317.
6. Wright, A. E.: The Causation and Treatment of Scurvy. The Lancet, London (1908), II, p. 725.
7. Lepper, E. H. and Zilva, S. S.: Biochem. J. *19,* 581 (1925).
8. Smith, Theobald: Bacilli of Swine Disease, U.S. Dept. Agr., Bur. Animal Industry, Ann. Rep. (1895–96) p. 172.
9. Holst, A. and Fröhlich, T.: Experimental Studies Relating to Ship Beriberi and Scurvy. J. Hygiene 7, 634 (1907). Ueber experimentellen Skorbut. Zeitschr. f. Hyg. u. Infektionskrankh. 72, 1 (1912).
10. American Pediatric Soc.: Collective Investigation on Infantile Scurvy in North America. Arch. of Pediatrics *15,* 481 (1898).
11. Hess, A. F. and Fish, M.: Amer. J. Dis. Child. *8,* 386 (1914).
12. Barnes, R. E. and Hume, E. M.: Lancet, London, ii, 323 (1919).
13. Harden, A. and Zilva, S. S.: J. Path. and Bacteriol. 22, 246 (1919).
14. Cohen, B. and Mendel, L. B.: J. Biol. Chem. 35, 425 (1918).
15. Drummond, J. C.: Biochem. J. *14,* 660 (1920).
16. Szent-Györgyi, A. and Haworth, W. N.: Nature *131,* 23 (1933).
17. Harden, A. and Zilva, S. S.: Biochem. J. *12,* 259 (1918).
18. Zilva, S. S.: Biochem. J. *18,* 632 (1924).
19. Bezssonoff, N.: Compt. Rend. Acad. Sci. Paris, *175,* 846 (1922).
20. Lepkovsky, S., *et al.*: J. Biol. Chem. *66,* 49 (1925).
21. Grettie, D. P. and King, C. G.: J. Biol. Chem. *84,* 771 (1929).

22. Delf, E. M.: Biochem. J. *14,* 211 (1920).

23. Hess, A. F.: Scurvy, Past and Present. Philadelphia (1920).

24. Daubney, C. G. and Zilva, S. S.: Biochem. J. *20,* 519 (1926).

25. La Mer, V. K., Campbell, H. L. and Sherman, H. C.: J. Amer. Chem. Soc. *44,* 172 (1922).

26. Hess, A. F.: Indust. Eng. Chem. 22, 1015 (1930); Scurvy, Past and Present, Philadelphia (1915).

27. McKinnis, R. B. and King, C. G.: J. Biol. Chem. *87,* 615 (1930).

28. Sipple, H. L. and King, C. G.: J. Amer. Chem. Soc. *52,* 420 (1930); Grettie, D. P. and King, C. G.: J. Biol. Chem. *84,* 771 (1930); Svirbely, J. L. and King, C. G.: *Ibid. 94,* 483 (1931–32).

29. Tillmans, J., Hirsch, P. and Jackisch, J.: Zeitschr. f. Untersuch. Lebensmittel *63,* 275 (1932).

30. Sherman, H. C. and Smith, S. L.: The vitamins, 2nd ed. (1931). Amer. Chem. Soc. Monograph.

31. Harris, L. J., Mills, J. I. and Innes, J. R. M.: Lancet, London, ii, 235 (1932).

32. Höjer, A. J.: Brit. J. Exper. Path. *7,* 356 (1926).

33. Coward, K.: The Biol. Standardization of Vitamins. Nut. Absts. and Rev. *4,* 705 (1935).

34. Szent-Györgyi, A.: Biochem. J. 22, 1387 (1928).

35. King, C. G. and Waugh, W. A.: Science *75,* 357 (1932); Waugh, W. A. and King, C. G.: J. Biol. Chem. *97,* 325 (1932).

36. Rygh, O., Rygh, A. and Laland, P.: Zeitschr. f. physiol. Chem. *204,* 105 (1932); Rygh, O. and Rygh, A.: *Ibid. 211,* 275 (1932).

37. Svirbely, J. L. and Szent-Györgyi, A.: Nature *129,* 576 (1932); Biochem. J. *26,* 865 (1932).

38. Waugh, W. A. and King, C. G.: Science *76,* 630 (1932).

39. Svirbely, J. L. and Szent-Györgyi, A.: Biochem. J. *27,* 279 (1933).

40. Waugh, W. A. and King, C. G.: J. Biol. Chem. *97,* 325 (1932).

41. Haworth, W. N.: Biochem. J. *22,* 576 (1928).

42. von Vargha, L.: Nature *130,* 847 (1932).

43. Cox, E. G., Hirst, E. L. and Reynolds, R. J. W.: Biochem. J. 22, 888 (1928).

44. Reichstein, T., Grussner, A. and Oppenheimer, R.: Helv. chim. Acta *16,* 1019 (1933).

45. Wolbach, S. B. and Howe, P. R.: Arch. Path. *1,* 1 (1926); Wolbach, S. B.: Amer. J. Pathol. (Suppl.) *9,* 689 (1933).

18

Investigations on the Etiology of Rickets

Vitamin D

THE EARLIEST RECORDED observation that bones differ greatly in quality seems to have been made by the Greek historian Herodotus (484–425 B.C.) (1). He visited the battlefield where Cambyses (525 B.C.) overcame the Egyptians, and inspected the skulls of the Persians and of the Egyptians who were there slain. He noted that the Persian skulls were so fragile that they broke even if struck with a pebble, whereas the skulls of the Egyptians were strong and could scarcely be broken even when struck with a stone. The Egyptians told Herodotus that this was due to their going bareheaded from childhood and exposing their heads to sunlight. The Persians, on the other hand, covered their heads with turbans, which shaded them and made them weak. Herodotus said he noticed the same contrasting quality in the skulls of soldiers killed by the army of Inarus the Libyan. Here again it was the Persians who had fragile skulls. This seems to be the first reference to the physiological effect of sunlight.

Soranus of Ephesus (2), in a treatise on the Diseases of Women written in the first century of our era, included a chapter on "Why the Majority of Roman Children are Distorted." He suggested that one cause was that their bodies were chilled from sitting on cold stone floors.

In 1650 Francis Glisson (1597–1677), Regius Professor of Physic at Cambridge University, wrote a treatise on rickets (3). He was the first to give a clinical description of the bone disorder. Glisson stated that the name was derived from the Old English word *wrikken,* which meant to bend or twist. The disease, which he believed to be new, had in his time become common in parts of England.

Glisson was a follower of the humoral pathology of Galen. He described rickets as a "cold distemper; moist, and consisting in penury or paucity of the spirits." No accurate conception of the ricketic lesion was possible until more was known about the structure of bones than was available to Glisson.

du Monceau's Observations on Bone Growth

Duhamel du Monceau (1700–1781) was by vocation Inspector of Mines in France, and by avocation the earliest investigator of diseases of plants. He improved the arts of making glue and of refining sugar. Having studied closely the manner of the growth of trees, he had the curiosity to inquire how bones grow. With this as his objective, he used madder to stain and study the bones of growing animals. This was the earliest work of its kind.

Madder (*Galium*, Ladies' bedstraw) was cultivated in Zeeland from early times for use in dyeing cotton. The steepwater in which the cloth had been dyed was used to wet bran for pig feeding. Lemnius, a physician in Zeeland, was the first to observe that madder, when fed to animals, produced a reddening of the bones (4). Dr. John Belchier, an English surgeon, also learned of this phenomenon while dining with a cotton printer. The printer explained that the presence of madder in food fed pigs caused the redness of bones in the pork served at the meal. Belchier tested this explanation by feeding madder to a pig, and found it to be true (5).

Duhamel said he learned about the bone-staining action of madder from Sir Hans Sloane, a British physician, and collector of plants, and so conceived the idea of studying bone growth by its use. He reported the results of his study in 1740 (6). Belchier had already published his account of the phenomenon in 1736.

The original feature of Duhamel's experiment was that he fed madder to fowls and pigeons for three-day periods, alternating with similar periods when none was fed. He described concentric layers of red and white in bones of animals so treated. Haller controverted Duhamel's statement (6a).

The Earliest Chemical Analysis of Bone

Boerhaave (1668–1738), in his *Elementa Chemae* (1732) described how, when bones were soaked in muriatic acid, the earthy salts were dissolved out and the organic matrix was left without change of shape. He said that this fact was well known in his time. For many years chemists believed the mineral matter of bones was a special kind of earth, but in 1768 J. G. Gahn of Sweden, a famous metallurgist who was largely responsible for developing the art of blow-pipe analysis of minerals, discovered that the principal part of the earthy matter of bones consisted of calcium phosphate.

The first man to undertake a chemical analysis of bone was Merat-Guillot (7), but unfortunately his method was superficial. In 1801, Berzelius (8) reported a much more correct proportion between calcium and phosphorus in bones, and suggested a chemical formula for their composition.

In 1801 Fourcroy and Vauquelin (9) discovered the presence of magnesium in bones. Five years later Gay-Lussac (10) verified the observation of Morichini, who had told him that when bone was treated with sulfuric acid, vapors were evolved which etched glass. This he correctly attributed to the evolution of hydrofluoric acid.

In 1844 von Bibra (11) published a book of 430 pages devoted to analyses of bones. He determined the presence of phosphate, lime, magnesia, carbonate, sulfate, the salts of sodium and potassium, and cartilage, in his samples, but not fluorine. He reported results for 143 specimens of mammalian bones, 135 from birds, 35 from reptiles, and 23 from fishes. He complied existing analyses of ricketic, osteoporotic, and osteomalacic bones, all of which deviated from the composition of normal bones in the proportion of organic to inorganic constituents. He added little of value to existing knowledge of the composition of the skeleton. Earlier observers were aware of the pronounced differences between strong bones of high breaking strength and inferior bones with little resistance to stress.

The Effect of Diet on Bone Structure

In Chapter 7 the experiment of Fordyce was described. He showed clearly that for successful egg production canary hens required more calcareous substance than they secured in a diet of seeds. Fordyce did not make any observations on the bones of his birds.

The earliest experimental study of the effect of food on the skeleton was made by Chossat (12) in 1842. He restricted pigeons to a diet of wheat, and observed that their bones became greatly rarefied. When the birds were given wheat plus a supplement of calcium carbonate their bones did not deteriorate. After 1860, when agricultural experiment stations were established, a number of trials were made on the effects resulting from the addition of ashes, bone meal, or calcium phosphate to farm rations. The objective of these trials was to increase the size of bones and their breaking strength. These tests proved the value of the practice, but added nothing to Chossat's observations.

Histologic Observations on Normal and Abnormal Bones

The chemical studies compiled by von Bibra, in which the mineral salts were dissolved out of bones by means of a mineral acid, leaving intact the organic matrix, had revealed that in osteomalacia the deficiency was in calcium salts rather than in osteoid tissue. The same technic when applied to osteoporotic bones showed the characteristic feature to be widening of the Haversian canals, with consequent rarefaction.

Knowledge of bone structure and bone growth was notably extended by publication in 1858 of the histological studies of Heinrich Müller (13). He devoted eighty-three pages to a description of the phenomena of bone growth, including the changes which occur in the healing of the ricketic lesion. Staining technics were still in the experimental stages at that period, but Müller's studies set a new standard for the investigation of normal and abnormal bone structure.

In 1858 Pommer (13a) advanced knowledge of the structure of bones in rickets, osteomalacia, and osteoporosis by carefully describing the distinguishing features of these disorders.

Schmorl's Classical Investigations on Healing of Ricketic Bones

Information about the histology of ricketic bones, beyond that already contributed by Pommer, was first described by Schmorl (14) in 1909. He extended the observations of Müller on the sequence of events in the development and healing of the lesion in the bones of ricketic infants. Schmorl pointed out that, in the ricketic child, when healing occurs, the initial deposition of calcium salts does not occur simultaneously throughout the extremity of the diaphysis (or shaft) of the long bone where it joins the epiphysis (or head) of the bone. The latter develops from a center of ossification distinct from that of the shaft, and separated from it by a layer of cartilage. Schmorl showed that calcification takes place at the cartilage-shaft junction. When the newly deposited calcium salts are stained with silver nitrate, they present, in longitudinal sections, a black line having somewhat the appearance of a section of honeycomb. Schmorl's description of the healing process was used by later investigators of the etiology of rickets in experimental animals, and by those testing for the antiricketic vitamin.

Unhygienic Conditions as the Cause of Rickets

Glisson inquired extensively into the conditions under which infants and children develop rickets. He pointed out that in Somersetshire, England, a beautiful pastoral country where agriculture flourished, and milk, butter, eggs, and vegetables were in ample supply, rickets of marked intensity was of high incidence. Hence he thought food could not be the cause of the abnormality. Cottages, he said, were generally built in valleys close to streams. In summer there was much rain and the air in the valleys was stagnant and oppressive. There was heavy morning and evening mist. Winters were long and severe, and an infant born in October was kept indoors during the winter months. From these observations, Glisson concluded that defective home environment and bad hygiene were the etiological agents of the rickets.

In 1917 Leonard Findlay (15) discussed the etiology of rickets, and said, "In spite of the most varied and extensive research we have practically no real knowledge of the nature of the causation of this widespread malady, or the factors which determine its onset." He concluded that bad housing and unhygienic conditions of life associated with industrialization might explain its distribution. Similarly, Dick (16), after an elaborate inquiry based on all recorded studies, concluded in 1922 that absence of sunlight, and deprivation of fresh air and the means of exercise, were the underlying factors in the etiology of the disease. He did not think the type of food was a cause.

Early Evidence that Rickets is a Dietary Disease

For a long time cod liver oil was considered to be medicinally valuable, and was at one time a popular remedy for tuberculosis. It was used therapeutically by Darby in 1789 at the Manchester Infirmary, but its usefulness at that time was not well defined.

Scheutte (17), in 1824, seems to have been the first to recommend the oil as a remedy for rickets. From that time forward it was widely used with varying results. In 1844 Gobley (18), famous for his discovery of lecithin, detected the presence of phosphorus in the liver oil of the ray. He used this oil successfully in the treatment of rickets.

However, not all clinicians were convinced of the remedial value of cod liver oil in the treatment of rickets. Thus, in 1920, Howland (19) wrote, "Cod liver oil has been used therapeutically for a long time. It is regarded by many physicians as a specific in the treatment of this disease (rickets). This is perhaps too strong a praise. But there is no doubt of its usefulness. Its effect, however, is not very prompt or marked."

Rickets in Caged Animals in Relation to their Food

In 1860 Röll (20) reported that young leopards developed rickets when fed meat without bones. The inclusion of bones in their diet prevented skeletal defects. For a long time this observation was overlooked, but it is now recognized as the earliest demonstration that muscle substance is not a complete food.

In 1863 Savory (21) restricted two young rats to a diet of lean veal with water. One died on the thirteenth day, the other on the twenty-third. Savory believed that lean veal was an adequate food for sustaining health, and that some unknown cause led to the death of his rats.

Bland-Sutton's Observations on Feeding Young Lions

In 1889 Sir John Bland-Sutton (22) reported results of his extensive inquiry into the incidence of rickets among wild animals in captivity in the Zoological Gardens in London. He noted that bone defects were common, and diagnosed as rickets the lesions of the skeleton seen in carnivora, ruminants, rodents, marsupials, and birds. Apparently he did not distinguish between rickets, osteomalacia, and osteoporosis, but diagnosed rickets solely on the basis of deformity.

Bland-Sutton recommended that lion cubs be given crushed bones and cod liver oil in addition to lean meat which had hitherto constituted most of their diet. The results of this test were dramatic.

For the first time lions born in captivity were reared without deformities so severe that they were unfit for exhibition. Sir John minimized the nutritive significance of feeding bones, and expressed his belief that rickets was caused by a deficiency of fat in the diet. His views left a strong impression on English thought which, along with the favorable results achieved by a number of clinicians using cod liver oil in the treatment of rickets in infants and children resulted in a general acceptance of his theory on the cause of rickets.

There is in medical literature a long and arid list of discussions of the etiology and treatment of rickets. It need only be mentioned here that lack of calcium, deficient absorption, acid intoxication, and deficiency of gastric acidity were the principal topics discussed, either on the basis of clinical observations or animal experiments. They contributed nothing to an understanding of the disease.

Elemental Phosphorus As a Remedy for Rickets

An astonishing method for treatment of rickets was recommended in 1872 by Wegner (23). In the course of necropsies of persons who had committed suicide by swallowing the tips of phosphorus matches, he made the chance observation that in several cases of phosphorus poisoning, hardening and enlargement of the bones occurred instead of the usual necrosis. He conducted experiments with rabbits and chickens, which he fed 0.00015 gram of white phosphorus per day. After a considerable period, the bones of these animals showed what he called a "phosphorus layer," which was a transverse band in the epiphyseal region. This phenomenon he found could be produced only in growing animals. Thus he believed that the development of new bone proceeded in the normal way, the peculiarity being that the proliferating cartilage cells had been changed into bone rather than into "lymph marrow."

In 1884 Kassowitz (24) applied Wegner's observation to the treatment of infantile rickets. He concluded that white (elemental) phosphorus was a specific remedy for this disease. He used cod liver oil as the carrier of the highly poisonous phosphorus. This method of treatment was widely adopted throughout Europe, and was recommended in textbooks in America after 1900. Medical opinion differed on phosphorus therapy for rickets. It was not until 1926 that Hess and Weinstock (25) demonstrated by histological studies that calcification caused by phosphorus was pathological in character. As a result, this therapy for rickets was abandoned.

Mellanby's Studies on Experimental Rickets

The earliest comprehensive investigation of the role of nutrition in the etiology of rickets was made by Edward Mellanby (26), whose first report of results and conclusions was published in 1919. He proved conclusively that rickets is a dietary deficiency disease, and showed that certain fats, notably cod liver oil, exerted marked preventive and curative effects.

Mellanby used puppies as experimental animals and prepared his experimental diets from natural foods. His standard diets were the following:

Diet 1	*Diet 2*
Whole milk, 200 ml.	Whole milk, 175 ml.
Porridge, oatmeal	White bread
Porridge, rice	NaCl, 1–2 grams
NaCl, 2 grams	
Diet 3	*Diet 4*
Separated milk, 175 ml.	Separated milk, 250–350 ml.
White bread (made from 70% extraction wheat)	White bread (made from 70% extraction wheat)
Linseed oil, 1 ml.	Linseed oil, 10 ml.
Yeast, 10 grams	Yeast 5–10 grams
NaCl, 1–2 grams	Orange juice, 3 ml.
	NaCl, 1–2 grams

The following is a list of the most important observations and interpretations made by Mellanby on the effects of feeding these diets to puppies:

1. All four diets produced rickets.
2. Diets 1 and 2 contained milk fat. Diets 3 and 4 contained a vegetable fat, linseed oil; the former supplied the fat-soluble vitamin A, the latter was devoid of it.
3. With diets like 1 and 2, decreasing the milk and increasing the cereal, especially oatmeal, increased the severity of rickets.
4. Inclusion of yeast, a rich source of the antiberiberi vitamin, did not prevent the development of rickets, but did improve the

general condition of the puppies and supported better growth. Rickets developed to more pronounced degree in animals which were growing well than in those stunted in growth.

5. The inclusion of certain foods in diet 4, which when fed alone produced well-marked rickets in a six-week old puppy within about six weeks, prevented or tended to prevent rickets, whereas other foods did not. Mellanby listed both classes of foods as follows:

Substances which do not prevent rickets in puppies	*Substances which prevent rickets to a varying extent in puppies*
Bread *ad lib.*	Whole milk, 500 ml. per day
Oatmeal	Cod liver oil
Rice	Butter
Separated milk *ad lib.*	Suet
Yeast, 10–20 grams a day	Olive oil
Linseed oil	Arachis (peanut) oil
Babassu oil	Lard
Hydrogenated fat	Cottonseed oil
Calcium phosphate	Meat
Sodium chloride	Meat extract
Meat protein	Malt extract
Milk protein	

Among the fats used, cod liver oil was by far the most effective in preventing rickets in puppies. Butter was next in rickets-preventing activity.

At the time of Mellanby's studies, three "accessory" food substances were known. They were fat-soluble vitamin A, the antineuritic or antiberiberi vitamin, and the antiscorbutic vitamin. The latter was supplied in diet 4 by orange juice. Of the three substances it seemed evident that the fat-soluble vitamin A was distributed among natural foods in striking accordance with their property of preventing rickets. There were discrepancies between Mellanby's findings and those of McCollum and Davis, notably in the substances found to be rickets-preventing. Mellanby listed under this heading lard, olive oil, meat, meat extract, and malt extract; the last three of which were essentially fat-free and devoid of the fat-soluble vitamin, as shown by their inability to prevent xeropthalmia in young rats.

In 1921, on the basis of available experimental evidence, Mellanby said, "It will be seen, therefore, that, although there is considerable evidence that fat-soluble A and the anti-rachitic factor are identical, further work is necessary, and the above difficulties must be cleared up before it can be stated definitely that they are the same." (26) Mellanby's experiments disposed finally of the theory that environment was the sole cause of rickets. He proved that, other conditions being constant, the diet could be so adjusted as to be the deciding factor in the development or prevention of this disorder.

The preventive action of the foods Mellanby listed, which were either free from the fat-soluble factor or were poor sources of it, indicated that the active principle was not vitamin A. Results obtained with these foods strongly suggested that the abnormal growth processes of bones in rickets were not caused solely by the presence or absence of a sufficient amount of a specific antiricketic substance. Although not so interpreted, Mellanby's data actually afforded convincing evidence that more than one dietary factor might influence the outcome of restricting young animals to a rickets-inducing dietary regimen.

In the interpretation of his early studies, Mellanby did not consider the possibility that unphysiological relationships in the inorganic moiety of his experimental diets might be important. He believed that both calcium and phosphorus were adequately supplied in all cases. Korenchevsky (27) questioned this view, and concluded that the calcium in diet 4 was sufficient to satisfy the needs of growing puppies only if it was assumed that there was 70 per cent absorption and retention, an efficiency not ordinarily attained.

The Significance of an Inorganic Factor in Rickets

The studies of the Johns Hopkins investigators made it evident that not only the amounts of calcium and phosphorus in the diet, but the proportions subsisting between them, had profound significance in bone growth. Mellanby's later studies on rickets were influenced by acceptance of this fact, and his conception of the etiology of rickets was modified accordingly.

Mellanby's "Toxamin" Theory of Disturbed Bone Calcification

Mellanby's experiments convinced him that the greater the proportion of cereal in the diet, the greater the rickets-producing tendency. In 1920 he introduced the term "toxamin" to designate an unidentified, harmful ingredient in cereals which prevented utilization of calcium and phosphorus, especially calcium. This ingredient was called an anti-calcifying substance (28). Eventually he concluded that this substance was the organic phosphorus-containing compound known as phytic acid, which occurs in the seeds of cereals and some other plants in the form of its calcium-magnesium salt, known as phytin. Its anti-calcifying property was attributed to the low solubility of calcium phytate, which prevented absorption of the calcium and phosphorus in this compound.

In 1922 McCollum and his associates demonstrated the existence of a second fat-soluble factor. It was named vitamin D and was shown to be essential for the normal ossification of the skeleton. Mellanby accepted the evidence for the existence of the new antiricketic factor. He postulated that its function was to antagonize the rickets-producing effect of phytic acid, and concluded that this was due to its facilitating the conversion of calcium phytate into inorganic phosphate, thus rendering its components available for absorption by the alimentary tract.

Rickets Studies Made by the Johns Hopkins Group

The cooperative investigation made at Johns Hopkins was based on a new approach to the study of the etiology of rickets, and a different interpretation of the factors involved. It had its inception in the chance observation by McCollum and Simmonds that when young rats were restricted to certain experimental diets composed principally of cereals, they developed gross skeletal changes which were believed to be of ricketic nature. Dr. John Howland, Pediatrician-in-Chief of the Johns Hopkins Hospital, examined some of these animals and concurred with the opinion that the thoracic and other long bone abnormalities which they exhibited were like those of acute and severe rickets in infants.

The mutual interest of Howland and McCollum in attempting to discover the specific cause for the development of rickets in young rats resulted in the planning of a cooperative investigation. This was designed to reveal how growing bones responded to various kinds of faulty diets. It was expected that the dietary factor of etiologic significance in rickets would emerge from the results obtained from such experiments. The most important objective of the study was the comparison of the histological deviations from normal bone structure in the region of new growth which resulted from a variety of dietary defects involving the nutrients then recognized. If an unrecognized nutrient was involved it was believed that this should come to light as the study advanced. Histological studies of growing bones in experimental animals was a new criterion of physiologic status in nutrition studies.

At the outset of their investigations the Johns Hopkins group was familiar with the following recorded observations on the etiology of rickets:

1. The studies of Mellanby, which have been described.
2. The observations of Glisson, Findlay, and others, which supported the view that rickets was caused by unhygienic conditions of life (e.g., confinement indoors, with consequent lack of sunshine and exercise, and poor ventilation).
3. The studies of Kassowitz (24), who commented on the progressive rise of rickets during the winter months.
4. The observations of Hansemann (24a) who reported that children born in the spring and dying in the fall were free from rickets, whereas children born in the fall and dying in the spring all showed rickets.
5. The writings of Palm (38) who in 1890 recorded the results of a topographic study of the distribution of rickets, and concluded that light should be regarded as a therapeutic agent in this disease. The experiments of Raczynski (39) in 1912, which consisted of testing the efficiency of sunlight as a rickets-preventive agent by keeping one puppy in the dark, and a litter-mate in sunlight, both being suckled by their mother. At the end of six weeks the calcium and phosphorus content of the puppy reared in sunlight was much greater than that of the one kept in darkness. Presumably, the incentive to exercise was less for the puppy in darkness, and this factor complicated this observation. Huldschinsky (40) had reported in 1919 that ultraviolet rays exerted a curative effect on rickets.

6. The general belief among clinicians that cod liver oil was a valuable therapeutic agent in the treatment of rickets.
7. The observation that lack of exercise caused abnormal bone growth. This was well known to breeders of bulldogs. Fanciers and judges of this breed had long favored animals manifesting outward bending of the legs. Breeders' experience had led to the common knowledge that pups of this and other heavy breeds of dogs have straight legs if allowed to exercise freely, but develop the desired deformities if kept chained. It was not clear at that time whether deformities in properly fed dogs which were confined to prevent exercise correspond in histological details to the lesions in the ricketic bones.
8. The results of a study reported in 1915 by McCollum and Davis (42) in which groups of young rats were fed a diet of constant composition in organic ingredients, but varied in several ways and over a fairly wide range in respect to inorganic elements. The variations included strongly acid and strongly alkaline mineral mixtures, a wide range of total amount of the inorganic moiety, and other differences in inorganic composition. The results showed that when growth, appearance, fertility, and rearing of young were used as criteria, rats were able to tolerate a wide variation in total ash-constituents of the diet, but exhibited marked responses to several maladjustments in the inorganic portion of the food.

McCollum and his associates had had over five years' experience in studying the biological values of individual foods and simple combinations of two or more of them. The method of biological analysis and the results which it yielded have been described in connection with the evolution of food analysis and the discovery of vitamins (Chapters 11 and 14). The Johns Hopkins group undertook investigations of the manner in which bones of growing rats respond to several defects in diet, by modifying cereal diets in different ways. It is important to remember in this connection that a single cereal or any mixture of wheat, oats, maize, and the like was improved as food for the rat by a supplement of calcium, vitamin A, or a protein which supplied certain amino acids not sufficiently abundant in cereal proteins. When all three of these were added to a cereal grain a ration resulted which was fairly satisfactory for growth and reproduction in the rat.

Park and Shipley, pediatricians in the Hopkins group, examined the histological structure of the tibial epiphyses of groups of young rats kept for varying periods on experimental diets derived from cereal mixtures with different supplements. The descriptions of details of the histological elements, viz., resting and vesicular cartilage, amount and distribution of osteoid tissue, bone trabeculae, details of calcification, when present, peculiarities of the vascular elements and their distribution, and the extent of activity of osteoblasts and osteoclasts, when present, revealed that the growing bone is altered in various ways by several kinds of nutritional disturbances.

Effects of Vitamin A and Calcium Supplements on Cereal Diets

When unsupplemented, a diet of cereal grains invariably caused the development of the eye condition designated as xerophthalmia. However, when butterfat (3–5 per cent) was added to the diet, the eyes remained normal; butterfat as the only supplement resulted in bone changes in young rats having some of the characteristics of rickets. Animals failed to grow satisfactorily unless a calcium salt was added to the cereal diet. When both butterfat and calcium were supplied, the cereal diet produced essentially normal bone development, thus suggesting that rickets might be caused by calcium starvation.

Contrasting Effects of Cod Liver Oil and Butterfat

It was soon discovered that young rats were protected from xerophthalmia and from rickets when fed a cereal diet in which cod liver oil (1–2 per cent) replaced butterfat and a calcium supplement was not used (31). This made it clear that in the experiments with butterfat, calcium starvation was not the cause of the ricketic lesions, but that the results were referable to defect in utilization of calcium for bone ossification (31–34). The conclusion was inescapable that whereas butterfat and cod liver oil prevented the eye symptoms, these fats were markedly different in their effect on bone development.

The Significance of the Calcium to Phosphorus Ratio

By the use of appropriate diets it was demonstrated that not only the actual amounts of calcium and phosphorus but also the ratios between them exerted an effect on bone growth. A disproportionate increase or decrease of either of these bone-forming elements in the diet resulted in rickets. When the calcium was low and the phosphorus high, rickets was complicated by tetany. The detrimental effect of unfavorable ratios of calcium and phosphorus in the food was in great measure prevented by including cod liver oil in the diet. Something present in abundance in cod liver oil exerted a regulatory influence which enabled the animals to withstand the effects of an unfavorable ratio between the two elements principally concerned in ossification. Even 20 per cent of butterfat was less effective than 2 per cent of cod liver oil in this respect. Its inclusion in a rickets-inducing diet prevented the unphysiological effects of faulty calcium to phosphorus ratios (31–34).

The Sherman-Pappenheimer Experiments

At Columbia University, Sherman and Pappenheimer (35) also reported producing rickets in young rats. They used a diet very low in phosphorus and high in calcium. It consisted of white flour (wheat) 95 per cent, calcium lactate 3 per cent, sodium chloride 2 per cent, with or without a small amount of ferric citrate. The addition of 0.4 per cent of potassium phosphate and removal of a corresponding amount of calcium lactate protected young rats against rickets.

In the experience of all investigators the lesion typical of rickets in bones develops only when the animals are growing. In addition to disproportionate amounts of calcium and phosphorus, the diet used by Sherman and Pappenheimer was inadequate in the quality of its protein, and grossly lacking in vitamins and inorganic nutrients required for growth. It seems remarkable that they succeeded in demonstrating the importance of the ratio between calcium and phosphate in the development of rickets by using a diet so obviously incompatible with growth. They did not study the influence of fats on the etiology of rickets as did the Johns Hopkins group.

The Destruction of Vitamin A by Oxidation

In 1920 F. G. Hopkins (36) found that when oxygen was passed through heated butterfat, vitamin A was readily destroyed. Mellanby (26) (1921) employed this means of destroying vitamin A in heated butter and cod liver oil, and found that while the former did not exert any protective influence against rickets, oxidized cod liver oil was still effective. He was undecided "whether this difference . . . . can be explained by the fact that cod liver oil contains a much greater quantity of the antirachitic vitamin than butter, or that the destructive change takes a longer time, or whether some other explanation must be sought."

McCollum and his associates sought to find the explanation for these results by testing both oxidized butterfat and oxidized cod liver oil for the prevention of xerophthalmia and for inducing healing in experimental rickets. Oxidized cod liver oil was of no value in the xerophthalmia test, but was still potent for curing rickets. From these results they concluded that the antiricketic substance was distinct from vitamin A. Since this was the fourth unidentified nutrient to be discovered, it was called vitamin D (37).

The Development of the "Line-Test"

In 1922 the group at Johns Hopkins developed a biological method for the assay of vitamin D in foods. This was based on two principles: in the absence of this organic nutrient and of ultraviolet rays, young rats given a ricketogenic diet develop a severe grade of rickets; they begin to recover from the disease promptly when given a source of vitamin D.

The Johns Hopkins group made use of the observations of Schmorl (p. 269) in developing a test for the antiricketic substance. In infants or animals, rickets may be of varying degrees of severity, and in its milder forms the bones may show some degree of calcification. Hence, for the development of the desired biological test, it was essential to formulate a diet which would invariably produce in young rats florid rickets in which the zone of provisional calcification was free from areas of calcium deposition. The addition of vitamin D would then initiate the normal process of calcification, and the amount of deposition in a stated period of time could be made the basis for estimating the amount of vitamin D administered. Examination of the bones of rats restricted to various dietary formulas of the rickets-producing type, showed that diet 3143 caused acute and severe rickets within nineteen to twenty-one days, and met all the requirements of the test (43). Diet 3143 had the following composition:

Whole ground wheat	33.0
Yellow maize, ground	33.0
Gelatin	15.0
Wheat gluten	15.0
Calcium carbonate	3.0
Sodium chloride	1.0

One hundred grams of this ration contained 1.22 grams of calcium and 0.30 grams of phosphorus. The weight ratio between these elements was Ca. : P. : : 4.04 : 1.0. The rickets produced was of the high-calcium, low-phosphorus type, and was uncomplicated by tetany.

Young rats were restricted to diet 3143 for a period of nineteen to twenty-one days, after which time they were given a source of vitamin D for six to eight days. At the end of this period they were killed, and longitudinal sections of the tibae were made and stained with silver nitrate. Exposure of bone sections so treated to light caused blackening of the intercellular matrix in the cartilage where there was newly deposited calcium salts, resulting from the initiation of the healing process. The amount of calcification was estimated by examination of the section under low magnification, and the dosage of vitamin D was estimated on the basis of the extent and degree of healing induced. This was called the "line test."

In 1925 Steenbock and Black (44) designed a simpler diet formula, 2965. It consisted of yellow maize 76 per cent, wheat gluten 20 per cent, calcium carbonate 3 per cent, and sodium chloride 1 per cent. This diet produced excellent results in the vitamin D assay procedure.

Bourdillon and others (45), in 1931, worked out the details of a method in which the bones of ricketic rats are photographed by X-rays before administration of the substance to be tested. The substance was given daily for fourteen days, after which time the bones were X-rayed again to determine the extent of calcium deposition.

In 1932 Kay (46) devised a method of assay based on determining the amount of the enzyme phosphatase in the blood serum in response to administration of vitamin D. The enzyme which hydrolyzes certain phosphoric acid esters is abnormally high in the serum of ricketic infants.

Chemical Changes in the Blood in Rickets

In 1919 Iversen and Lenstrup (47) reported that the inorganic phosphate of the blood of ricketic infants was increased after the administration of cod liver oil. Kramer (48, 49) confirmed these observations and analyzed the bloods of normal and ricketic rats from among the experimental animals used in the Johns Hopkins tests. The results showed that the calcium and phosphate of the blood serum corresponded with the histological observations of bones. It was also noted that (a) the concentration of inorganic phosphorus and calcium in the serum cannot be made to exceed that regarded as normal; (b) when the concentration of either calcium or inorganic phosphorus in the serum is low, it may be increased by increasing the amount of the respective element in the diet; (c) when the inorganic phosphorus of the serum is low it may be increased by starvation, by addition of inorganic phosphate to the diet, or by administration of certain fats (e.g., cod liver oil or butter fat), and also by exposure of the animals to radiations of the requisite quality; (d) when the calcium content of the serum is low, it can be raised by dietary adjustments.

The Therapeutic Value of Sunlight in Rickets

In 1921 Shipley and his associates (50) tested the effects of the exposure of ricketic rats to sunlight. They kept two groups of young rats on diet 3143. One group, kept under laboratory conditions, developed severe rickets in three weeks. The other group was exposed to summer sunshine daily, at four hour periods, for 62 to 67 days; the bones of these animals showed no signs of rickets, although the rats were undersized. They had not benefitted as much from sunlight as they would have done from a suitable dosage of cod liver oil. Thus it was concluded that cod liver oil contains something which is necessary for optimal cellular functioning.

In 1922 Hume (51) observed that young rats on a diet which caused faulty bone growth were benefitted by exposure to ultraviolet rays. However, these rays did not prevent the development of xerophthalmia. Two years later Hume and Smith (52) discovered that young rats which were housed in previously irradiated glass jars containing sawdust (and, presumably, feces), grew as well on a diet deficient in vitamin D as did animals fed the same diet and exposed directly to ultraviolet light. Bone development was equally good in both groups. At first Hume and Smith suspected an important effect of irradiated air, but this was soon disproved.

In 1923 Goldblatt and Soames (53) found that the livers of irradiated rats on a rickets-producing diet had acquired antiricketic properties, whereas livers from non-irradiated animals similarly fed were without this property. This important discovery was confirmed by Steenbock and Black in 1924 (54). They extended their experiment to direct irradiation of rat liver, and also irradiation of the deficient diet. This treatment induced antiricketic activity in both liver and the ricketogenic diet. It soon emerged that irradiation resulted in the formation of vitamin D, but not vitamin A. Simultaneously with the Steenbock-Black report, the same observations and interpretations of their meaning were made by Hess and Weinstock (55).

Further inquiry showed that production of antiricketic properties in foods by irradiation was limited to the fat fraction, and also that pure fats were not "activated" by irradiation. The property of generating vitamin D by irradiation resided in the non-saponifiable matter after removal of fatty acids. It was soon traced to the sterol fraction in fats of both animal and vegetable origin.

Ergosterol, a Precursor of Vitamin D

In 1926 Rosenheim and Webster (56) found that when cholesterol was irradiated, as much as 99 per cent of it remained unchanged. By using digitonin to precipitate cholesterol from irradiated material, they were able to concentrate all the antiricketic property in a very small amount of material not precipitated by this reagent. Nelson and Steenbock (57) had found that digitonin did not precipitate vitamin D from cod liver oil, although it separated the cholesterol. In this manner Rosenheim and Webster secured from irradiated cholesterol a preparation which met the antiricketic requirements of rats when given in daily doses of 0.01 mg.

Rosenheim and Webster (56) also tested on rats the curative value of irradiated ergosterol. This is the characteristic sterol of fungi, so named because it was first isolated from oil of ergot. They found it "highly protective even in doses of one milligram." These interesting observations led to intensive studies which have been reviewed by Park (57a). They entailed the use of spectrographic technic, and revealed the fact that ordinary cholesterol, even after extensive purification, still contained an impurity which was associated with the antiricketic property. But when the highly purified cholesterol was treated with bromine, this impurity was removed. The cholesterol thus obtained showed no absorption bands in the ultraviolet region of the spectrum and was not activated by irradiation. Rosenheim and Webster were able to concentrate this impurity from ordinary cholesterol by repeated recrystallizations. With its concentration the antiricketic property was greatly increased.

In 1926 the same two investigators made further studies of ergosterol, which is trebly unsaturated and can be destroyed by bromine. Irradiation rendered it antiricketic, and it was reported that 0.0001 mg. per day of this material protected young rats against rickets.

Heilbron, Kamm, and Morton (58) described their spectrographic studies with cholesterol purified to different degrees, and confirmed that ordinary cholesterol contained an impurity, the absorption spectrum of which they described. Hess, Weinstock, and Helman (59), Schlutz and Morse (60), and Schlutz and Ziegler (61) also described the ultraviolet absorption phenomena of ordinary and irradiated cholesterol. Bioassays were made of various preparations from cholesterol, and from ergosterol, irradiated and unirradiated, by the investigators mentioned. The identification of ergosterol with provitamin D was announced independently in 1927 by Rosenheim and Webster (62) and by Windaus and Hess (63). Irradiation with ultraviolet rays transformed ergosterol into the vitamin. Pure vitamin D, or activated ergosterol, was first isolated in crystalline form in 1930 by Bourdillon and his associates (64), who used a molecular distillation procedure.

Vitamin D in Fish Liver Oils

In 1927 Bills (65), using the "line test" procedure, assayed many kinds of fish-liver oils. He made the remarkable discovery that there is great variation in the content of this vitamin in the liver oils of different species. Blue-fin tuna-liver oil assayed as containing 40,000 International Units of vitamin D per gram; yellow-fin tuna-liver oil 10,000 I.U. In comparison, cod liver oil contained an average of about 100 I.U. per gram. Sturgeon liver oil contained no vitamin D. All other liver oils fell between these extremes in their content of vitamin D.

The Discovery of How Ultraviolet Rays Prevent Rickets

Many surprising developments occurred during the period of investigation of the chemical nature of the antiricketic substances. "Vitamin D" was one of the first terms used, and it was thought for a time that only one chemical substance possessed this protective and curative property. As a result of attempts to isolate the vitamin from irradiated ergosterol, the fact emerged that in the process of ultraviolet irradiation a series of degradation products were successively formed. The term vitamin D_1 was applied to the first antiricketic substance isolated from irradiated ergosterol. It was found that this consisted of a molecular compound of the vitamin and a second irradiation product called lumisterol. The molecular compound later proved to be calciferol, known also as vitamin D_2.

From the numerous experiments on the production of antiricketic substances by irradiation of different sterols, it was found that in addition to ergosterol, 7-dehyrocholesterol yielded a characteristic product. This was called vitamin D_3. Still another potent antiricketic substance, known as vitamin D_4, was prepared by irradiation of 22-dihydroergosterol (22-dihydrocalciferol).

As experiments progressed the term provitamin D, with appropriate subscript, was adopted. The problem of identifying the provitamin D which occurs in skin stimulated many investigations. Windaus and Bock (66) proved that the provitamin D in hog skin is 7-dehydrocholesterol. Boer and his associates (67) also isolated the provitamin from cholesterol, the principal animal sterol. It is this sterol which is activated to form D_3 when skin, feathers, hair, or wool are acted upon by ultraviolet rays. Vitamin D_3 is produced when butter, brain, fish oils, and other foods of animal origin are irradiated. The provitamin D of fungi (such as ergot and yeasts) and of higher plants is ergosterol, not 7-dehydrositosterol, as might have been anticipated.

In 1930 Mussehl and Ackerson (68) reported that the amount of antiricketic vitamin from irradiated yeast (i.e., ergosterol) and of isolated ergosterol, when calculated on the basis of assays made with ricketic rats, was equivalent to that which would have been supplied by 50 per cent of cod liver oil in the diet but did not cause normal bones in chicks. Massengale and Nussmeier (69), working in Bills' laboratory, confirmed this observation by showing that it was necessary to give chicks activated ergosterol equivalent to 200 per cent cod liver oil in order to get the same degree of protection in bone growth as is given by 2 per cent of cod liver oil. A critical study by Bethke and his associates (70) provided further evidence that the antiricketic substance formed from ergosterol by irradiation is greatly inferior to the form existing in cod liver oil in protecting chicks against rickets. The numerous investigations relating to antiricketic vitamins and their physiological significance have been admirably reviewed by Bills (71) and by Park (57a).

REFERENCES

1. Herodotus: History Trans. by George Rawlinson, New York (1928), pp. 149–150.
2. Soranus of Ephesus: Diseases of Women; Die Gynakologie. J. H. Lehmann, Munich (1894), Trans. by H. Lueneburg.
3. Glisson, F.: De Rachitide sive Morbo Puerili que vulgo, The Rickets dicitur, Tractatus. London (1564) 1650.
4. Lemnius: de *Miraculis Occultis Naturae* (From W. B. Johnson: The History and Present Status of Animal Chemistry. 3 vols. London (1803), vol. *1,* p. 343).
5. Belchier, J.: Philos. Trans. 39, 287 (1736).
6. Louis Duhamel du Monceau: Philos. Trans. *41,* 390 (1740).

6a. Haller, A. von: Elements of Physiology *4,* xxix, 33–36 (1759–66).

7. Merat-Guillot: Ann. de chim. *34,* 64 (1795).
8. Berzelius, J.: Djurkemie (Animal Chemistry) ii, 120 (1801).
9. Fourcroy, A. and Vauquelin, L. N.: Ann. de chim. *47,* 244 (1801).
10. Gay-Lussac, J. L.: Philos. Mag. 23, 264 (1806).
11. Von Bibra, E.: Chemische Untersuchungen ueber die Knochen und Zahne, etc. (1844) p. 430.
12. Chossat, C.: Compt. rend. Acad. sci. *14,* 451–54 (1842); Mém. présentés à l'acad. des Sci. de l'Inst. de France *8* (2) 438–440 (1843).
13. Müller, H.: Zeitsch. f. wiss. Zoologie *9,* 147 (1858).

13a. Pommer, G.: Untersuchungen über Osteomalacie und Rachitis, Leipzig (1918).

14. Schmorl, G.: Ergebnisse d. inn. Med. und Krankh. *4*, 403 (1909).
15. Findlay, L.: Med. Res. Committee. Special Rep. Ser. No. 20, p. 9 (1918).
16. Dick, J. L.: Rickets. New York (1922).
17. Scheutte, D.: Arch. med. Erfahrung, *79*, 80 (1824).
18. Gobley, M.: Jour. de Pharm. et de Chim. *5*, 306 (1844).
19. Howland, J.: Nelson's Loose-Leaf Living Medicine *3*, 127 (1920).
20. Röll, M. F.: Die Knochenweiche (Rachitis). Lehrbuch der Pathol. und Therapie die Hausthiere. 2nd ed. (1860) p. 85.
21. Savory, W. S.: Lancet (London) ii, 381 and 412 (1863).
22. Bland-Sutton, J.: Journ. Comp. Med. and Surgery *10*, 1 (1889).
23. Wegner, G.: Arch. pathol. Anat. u. Physiol. *55*, 11–45 (1872).
24. Kassowitz, M.: Zeitschr. f. klin. Med. *7*, 36–74, 93–139 (1884).
24a. Hansemann, D.: Berlin Klin. Wochnschr. *43*, 629, 670 (1906).
25. Hess, A. F. and Weinstock, M.: Amer. J. Dis. Child. *32*, 483 (1926).
26. Mellanby, E.: Proc. Physiol. Soc. (1918), pp. 1–26; J. Physiol. *52*, xi (1918); Lancet (London) i, 407 (1919); Experimental Rickets. Spec. Rep. Ser. No. 61, Privy Council Med. Res. Comm. (1921).
27. Korenchevsky, V.: Special Rep. Ser. Med. Res. Council (London) No. 71 (1922).
28. Mellanby, E.: J. Physiol. *61*, xxiv (1926).
29. Mellanby, E.: A Story of Nutritional Research. Baltimore (1950) p. 256.
30. McCollum, E. V. and Davis, M.: J. Biol. Chem. *21*, 615 (1915).
31. McCollum, E. V., Simmonds, N., Parsons, H. T., Shipley, P. G. and Park, E. A.: J. Biol. Chem. *45*, 333 (1921).
32. Shipley, P. G., Park, E. A., McCollum, E. V., Simmonds, N. and Parsons, H. T.: J. Biol. Chem. *45*, 343–348 (1921), Johns Hopkins Hosp. Bull. XXXII, 1 (1921).
33. McCollum, E. V., Simmonds, N., Shipley, P. G. and Park, A. E.: Proc. Soc. Exp. Biol. and Med. *18*, 275–77 (1921).
34. McCollum, E. V., Simmonds, N., Shipley, P. G. and Park, E. A.: J. Biol. Chem. *47*, 507–27 (1921).
35. Sherman, H. C. and Pappenheimer, A. M.: Proc. Soc. Exp. Biol. and Med. *18*, 193 (1921); J. Exp. Med. *34*, 189 (1921).
36. Hopkins, F. G.: Biochem. J. *14*, 725 (1920).

37. McCollum, E. V., Simmonds, N., Becker, J. E., Shipley, P. G. and Park, E. A.: J. Biol. Chem. *54,* 249 (1922).

38. Palm, T. A.: The Geographical Distribution of Rickets. Practitioner, *65,* 270, 321 (1890).

39. Raczynski, J.: Compt. rend. de l'Assoc. Internat. de Pediat. (1913) p. 308.

40. Huldschinsky, K.: Deutsche med. Wochenschrift *45,* 712 (1919).

41. Findlay, L.: Lancet (London) i, 825 (1922).

42. McCollum, E. V. and Davis, M.: J. Biol. Chem. *21,* 615 (1915).

43. McCollum, E. V., Simmonds, N., Shipley, P. G. and Park, E. A.: J. Biol. Chem. *51,* 41 (1922).

44. Steenbock, H. and Black, A.: J. Biol. Chem. *64,* 263 (1925).

45. Bourdillon, R. B., Bruce, H. M., Fischmann, C. and Webster, T. A.: Spec. Rep. Ser. Med. Res. Council (London) No. 158 (1931).

46. Kay, H. D.: Physiol. Rev. *12,* 384 (1932).

47. Iversen, P. and Lenstrup, E.: Fordh. Nordiske Kongres for Paediatri. Hosp. Tidende *62,* 1079 (1919).

48. Kramer, B., Tisdall, F. and Howland, J.: Amer. J. Dis. Child. *22,* 431 (1921).

49. Kramer, B. and Howland, J.: Bull. Johns Hopkins Hosp. 33, 313 (1922).

50. Shipley, P. G., Park, E. A., McCollum, E. V. and Simmonds, N.: Proc. Soc. Exp. Biol. and Med. *19,* 43 (1921); Shipley, P. G.: J. Amer. Med. Assoc. *79,* 1563 (1921).

51. Hume, E. M.: Lancet (London) ii, 1318 (1922).

52. Hume, E. M. and Smith, H. H.: Biochem. J. *18,* 1334 (1924).

53. Goldblatt, H. and Soames, K. M.: Biochem. J. *17,* 446 (1923).

54. Steenbock, H. and Black, A.: J. Biol. Chem. *61,* 405 (1924).

55. Hess, A. F. and Weinstock, M.: J. Biol. Chem. *62,* 301 (1924).

56. Rosenheim, O. and Webster, T. A.: Biochem. J. *20,* 537 (1926).

57. Nelson, E. M. and Steenbock, H.: J. Biol. Chem. *62,* 575 (1925).

57a. Park, E. A.: Physiol. Rev. 3, 106–163 (1923).

58. Heilbron, I. M., Kamm, E. D. and Morton, R. A.: Chem. Ind. *45,* 932 (1926); Biochem. J. *21,* 78 (1927).

59. Hess, A. F., Weinstock, M. and Helman, F. D.: J. Biol. Chem. *63,* 305 (1925).

60. Schlutz, F. W. and Morse, M.: Am. J. Dis. Child. *30,* 199 (1925).

61. Schlutz, F. W. and Ziegler, M. R.: J. Biol. Chem. *69*, 415 (1926).
62. Rosenheim, O. and Webster, T. A.: Biochem. J. *21*, 389 (1927).
63. Windaus, A. and Hess, A. F.: Nachr. Ges. Wiss. Göttingen. Math. Physik. Klasse 2, 175 (1927).
64. Bourdillon, R. B., Jenkins, R. G. C. and Webster, T. R.: Nature *125*, 635 (1930).
65. Bills, C. E.: J. Biol. Chem. *72*, 751–58 (1927); Physiol. Rev. *15*, 1–97 (1935).
66. Windaus, A. and Bock, F.: Zeitschr. f. physiol. Chem. *245*, 168 (1937).
67. Boer, A. G., Reerink, E. H., van Wijk, A. and van Niekerk, J.: Proc. Acad. Sci. Amsterdam *39*, 622 (1936).
68. Mussehl, F. E. and Ackerson, C. W.: Poultry Sci. *9*, 334 (1930).
69. Massengale, O. N. and Nussmeier, M.: J. Biol. Chem. *87*, 423 (1930).
70. Bethke, R. M., Record, P. R., Kirk, C. H. and Kennard, D. C.: Poultry Sci. *15*, 326 (1936).
71. Bills, C. E.: Physiol. Rev. *15*, 1–97 (1935).

19

Riboflavin

On the basis of results obtained by feeding rats a diet of polished rice, supplemented in various ways, McCollum and Davis believed that there were only two unidentified nutrients necessary for the rat. After studying the behavior of pigeons restricted to several types of experimental feedings, McCollum and Kennedy (1), in 1916, expressed the view that the antineuritic substance which cured pigeons of polyneuritis, and the water-soluble substance essential for rats which must be added to polished rice in addition to supplements of amino acids (protein), mineral salts and the fat-soluble vitamin, were identical, and that for both species but two unknowns existed. This view was widely accepted for a time. However skepticism was soon expressed by several investigators, and its incorrectness was established by a number of approaches to the problem of what constitutes an adequate diet. Examples of such studies have been given in the chapters in which the etiology of scurvy, beriberi, rickets, and pellagra are discussed. The existence of still another unsuspected nutrient, designated at various times as vitamin B_2, P-P (pellagra-preventive factor), and vitamin G was the subject of experiment and discussion between 1919 and 1933. The term B_2 was adopted by English investigators, while vitamin G was commonly used by Americans. Here the English usage will be employed. The name finally adopted was riboflavin.

In retrospect it is easy to see why it was so difficult to determine the number and natures of the essential nutrients. In order to discover the existence of any new vitamin, it was first necessary to plan an experimental diet which lacked that substance but provided all other essentials. Under such conditions experimental animals would develop an unique type of malnutrition, the symptoms of which could be duplicated under no other circumstances.

Actually, in the approximately three thousand experimental diets which McCollum and his co-workers fed to rats before 1920, several strongly contrasting states of malnutrition were produced. These were not adequately described because the chemical viewpoint overshadowed the pathological viewpoint, and chemists were not prepared by training or experience to understand the meaning of symptoms as diagnostic of the specific types of physiological disturbance which they represented. Other nutrition investigators had similar experiences. Pathologists in the first two decades of the twentieth century were, with few exceptions, not equipped by training to comprehend even the simplest principles of biochemistry, and could not visualize physiological failure arising from malnutrition other than under-nutrition or starvation. Indeed, until about 1920 they were not interested in participating in studies of malnutrition. In such experiments, chemists took the initiative and produced either entirely new syndromes or certain ones which bore resemblances to pathological conditions seen in human subjects.

The earliest examples of adequate contributions by anatomists and pathologists to experimental nutrition studies were those provided by Holst and his co-workers (1912) on scurvy in guinea pigs, and by E. A. Park and P. G. Shipley (1918–1925) on rickets in the rat. Their leadership led other investigators to undertake nutrition studies from the point of view of the pathology produced. R. McCarrison, during the years 1919–1930, was a pioneer in this field. H. M. Evans, in his studies of vitamin E deficiency (Chapter 23) reached a high standard of achievement in the new field of investigation.

The researches which revealed the cause, cure, and prevention of pellagra, and those which brought to light the existence of a new and unsuspected nutrient, riboflavin, illustrate well the extreme complexity of the problem involved in determining what constituted a specific syndrome caused by lack of a single, indispensable, and unidentified nutrient. Inadequate diets derived from single or multiple sources caused malnutrition; but in most instances the diets then used which were thought to be inadequate in only one respect were deficient or unbalanced in other unrecognized nutrients. In such circumstances, multiple deficiency states were observed, but the symptoms of the experimental animals could not be satisfactorily interpreted. When mixtures of the then known nutrients in purified form were fed, complex physiological disturbances developed. Seldom did extracts or concentrates of natural foods, when added to such diets, provide all of the missing dietary factors or provide them in sufficient amounts. Because some factors were present in adequate amounts, others in inadequate amounts, and still others lacking entirely, complete alleviation of all symptoms was not effected. Furthermore, the lack or inadequate amount of an unrecognized nutrient might actually be the limiting factor in a ration that had been designed to produce a deficiency of a known dietary factor. This would not have occurred had symptoms been minutely observed and competently interpreted.

Evidence Refuting the Two-Vitamin Theory

The two-vitamin theory was first challenged by Mitchell (2) who, in 1919, published an excellent critical discussion of the evidence which indicated that "water-soluble B" was multiple in nature. He based his conclusions on data reported by several investigators (Eijkman, Grijns, Funk) concerning the relative richness of many foods in the dietary factor, which prevents or cures polyneuritis in pigeons fed only polished rice and water, and in their content of the "growth-promoting" substance studied by McCollum and his associates. Mitchell made the following points: 1. in comparison with cereal grains, green vegetables, e.g., cabbage and spinach, are rich in the growth-promoting factor concerned in the complete supplementing of polished rice, but these vegetables are poor in the antineuritic factor which cures pigeons of polyneuritis. Carrot is poor in the latter factor but rich in the former, as indicated by rat tests. 2. The paralytic symptoms observed in rats on B-deficient diets are not necessarily the result of deficiency of the antineuritic vitamin demonstrable by the pigeon test. 3. There is a lack of carefully-controlled experiments on the solubility and thermostability of the two substances, so it is impossible to draw definite conclusions as to whether they are identical.

In 1917 Emmett and McKim (3) provided evidence that extracts of rice polishings, tested with both pigeons and rats, contained two vitamins, one which cured polyneuritis (pigeon) and the other which stimulated growth (rat). Three years later, Emmett and associates (4) reported the first investigations which clearly showed that the two factors discussed by Mitchell are not equally susceptible to destruction by heat.

In 1923 Levene and Mulfield (5) found by numerous experiments that antineuritic and growth-promoting substances were present in greatly varying amounts in different samples of both bakers' and brewers' yeast, and that the two properties were not proportional in the samples tested; hence the necessity of regarding them as distinct dietary essentials.

In 1926 Hauge and Carrick (6) produced another kind of evidence in support of the view that two factors existed. They used a yeast which when tested with baby chicks was found to be poor in the antineuritic principle. They showed that maize was relatively rich in the antineuritic factor but poor in the growth-promoting one. Yeast and maize supplemented each other and provided a combination sufficiently rich in the growth-promoting and antineuritic factors to meet the nutritional requirements of the growing chick.

Evidence that There is a Heat-Stable and a Heat-Labile Factor in Yeast

In 1926 Smith and Hendrick (7) described still another kind of experiment which proved clearly that two substances were involved in supplementing suitable experimental diets with a water-extract of some natural product. They were the first to use a pure derivative of the antineuritic vitamin in nutrition experiments with rats.

In 1919 Osborne and Wakeman made a preparation which represented about 6 per cent of the weight of the yeast used and which contained about 90 per cent of its antineuritic potency. In 1916 Seidell adsorbed on fuller's earth the antineuritic substance from yeast extract, and obtained a highly potent preparation. He prepared a silver compound of the vitamin, which showed high potency. With Bertrand (1923) Seidel prepared a picrate of the antineuritic vitamin.

It was this picrate which Smith and Hendrick (7) used in their study of the effect of dietary deficiencies on susceptibility to tuberculosis in rats. They used a diet composed of rolled oats 40 per cent, supplemented with purified casein 10 per cent, together with a source of vitamin A, inorganic salts, and dextrin. This diet, which had been devised by McCollum and associates, induced only subnormal growth in young rats. All the unidentified water-soluble nutrients were derived from the oat moiety of the diet. A marked improvement in growth resulted from a supplement of yeast which had been autoclaved at fifteen pounds pressure to destroy its antineuritic property. Addition of isolated yeast protein was not as effective as was the heated whole yeast. Again, the observed results could be accounted for only on the assumption that the heated yeast provided some essential nutrient distinct from the antineuritic factor.

When fed to rats along with a mixture of purified food substances, autoclaved yeast was inadequate as the sole source of water-soluble vitamins. But this combination when further supplemented with the antineuritic picrate of Seidell, a single chemical entity, was nutritionally complete for these animals.

In 1927 Salmon (8) prepared from extracts of natural foods an adsorbate on fuller's earth which cured polyneuritic pigeons but did not induce growth response in rats on his diet. The next year Hogan and associates (9) reported that irradiated substances retain their antineuritic, but not their growth-promoting properties. Either irradiated or autoclaved vitamin B preparations used alone were found to be inadequate to complete a diet of the well-known nutrients, but when used together they were adequate. Salmon, Guerrant, and Hays (10) devised a method to separate the antineuritic substance from B_2 by adsorbing each on fuller's earth at different hydrogen ion concentration. The work of these two groups of investigators extended that of Smith and Hendrick and gave further proof that there must be at least two water-soluble vitamins. The antineuritic factor was subsequently designated B_1 or thiamine, and the growth-promoting vitamin was called B_2, or riboflavin.

An Assay Procedure for Vitamin B_2

In 1928 Chick and Roscoe (11) devised an experimental diet with which they could estimate the amount of B_2 contained in a preparation. After three or four weeks on this diet plus a B_1 supplement, young rats developed a state of extreme malnutrition. It was characterized by loss of hair from the eyelids, sealing shut of the eyelids by a sticky exudate, dermatitis of ears and digits, and blood-stained urine. Administration of a source of B_2 to these animals cured all the symptoms. The assay was based on finding the relative amounts of different foods which would induce recovery sufficient to produce a gain of 10–12 grams weight per week. The supplement of antineuritic substance which they used was a preparation described in 1927 by Kinnersley and Peters. It was made by adsorbing the vitamin from yeast extract on activated charcoal, and was known as Peters' eluate. Bourquin and Sherman (12) also designed a diet suitable for assaying foods for their content of the new heat-stable, vitamin B_2.

Confusion Over the Relation Between B_2 Deficiency and Pellagra

In 1926 Goldberger and Lillie (13) described a state of malnutrition in rats characterized by arrest of growth, ophthalmia, some loss of hair on ears, neck, chest, forearms, et al. The fur became matted and fell out, leaving a denuded, pale pink, glistening skin. In some animals there was fissuring and ulceration at the mouth angles, together with a lesion at the tip of the tongue which often progressed and ended in a yellow slough. Inflammation of the anterior floor of the mouth and diarrhea were observed in some animals. This condition Goldberger and Lillie diagnosed as rat pellagra. It could be cured by administration of lean meat, yeast, or aqueous yeast extract. Recovery was also effected by feeding rats a fuller's earth adsorbate from yeast extract after the antineuritic factor had been destroyed by heating.

It was on the basis of such observations that Goldberger and Lillie designated the curative agent as the pellagra-preventive (P-P factor) factor. Later investigations showed that this condition in the rat is not analogous to pellagra in man or blacktongue in dogs, but is due to deficiency of a greenish-yellow pigment now known as riboflavin.

It would be unprofitable to report further the experimental studies describing the production of dermatitis, denudation, and the other symptoms noted in rats by Goldberger and others. Suffice it to say, as is related in Chapter 20, that there was confusion of the symptoms caused by vitamin A deficiency in dogs (Chittenden and Underhill) with those caused by nicotinic acid deficiency in that species (Goldberger and associates), and the dermatitis and other symptoms produced in rats by deficiency of vitamin B_2 or G. During the period 1926–1933 these symptoms were all believed to represent pellagra in the dog and rat. The earliest clue to the nature of the substance which would prevent a nutritive failure of rats on such diets as those of Chick and Roscoe, and of Bourquin and Sherman, came from the discovery by Booher that the rat deficiency disease was prevented or cured by a yellow pigment.

In 1933 Booher (14) described studies with several concentrated preparations from whey powder, which showed high supplemental values for the Bourquin-Sherman diet. She pointed out that the values of her preparations paralleled the intensity of their yellow pigmentation. Her experiments afforded the key to the solution of the problem of the nature of the heat-stable factor which was attracting increasing attention of investigators.

Discovery of a Yellow Pigment in Milk

In 1879 Blyth (15) called attention to the yellow pigment in milk, which he named lactochrome. It did not attract the attention of chemists and was not again investigated until 1925 when Bleyer and Kallman (16) separated the milk pigment and described its more obvious properties. No one suspected at that time that this pigment was of outstanding physiological significance.

Isolation, Chemical Identification, and Synthesis of Riboflavin

In 1932 Warburg and Christian (17) described a new oxidation enzyme which they isolated from bottom yeast aqueous extracts. In water solutions the pigment was yellow with a green fluorescence. The pigment portion they found to be easily detached from protein by treatment of its aqueous solution with alcohol (18). The yellow pigment thus liberated and the protein fraction had no enzyme activity. Irradiation changed the pigment to a chloroform-soluble pigment which they called lumiflavin.

An interest in the yellow pigments from various sources as of possible significance in animal nutrition, led investigators to prepare the water-soluble, yellow substances from heart muscle, liver, kidney, yeast, etc. Eventually these were found to be identical.

In 1933 Kuhn and associates (19) isolated the yellow pigment in pure form and noted its spectrographic similarity to the Warburg-Christian pigment. Its distribution and properties were similar to those of vitamin B_2. Preparing the pigment from spinach, kidney and liver, they concluded that it was vitamin B_2. Simultaneously Booher (14) arrived at the same conclusion.

In 1935 Karrer (20) and Kuhn (21), almost simultaneously, accomplished the synthesis of riboflavin, and György (22) showed by animal experiments that the synthetic substance had the same biologic activity as did the naturally occurring pigment. Chemically, riboflavin was identified as a compound containing iso-alloxazine and d-ribose.

Pathology of Experimental and Spontaneously Occurring Riboflavin Deficiency

In 1936 Dann (23) reported that riboflavin is ineffective in the treatment of human pellagra. In rats riboflavin deficiency results in retarded growth, dermatitis, and cataract. Phillips and Engel (24) found that chicks fed a diet low in riboflavin develop a rapidly acute paralysis involving the main peripheral nerve trunks which is characterized as neuromalacia. A gradual depletion of riboflavin results in 'curled toe' paralysis in chicks. These manifestations can be prevented by the addition of crystalline riboflavin to the diet.

Street, Cowgill, and Zimmerman (25) studied the pathology of both acute and chronic riboflavin deficiency in dogs. They observed that dogs on a diet very low in this vitamin collapse and die suddenly after six to eight weeks. Prolonged riboflavin deficiency results in neurologic abnormalities accompanied by myelin degeneration of the peripheral nerves and the posterior columns of the spinal cord. They also observed opacity of the cornea in dogs as well as in rats.

In 1939 Bessey and Wolbach (26) studied the vascular changes in the eyes of albino rats in both vitamin A and riboflavin deficiency. On riboflavin-deficient diets young rats ceased to grow after about three weeks. At the end of the fourth week a marked radial ingrowth of capillaries into the cornea from the limbus vessels could be seen with the slit lamp. Later, corneal turbidity due to leucocytic infiltration developed. The corneal turbidity usually cleared within 48 hours after riboflavin was restored to the diet, and the ingrowth of blood vessels disappeared after two weeks. The vascularization in riboflavin deficiency is similar to that in vitamin A deficiency. The role of riboflavin as a respiratory carrier and the altered physiology following keratinizing metaplasia in vitamin A deficiency suggested that vascularization in each case might be response to asphyxia of the corneal stroma.

In man the symptoms of riboflavin deficiency include inflammation of the lips, fissures at the mouth angles, glossitis, dermatitis, and vascularizing keratitis (27). Sydenstricker and associates (28) found vascularization of the cornea to occur in riboflavin deficiency in human subjects.

The observations made by Bessey and Wolbach suggested to Kruse and his associates (28) that riboflavin deficiency in the human could be diagnosed by observing corneal vascularization. They described in detail the vascularization of the cornea and other pathological changes in human eyes when deficiency of riboflavin exists. The changes were closely similar to those described in rats in this deficiency state. Further study by this group indicated that riboflavin therapy reversed the changes in the eyes, with a resulting return to normal.

They also distinguished carefully the oral lesions seen in ariboflavinosis and those seen in nicotinic acid deficiency (pellagra). In the former state glossitis can often be recognized before other signs are manifest. The tongue is clean, the papillae flat or mushroom-shaped, rather than atrophied, and the color is purplish-red as compared with the scarlet-red of nicotinic acid deficiency. Kruse and associates stated that the eye changes in riboflavin deficiency were those which had often been ascribed to "toxic states," "focal infection," and "eye-strain." Later investigators were to discover that corneal vascularization is not a conclusive sign of ariboflavinosis. It may arise from other causes such as excessive exposure to light, wind, and dust. But it is evident from the clinical study of pellagrins, that riboflavin deficiency is often a complication of that disease.

The Role of Riboflavin in Human Pellagra

In the account of investigations of the cause of pellagra (Chapter 20) it is recorded that there was confusion because of variations in symptoms presented by different patients. In the Rankin Farm experiment of Goldberger and associates, erythema was not noted; in other studies mouth and eye symptoms were not always the same. The subject was illuminated in 1938 by the observation of Schmidt and Sydenstricker (29). They noted that certain pellagrous patients who had apparently been cured with nicotinic acid, and were kept on maintenance dosage of that vitamin, suffered relapse. They developed fissures at the mouth angles, sore tongues, cracking and peeling of the lips, and conjunctivitis. This condition was what Goldberger and Wheeler had called *pellagra sine pellagra.* Sebrell and Butler (30), after studying uncomplicated riboflavin deficiency in dogs, were able to point out that the relapsed patients of Schmidt and Sydenstricker were in riboflavin deficiency. A supplement of this vitamin in addition to nicotinic acid brought about prompt cures. This clinical study revealed that what had been diagnosed as pellagra was frequently a state of multiple vitamin starvation.

It is of interest to recall that vitamin A potency was found by animal experiments to be associated with yellowness in plant tissues and was traced to carotene, the precursor of this vitamin in the body. With the discovery of the nutritional significance of riboflavin, a second plant and animal pigment was added to the list of essential nutrients.

REFERENCES

1. McCollum, E. V. and Kennedy, C.: J. Biol. Chem. *24,* 491 (1916).
2. Mitchell, H. H.: J. Biol. Chem. *40,* 399 (1919).
3. Emmett, A. D. and McKim, L. H.: J. Biol. Chem. 32, 409 (1917).
4. Emmett, A. D. and Luros, G. O.: J. Biol. Chem. *43, 265* (1920), Emmett, A. D. and Stockholm, M.: *Ibid. 43,* 287 (1920).
5. Levene, P. A. and Mulfield, M.: J. Biol. Chem. *57,* 341 (1923).
6. Hauge, S. M. and Carrick, C. W.: J. Biol. Chem. *69,* 403 (1926).
7. Smith, D. T. and Hendrick, E. G.: Pub. Health Repts. (U.S.) *41,* 201 (1926).
8. Salmon, W. D.: J. Biol. Chem. *73,* 483 (1927).
9. Hogan, A. G. and Hunter, J. E.: J. Biol. Chem. *78,* 443 (1928), Hogan, A. G. and Richardson, L. R.: J. Nut. *8,* 385 (1934); Nature *136,* 186 (1935).
10. Salmon, W. D., Guerrant, N. B. and Hays, I. M.: J. Biol. Chem. *80,* 91 (1928).
11. Chick, H. and Roscoe, M. H.: Biochem. J. *22,* 790 (1928).
12. Bourquin, A. and Sherman, H. C.: J. Amer. Chem. Soc. *53,* 3501 (1931).
13. Goldberger, J. and Lillie, R. D.: Pub. Health Repts. *41,* 1025 (1926).
14. Booher, L. E.: J. Biol. Chem. *102,* 39 (1933).
15. Blyth, A. W.: J. Chem. Soc. London 35, 530 (1879).
16. Bleyer, B. and Kallman, O.: Biochem. Zeitschr. *155,* 54 (1925).
17. Warburg, O. and Christian, W.: Biochem. Zeitschr. *254,* 438 (1932).
18. Warburg, O. and Christian, W.: Naturwissensch. *20,* 980 (1932).
19. Kuhn, R., György, P. and Wagner-Jaureg, T.: Ber. d. deutsch. chem. Ges. *66,* 317, 576, 1034, 1577 (1933).

20. Karrer, P. and Quibell, T. H.: Helvet. chim. acta. *19,* 1034 (1936); Karrer, P. and Becker, B., Benz, F., Frei, P., Saloman, H., and Schöpp, K.: *Ibid. 18,* 1435 (1935).

21. Kuhn, R., *et al.:* Ber. d. deutsch. chem. Ges. *68,* 1765 (1935).

22. György, P.: Zeitschr. f. Vitaminforsch. *4,* 223 (1935).

23. Dann, W. J.: J. Nut. *11,* 451 (1936).

24. Phillips, P. H. and Engel, R. W.: J. Nut. *16,* 451 (1938).

25. Street, H. R., Cowgill, G. R. and Zimmerman, H. M.: J. Nut. 22, 7 (1941).

26. Bessey, O. and Wolbach, S. B.: Exper. Med. *69,* 1 (1939); Am. J. Ophth. 22, 322 (1939).

27. Sebrell, W. H. and Butler, R. E.: Pub. Health Repts. 53, 2282 (1938).

28. Kruse, H. D., Sydenstricker, V. P., Sebrell, W. H. and Cleckley, H. M.: Pub. Health Repts. 55, 157 (1940).
Sydenstricker, V. P., Sebrell, W. H., Cleckley, H. M. and Kruse, H. D.: J. Amer. Med. Assoc. *114,* 243 (1940).

29. Schmidt, H. L. and Sydenstricker, V. P.: J. Amer. Med. Assoc. *110,* 2065 (1938).

30. Sebrell, W. H. and Butler, R. E.: U.S. Pub. Health Repts. Washington 53, 2282 (1938).

20

Investigations on Pellagra

PELLAGRA IN NORTHERN SPAIN was described by Casal in 1735, but for many years it was more commonly seen in Italy. It also occurred in France, the Balkans, Roumania, and Egypt. In September, 1786, Goethe wrote in his "Italian Journeys," "I know little if anything, pleasing to say about the people. As soon as the sun rose over the Brenner Pass in the Alps I noticed a decided change in their appearance, and especially displeasing to me was the brownish tan color of the women. Their features indicated misery, and the children were just as pitiful to behold; the men are little better, though their general features were regular and good. I believe the cause of this sickly condition is found in the continued use of Turkish and heath corn."

Dermatitis, diarrhea, dementia, death — these were the terms most used by the numerous writers who discussed pellagra for more than a century and a half (1). Italian investigators favored the view that the disease was caused by eating moldy maize. Many believed it to be caused by infection. From the time of Casal (1762) onward, the idea was often expressed that sensitization to sunlight was a factor in its etiology.

The earliest symptom to appear was inflammation and soreness of the mouth, followed by symmetrical erythema on those parts of the body, face, neck, hands, arms, and feet which were exposed to light. There was progressive injury to the nervous system as evidenced by damage to the digestive tract, spinal cord, and central nervous system. The details of the lesions are discussed in every textbook on pathology, and, therefore, will not be considered here.

For over a century, proponents of the opposing theories as to the cause of the disorder were unable to prove the correctness of their views. When between 1905–1910 there was an explosive outbreak of pellagra in the United States, principally confined to the Southern States, medical opinion was about equally divided on the "corn-poison" and the "infection" theory.

Pioneer Dietary Studies with Human Pellagrins

In 1914 Voegtlin (2) reported the earliest study which proved that human pellagra is unquestionably caused by a dietary deficiency. In a hospital in Spartanburg, S. C., he tested the effects on pellagrins of two contrasting diets. One diet was composed of wheat bread 300, butter 30, cabbage 100, corn meal (maize) 50, ham 25, hominy 75, corn syrup 75, pork 50, potato 150, prunes 30, turnip tops 100, sugar 40, and milk 40 grams respectively. The other consisted of wheat bread 300, butter 45, corn meal 50, egg 100, meat 100, orange juice 100, potato 150, prunes 30, sugar 40, and milk 1000 grams respectively. The outstanding difference between these two diets was the egg, meat, and milk content of the second diet. Voegtlin's diets were planned before McCollum and associates had discussed foods on the basis of quality as revealed by their biological method of analysis; however, the first of the fat-soluble vitamins had been discovered. The relation of polished rice to beriberi was then well known.

Voegtlin restricted patients to the first diet, and observed that "almost without exception the general clinical condition remained either stationary or gradually became more aggravated, simultaneously with an increase in the pellagrous manifestations." After a time the patients were changed to the second diet. On this they showed gradual improvement and in many cases experienced complete disappearance of all the symptoms of the disease. Next he placed patients on the first diet for a time, and when they were in stationary clinical condition, or were growing worse, he administered (a) a fat-free alcoholic extract of yeast or rice polishings, or (b) a fat-free alcoholic extract of liver or thymus gland. These were made by first extracting the yeast or polishings and the glands with alcohol, and then removing the ether-soluble substances from the extracted materials. Voegtlin stated that preparation (a) contained the anti-beriberi vitamin, but no fat-soluble A vitamin; whereas preparation (b) provided in abundance both of these substances. Preparation (a) was of no benefit to the patients, whereas (b) was curative. From these observations he concluded that pellagra was caused by lack in the diet of "a substance distinctly different from, and probably more complex than the one causing human beriberi." He did not imply that he believed pellagra to be due to lack of a specific unidentified vitamin, but rather that the syndrome of pellagra results from a combination of deficiencies in some of the well-recognized food factors.

Voegtlin's experiments cannot be satisfactorily interpreted because yeast was proven by Goldberger to be an effective remedy for pellagra, and the curative substance, later identified as nicotinic acid, is contained in yeast and is easily extracted by alcohol. His yeast and rice polishings extracts made with alcohol must have been fairly rich in the anti-pellagra substance, and should have cured his patients. But his results clearly proved that small doses of liver or spleen extracts were curative, and he thus showed that pellagra was a dietary deficiency disease.

Goldberger's Institutional Studies

Unconvinced by Voegtlin's experiments, Goldberger and his associates (3) in 1915 undertook a study to determine whether pellagra might be caused by faulty diet. They investigated the incidence of the disease and the character of the diets given to patients and medical and nursing staffs in State Asylums in South Carolina, Georgia, and Mississippi; they were soon convinced that pellagra was a disease caused by malnutrition. Although the diets of patients and staff were supposed to be alike, it was soon noted that inadequate supplies of milk, meat, and eggs, and some other better class foods found their way to the table of the staff, while the patients subsisted mainly on cereals. There was no pellagra among the former group even when there was a high incidence among the latter, who ate very little food of animal origin.

In an orphanage in Mississippi where pellagra was rampant among the children of 6–12 years of age, Goldberger and his associates were able to eradicate the disease by providing liberal amounts of milk, meat, and eggs in the diet. They concluded that pellagra is a deficiency disease rather than one due to poisoning or to infection.

The Rankin Farm Experiment

In 1915 Goldberger and his associates (4) carried out an experiment on human subjects to test the dietary theory of the cause of pellagra. On promise of pardon by the Governor, eleven adult men prisoners in the Rankin Farm Prison in Mississippi volunteered to take during a six-month period such a diet as Dr. Goldberger might prescribe. This diet consisted of bolted wheat flour, degerminated cornmeal (maize), polished rice, starch, sugar, molasses, pork fat, sweet potatoes, collards, turnip greens, and coffee. The men showed preferences among these foods and to some extent traded one article for another. Hence they did not all eat the same diet. At the end of the six-month period seven of the men had developed certain of the symptoms of pellagra, and responded to treatment with dietary supplements of 30 grams of yeast, 200 grams of meat, or 2 pints of milk daily.

Erythema in Pellagrins Caused by Light Exposure

The results of Goldberger's study were not convincing to many medical men. One reason for their skepticism was mildness or the absence of erythema, a prominent symptom in most pellagrins. This deviation from the usual symptoms of pellagra was explained by experimental studies of Smith and Ruffin (5) in 1937.

The relation of pellagra to sunlight was frequently commented upon in clinical literature. Some believed the disease to be caused by exposure to sunlight. It had been observed that erythema and dermatitis appeared earlier in relation to other symptoms in persons who were exposed to direct sunlight. Smith and Ruffin showed that the dermatitis of the exposed parts of the body was closely dependent upon the action of sunlight on the patient's skin. Spies (6) studied the problem and stated that pellagrous lesions appear in the absence of sunlight or ultraviolet radiation. He emphasized that pellagra should be considered a systematic disease and not a cutaneous condition and that under certain circumstances, still matters for conjecture, sunlight might act as an irritant and precipitate the cutaneous lesions of the disease. The role of light in pellagrous lesions of the skin was, however, conclusively shown by Smith and Ruffin.

In the Rankin Farm experiment Goldberger had not exposed his subjects to sunlight. Accordingly the erythema ordinarily observed in human subjects was either absent or so mild that his diagnosis was not convincing to dermatologists and clinicians.

Notwithstanding the convincing evidence brought out by the institutional studies mentioned, the Thompson-McFadden Commission, in 1917 (7) reported, after an extensive epidemiological study in pellagrous areas, that the disease was transmitted by the stable fly.

The Commission noted that pellagra tended to occur in spring when the fly appeared, and to disappear in summer and autumn, only to recur on the anniversary of the first or later attack when the fly again appeared. Goldberger suggested altering the statement "occurs in spring" to "occurs at the end of winter," to emphasize his belief that the recurrence was an aftermath of inferior winter diet among the afflicted people.

Goldberger and his associates (8) in 1916 reported the results of heroic efforts to transmit pellagra to themselves by inoculation with blood, nasopharyngeal secretions, feces, urine, and desquamating epithelium from pellagrins. The attempt was unsuccessful, thereby disposing of the infection theory.

Blacktongue in Dogs

In 1916 T. N. Spencer (9) a veterinarian of Concord, North Carolina, first called attention to the similarity between the symptoms of a spontaneous canine disease known to veterinarians as "blacktongue" and those of human pellagra.

He diagnosed "blacktongue" as pellagra in dogs, and from his success in curing the animals by giving them milk, eggs, and meat he concluded that it was caused by a diet low in nitrogen. In his article on the subject he stated that some years previously Dr. Walter Barstow Houston, a dentist in Monroe, North Carolina, had cured himself of pellagra by taking a "high nitrogenous" diet, and that others who followed his advice were also cured of the disease.

Experimental Production of a Pellagra-Like Syndrome in Dogs

In 1917 Chittenden and Underhill (10) described the symptoms produced in dogs by restricting them to an experimental diet consisting of cracker meal (from bolted white flour), cooked dried peas, and cottonseed oil. They expressed the belief that they had produced by this inadequate diet the analogue of human pellagra. They did not mention blacktongue as a disease in dogs. Goldberger accepted this as evidence that blacktongue was dog pellagra. Thenceforth he employed the dog as an experimental animal for the purpose of analyzing the diets which produced blacktongue and discovering the nature of the nutrient which was involved in the etiology of the disease. Apparently he did not know of the publication of Spencer (9).

A puzzling feature of human pellagra, and of the supposed analogue, blacktongue, was the variability of certain features of the disorder. Dermatitis was sometimes prominent and at other times absent or nearly so. Chittenden and Underhill (10) described in their dogs severe inflammation of the mouth, with sloughing of the mucosa, diarrhea, and skin changes which they believed corresponded to the erythema and bronzing often seen in pellagra.

In 1925 Underhill and Mendel (11) sought to discover what was wrong with the cracker-peas-cottonseed-oil diet which produced in dogs the severe symptoms described earlier (10). They found that the condition could be alleviated by a supplement of fresh butter fat, egg yolk, boiled unpeeled carrots, a lard extract of carrots (yellow from its content of carotene), or by a supplement of crystallized carotene. On the other hand, yeast, which Goldberger had found to be effective as a remedy for human pellagra, Underhill and Mendel found to be of no benefit to their dogs.

For the production of canine blacktongue, Goldberger (12) and associates used a diet composed of the following foods:

Whole white maize	400 gm.
Cow peas (black-eyed)	50
Casein	60
Sucrose	32
Cottonseed oil	30
Cod liver oil	15
NaCl	10
$CaCO_3$	3

They described an initial reddening of the mucosa of the upper lip, which was sometimes intermittent or relapsing. The tongue was but slightly affected until the attack was well advanced. A reddening of the mucosa of the cheeks and the floor of the mouth was followed by the development of irregular patches of superficial necrosis within the reddened areas. Necrotic patches appeared also on the base of the tongue, the soft palate, fauces, and gums. A fetid odor and increase of buccal secretion developed, with drooling of a secretion resembling egg-white. The mouth became very inflamed and the dog put its muzzle into water as if it desired to drink, but made no effort to do so. Hiccups sometimes occurred. The temperature was but slightly elevated until shortly before death. Constipation followed diarrhea and even bloody discharges. An itching or burning sensation caused scratching or biting, producing self-inflicted dermatitis. There was an eruption on the scrotum. The attack was usually acute and rapid, causing the dog to die within ten days.

In 1925, Goldberger and Tanner (13) classified common foods on the basis of their effectiveness in preventing or curing human pellagra. They studied the effects of supplementing a pellagra-producing diet with dried beans, dried peas, casein, dried milk, and dried yeast. Among these only the yeast stood out as highly effective, but some protective action was seen with milk, and less with casein. Beans and peas were of little value. From these results they concluded that food protein was not the sole factor involved in preventing or curing pellagra. Their results supported the view that there exists a specific dietary factor of unknown nature which yeast contains in abundance, lean meat and milk in lesser amounts, and peas and beans in very small amounts. Butter and cod liver oil were found to be of no value in relieving the symptoms of pellagrins.

On the basis of his tests, Goldberger expressed the belief that all vegetables, such as potatoes, turnips, string beans, tomatoes, cabbage, collards, turnip greens, and spinach, contain the pellagra-preventive vitamin, but only in small amounts.

Following the work of Smith and Hendrick (14) indicating the growth-promoting action of heated yeast, Goldberger and Wheeler (15) found that dogs with blacktongue could be cured by either autoclaved yeast (in which the anti-beriberi vitamin was destroyed) or by water extracts of heated yeast. They absorbed the active principle from autoclaved yeast extract upon fuller's earth. This preventive and curative factor they designated P-P factor (pellagra-preventing).

Discovery of a Heat-Stable Vitamin Distinct from the Anti-Beriberi Factor

In 1926 Smith and Hendrick (14) published their investigations on the influence of dietary deficiencies on experimental tuberculosis. Their results left no doubt that what had been considered a single substance, vitamin B (the antineuritic substance) consisted of a heat-labile and a heat-stable substance, both of which were essential in the diet of the rat. They used a diet of rolled oats 40, casein 10, an inorganic salt mixture, and butter fat (to provide vitamin A). In the early experiments (1917) of McCollum, Simmonds, and Pitz (16) it was noted that although wheat, maize, and oats were deficient as sources of protein, calcium, and vitamin A, rats responded less favorably to oats supplemented with the three factors named than to the other seeds. Smith and Hendrick found this to be true, and showed that a supplement of 5 per cent of dried yeast induced a good response with the diet. They then tested separately the value of yeast protein and of yeast which had been heated in an autoclave to destroy the anti-beriberi vitamin. The heated yeast was as effective as the unheated. A supplement of yeast protein, on the other hand, did not improve the condition of the rats. It was thus apparent that there was a heat-stable factor which was effective in small amounts, and that 40 per cent of rolled oats did not contain enough of it to meet the requirements of young rats.

Heat-Stable Factor: The Anti-Pellagra Vitamin

Between 1915 and 1920 Goldberger and his associates suspected that deficiency of protein, or of protein of high quality, might be the cause of pellagra. However, this view was abandoned when in 1920 Voegtlin, Neill, and Hunger (17) discovered that pellagra could be cured by daily doses of 15 to 30 grams of dried yeast, or by 15 grams of a water extract of yeast, which supplied not more than seven grams of protein, whereas a daily supplement of 75 grams of casein was much less effective (12).

Two years later Goldberger and his associates (18) reported that yeast or a water extract of yeast was equally effective in curing pellagra. The yeast extract supplied so little nitrogen that it seemed clear the curative principle must be something other than protein, and that it must be effective in very small doses. The idea was implied that this substance was contained in foods of animal origin, and was much less abundant or absent entirely in various cereal foods. Attention was then directed to the B vitamins, and Goldberger, Wheeler, Lillie, and Rogers (19) identified the pellagra-preventive principle with the heat-stable factor in yeast which Smith and Hendrick had described.

Goldberger and associates, having produced blacktongue in dogs, found that the same dietary supplements which cured pellagra in humans cured the disease in dogs. Food extracts which failed to relieve the condition in one species failed in the other. Such results supported the view that blacktongue in dogs was the analogue of human pellagra. By restricting dogs to a diet similar to the type which causes pellagra in man and blacktongue in dogs, Goldberger and Lillie (20) produced in rats a disorder which they diagnosed as rat pellagra. Later observations proved that the ophthalmia and bilaterally symmetrical denudation produced in their animals was not pellagra — it was ariboflavinosis, which is discussed in the chapter on riboflavin.

A further complication of the pellagra story developed in 1927 when Boas (21) described a syndrome in rats caused by feeding them raw Chinese egg-white as a source of protein. The chief symptoms produced in the animals were eczematous dermatitis, alopecia, blepharitis, spasticity, and in some cases edema of the feet and hemorrhages into the skin. On diets similarly constituted but containing proteins other than egg-white, the animals appeared normal. Though some of the abnormalities which developed on the raw egg-white diet suggested the pellagra syndrome, later studies showed they resulted from biotin deficiency. This is discussed in Chapter 27.

Nicotinic Acid: The Pellagra-Preventive Vitamin

In 1914 Voegtlin (2) prepared an extract of liver for the treatment of pellagra and reported with it fairly good results. Goldberger found that liver was one of the most effective remedies for the treatment of the disease and that it also quickly cured blacktongue in dogs. Other clinicians confirmed and extended these observations. Spies succeeded in curing pellagrins by injecting intravenously or intramuscularly small amounts of liver concentrate, which was then beginning to be used for the treatment of pernicious anemia.

The series of investigations which finally led to discovery of the nature of the pellagra-preventive substance began with a report by Huber (22) in 1867, who described the preparation of crystalline salts of an organic acid which was formed when nicotine, the alkaloid from tobacco, was oxidized with potassium dichromate and sulfuric acid. Huber described the physical properties of the new substance and determined the percentage of the elements in its composition. It was called nicotinic acid.

Funk, who in 1911 coined the word *vitamine* to designate the substance which protects against beriberi, suggested, but without experimental evidence, that pellagra might also be due to deficiency of some unidentified substance. In 1912 he isolated nicotinic acid from rice polishings. He found that this substance did not cure beriberi, but that when it was administered in addition to the concentrates containing the antineuritic vitamin, the cures effected were more rapid than when only the latter was given.

In 1912 Suzuki, Shimamura, and Ohdake (23) precipitated from a water extract of rice bran, in the form of its picrate, a substance which was found to cure the polyneuritis (experimental beriberi) in fowls or pigeons due to a diet of polished rice. The crude precipitate formed by adding phosphotungstic acid to an aqueous solution of an alcoholic extract of rice bran was found to contain nicotinic acid, which they isolated and identified. However, this did not cure pigeons sick with the rice disease.

In 1935 von Euler, Albers, and Schlenck (24) studied the preparation of *cozymase,* the coenzyme which is necessary for the alcoholic fermentation of glucose by *apozymase,* shown later to be diphosphopyridine nucleotide, DPN. On hydrolysis, cozymase yielded nicotinic acid. This was the first evidence that nicotinic acid (in the form of its amide) formed a part of the structure of an enzyme, and placed it among the organic compounds of great importance in biological chemistry.

In 1936 Warburg and Christian (25) demonstrated that nicotinic acid was a product of hydrolysis of their *fermentation-co-ferment,* later shown to be triphosphopyridine nucleotide, TPN (coenzyme II, or codehydrogenase II), or Warburg's coferment. Here was a second biological substance in which nicotinic acid in the form of its amide occurred as a structural unit.

In 1937 Subbarrow (26) reported the isolation of nicotinic acid from liver. In the same year Elvehjem, Madden, Strong, and Woolley (27) reported that dogs suffering from blacktongue made a phenomenal response to a single dose of 30 mgm. of nicotinic acid. Further dosage of nicotinic acid produced uninterrupted recovery. Nicotinic acid amide also proved effective in the cure of blacktongue. They pointed out that since nicotinic acid amide is a component of enzyme systems, it is not surprising that it is an indispensable constituent of the diet. The new discovery was soon confirmed by Street and Cowgill, Margolis, Smith, Dann, and others.

In 1938 Smith and Smith (28) reported that 0.1 mgm. of nicotinic acid per kilogram of body weight given daily for ten days failed to cure blacktongue in dogs, 0.2 mgm. per kilogram was slowly curative, and 0.5 mg. per kilogram gave rapid and dramatic cures. This proved to be the maximum dose of advantage in causing recovery from blacktongue in dogs. These investigators also reported the first successful treatment of human subjects with pellagra by means of nicotinic acid. One and a half mg. per kilogram of weight was effective in bringing about cures.

Pellagra in Swine

In 1937 Birch, Chick, and Martin (29) restricted weanling swine to a pellagra-producing diet similar to the blacktongue and pellagra-producing diets employed by Goldberger, and observed that this species also develops the pellagra-like syndrome. They advanced knowledge in this field, however, by stating that their results indicated that "the nutritive failure of the above maize diets for rearing young pigs is not due to defects in the amount or quality of the protein, but to a deficiency in some constituent of the heat-stable vitamin B_2 complex other than lactoflavin (riboflavin), and that a corresponding amount of a mixture of wheat and barley contains just sufficient of it to support satisfactory growth." The following year, Chick and her co-workers (30) experimented with two pigs which, having been on a maize diet, were losing weight and had diarrhea and dermatitis. The animals chosen for this test were expected to die within two or three days, but the administration of nicotinic acid caused a prompt and dramatic response. Within twenty-four hours after the first intramuscular injection of 100 mg. of nicotinic acid, appetite returned and there followed a steady recovery. After six weeks' treatment, the pigs appeared quite healthy.

Confusion of Symptoms of Vitamin A and of Nicotinic Acid Deficiency Syndromes

Lack of constancy in the clinical manifestations of human and animal pellagra remained unexplained for a few years. E. Mellanby (31) described, in 1931, anatomical changes in the spinal cords of rabbits corresponding to those seen in human pellagra. These changes he brought about by producing vitamin A deficiency in the animals. He theorized that vitamin A deficiency might play a part in the etiology of pellagra and in its treatment, at least in respect to its nervous manifestations. Mellanby stated further that pellagra might be due to a double deficiency of essential nutrients, the skin changes being a result of B_2 (riboflavin) deficiency and the nerve changes to vitamin A deficiency. Basing his experiments on the discovery by

Steenbock that yellow pigmentation was associated in plant materials with vitamin A potency, Mellanby showed by animal experiments that when white maize was used the nerve changes appeared, but not when yellow maize was substituted for the white variety. He pointed out that in the United States, where pellagra was commonly seen, white maize was usually eaten, whereas in Java where Jansen and Donath found no pellagra, the people ate yellow maize.

A notable contribution to the solution of the etiology of pellagra was made in 1932 by D. T. Smith (32). In a review of the literature on oral spirochetes and related organisms in fuso-spirochetal disease, he pointed out that this group of organisms grow profusely in the mouths of dogs with blacktongue produced by either the Goldberger or the Chittenden-Underhill types of faulty diets. He stated there is a symbiotic relation among these organisms in Vincent's angina, pyorrhea, and fuso-spirochetal disease of the lungs.

Miller and Rhoads (33), who observed the characteristic oral flora seen in dogs with blacktongue, found that they could not infect normal dogs with these organisms by inoculating them under the labial mucous membrane. Smith and associates (34) then restricted one group of dogs to the Chittenden-Underhill-Mendel type of diet, and another group to the Goldberger diet for producing experimental blacktongue. They observed that the clinical and bacteriological findings in the oral cavity were identical. There were enormous numbers of the fuso-spirochetal organisms in the oral lesions of dogs on both diets. Smith also attached significance to the occurrence of similar organisms in the lesions of human pellagra, and noted that on treatment with a curative substance these organisms disappear. It was now apparent that the oral lesions seen in pellagra and in blacktongue were not specific, but occurred in vitamin A deficiency (the Yale studies), as well as in pellagra (blacktongue) produced by Goldberger's type of diet. The fuso-spirochetal flora invade the oral cavity when the individual is debilitated by any of several deficiency states. Such studies as those of Mellanby and of Smith and his associates set the stage for more critical examination of the pathological states induced by faulty diets than had hitherto been comprehended.

Goldberger's Error in Diagnosing Rat Pellagra

Nicotinic acid amide is associated with certain dehydrogenase systems. In these it forms an integral part of the co-enzyme molecule, combined with adenine, ribose, and phosphoric acid. Human pellagrins, as has been stated, were in many cases found to respond dramatically with cures when nicotinic acid or its amide was administered. The same astonishing results occurred in dogs and pigs when brought into experimental pellagra by restricting them to certain diets. It was, therefore, a most unlooked-for discovery when several investigators, using rats as subjects, found that this species is immune to nicotinic acid deficiency, and that a form of malnutrition in rats manifesting symptoms which suggested "rat pellagra" did not respond to this treatment as do humans, dogs, and swine.

Thus in 1926 Goldberger and Lillie (20) described a pellagra-like condition in albino rats which included as the most characteristic symptoms ophthalmia and bi-laterally symmetrical loss of hair together with dermatitis on various areas. Since these lesions appeared in rats restricted to diets not then distinguishable from other so-called "pellagra-producing" diets, it appeared logical to consider the lesions as manifestations of pellagra in the rat. In this animal the symptoms were prevented or cured by either lean meat or yeast, and by administration of certain absorbates on fuller's earth from yeast extracts which had been freed from the beriberi-curative principle by heating. Thus, Goldberger thought that the symptoms and curative agencies were such as to warrant belief that the types of malnutrition under consideration as seen in the dog and rat had a common origin.

During the years 1937–1938, as a result of experimental studies by the investigators mentioned, the nutritive significance of nicotinic acid or its amide was fully established for man, dog, and swine. A finding of extraordinary interest, therefore, was that of Macrae and Edgar (35) that neither nicotinic acid, nicotinamide, nor co-dehydrogenase II could replace yeast, nor other substances which supplied water-soluble vitamins, in the diet of the rat. With their experimental diet an amyl alcoholic extract of liver concentrate was shown to contain a substance necessary for the rat which was different from the anti-blacktongue factor contained in such preparations, and which had been identified by Elvehjem *et al.* as nicotinamide. In the same year Cook, Clarke, and Light (36) presented experimental evidence that the rat does not need nicotinic acid or its derivatives in its diet as do man, dog, and swine. Thus, a species difference in nutritive requirements was brought to light, comparable to that seen in man, monkey, and guinea pig, which are susceptible to scurvy, whereas other common species of animals are able to synthesize the antiscorbutic substance (Vitamin C, ascorbic acid).

New difficulties immediately presented themselves to investigators of the pellagra problem when it was found that while maize is greatly inferior to wheat in its content of nicotinic acid, it is richer in this substance than oats or rye, high consumption of which had never been associated with the occurrence of pellagra, as had been high maize consumption. In fact, commercial degerminated corn meal is not inferior in its nicotinic acid content to refined wheat flour of 70 per cent extraction, nor to polished rice, nor the millets, yet people who employ these cereal products as staple foods have not, in general, had pellagra as a health problem. These facts could not be harmonized with the high incidence of the disease among maize-eating peoples in several parts of the world. Surprisingly enough, light was cast upon this puzzling problem by experiments on rats, which are, under most dietary situations, immune to pellagra.

Experimental Pellagra in the Rat

In 1938 Chick, Macrae, Martin, and Martin (37) observed that rats thrive on certain supplemented maize diets which cause pellagra in man, pig, or dog. However, when rats were restricted to a diet of purified foodstuffs, which was low in protein and nicotinic acid, the replacement of 40 per cent of the food by maize grits (endosperm) caused retardation of growth and evidences of malnutrition, which could be relieved in either of two ways. The addition of a supplement of nicotinic acid or of the amino acid tryptophan enabled the rats to improve in health and to resume growth. Krehl and associates (38) showed that no other amino acid could replace tryptophan in this situation. Further investigations proved that tryptophan, a digestion product of most proteins, can replace nicotinic acid in the diets of pellagra-susceptible species, and the conclusion was warranted that this was due to the ability of the body to convert tryptophan to nicotinic acid. That this is true was established by studies on the effects of administration of tryptophan on the excretion of nicotinic acid. The output of nicotinic acid is increased after dosage with tryptophan in the horse, calf, and man. The guinea pig is the only species thus far studied which seems to be unable to bring about conversion of this amino acid to nicotinic acid. Chick (39) has discussed this conversion.

Broadened Concepts of the Pathology of Nutritional Deficiencies

The recording of clinical, biochemical, and animal feeding studies served not only to clarify the cause and prevention of human pellagra, but to bring to light a new era in one segment of preventive medicine. As a result, nutrition investigators and pathologists, and pioneers in preventive medicine, saw a wealth of new opportunities for specific investigators in the pathology of nutritional disorders. This renewed hope of achievement, together with the increase of resources and opportunity, encouraged investigators to study malnutrition with a twofold purpose: to make basic discoveries in physiology and metabolism, and in the ways by which the body responds in specific deficiencies of each of the known, indispensable chemical substances which the diet must provide if optimal health is to be realized and maintained.

REFERENCES

1. Roberts, S. H.: Pellagra, St. Louis, 1912.
2. Voegtlin, C.: J. Amer. Med. Assoc. *63,* 1094 (1914).
3. Goldberger, J., Waring, C. H. and Willets, D. G.: Public Health Rpts. (U.S.) *30,* 3117 (1915).
4. Goldberger, J. Waring, C. H. and Willets, D. G.: Pub. Health Repts. (U.S.) *30,* 3117 (1915); U.S. Public Health Serv. Hyg. Lab. Bull. No. 120 (1920); Pub. Health Repts. *31,* 3336 (1915).
5. Smith, D. T. and Ruffin, J. M.: Arch. Intern. Med. *59,* 631 (1937).
6. Spies, T. D.: Arch. Intern. Med. *52,* 845 (1933).
7. Thompson Pellagra Commission of the New York Post-Graduate Medical School and Hospital (1917).
8. Goldberger, J.: Public Health Repts. *31,* 3159 (1916).
9. Spencer, T. N.: Amer. Journ. Vet. Med. *11,* 325 (1916).
10. Chittenden, R. H. and Underhill, F. P.: Amer. Journ. Physiol. *44,* 13 (1917).

11. Underhill, F. P. and Mendel, L. B.: (U.S.) Pub. Health Repts. *40,* 1087 (1925); Amer. Journ. Physiol. *83,* 589 (1928).

12. Goldberger, J., Wheeler, G. A., Lillie, R. D. and Rogers, L. M.: Public Health Repts. *43,* 1385 (1928).

13. Goldberger, J. and Tanner, W. F.: Pub. Health Repts. *40,* 54 (1925).

14. Smith, M. I. and Hendrick, E. G.: Pub. Health Repts. (U.S.) *41,* 201 (1926).

15. Goldberger, J. and Wheeler, G. A.: Pub. Health Repts. (U.S.) *43,* 172 (1928).

16. McCollum, E. V., Simmonds, N. and Pitz, W.: J. Biol. Chem. *30,* 13 (1917).

17. Voegtlin, C., Neill, M. H. and Hunger, A.: U.S. Public Health Serv. Hyg. Lab. Bull. No. 116, p. 7 (1920).

18. Goldberger, J.: Journ. Amer. Med. Assoc. *78,* 1676 (1922).

19. Goldberger, J., *et al.:* Journ. Amer. Med. Assoc. *41,* 297 (1926).

20. Goldberger, J. and Lillie, R. D.: Pub. Health Reports *41,* 1025 (1926).

21. Boas, M.: Biochem. J. *21,* 712–24 (1927).

22. Huber, C.: Ann. d. Chem. u. Pharm. *141,* 271 (1867).

23. Suzuki, U., Shimamura, T. and Ohdake, S.: Biochem. Zeitschr. *43,* 89–153 (1912).

24. von Euler, H., Albers, H. and Schlenck, F.: Zeitschr. f. physiol. Chem. *237,* 1–11 (1935).

25. Warburg, O. and Christian, W.: Biochem. Zeitschr. *285,* 156 (1936).

26. Subbarrow, Y.: Personal communication to Smith and Ruffin. J. Amer. Med. Assoc. *109,* 2054 (1937).

27. Elvehjem, C. A., Madden, R. J., Strong, F. M. and Woolley, D. W.: J. Biol. Chem. *123,* 137–149 (1938); J. Amer. Chem. Soc. *59,* 1767–1768 (1937).

28. Smith, D. T. and Smith, S. G.: Science *88,* 436–437 (1938) (In Soc. Proc.); Margolis, L. H., Margolis, G. and Smith, S. G.: J. Nut. *17,* 63–73 (1939).

29. Birch, T. W., Chick, H. and Martin, C. J.: Biochem. J. *31,* 2065–2079 (1937).

30. Chick, H., Macrae, T. F., Martin, A. J. P. and Martin, C. J.: Biochem. J. 33, 10–12 (1939).

31. Mellanby, E.: Brain *54,* 1, 247 (1931).
32. Smith, D. T.: Oral Spirochetes and Related Organisms in Fuso-spirochetal Disease. Baltimore, 1932.
33. Miller, D. K. and Rhoads, C. P.: J. Clin. Investigation *14,* 153–172 (1935).
34. Smith, D. T., Persons, E. L. and Harvey, H. I.: J. Nut. *14,* 373 (1937).
35. Macrae, T. F. and Edgar, C. E.: Biochem. J. *31,* 2225–31 (1937).
36. Cook, C. A., Clarke, M. F. and Light, A. E.: Proc. Soc. Exper. Biol. and Med. *37,* 514 (1937).
37. Chick, H., Macrae, T. F., Martin, A. J. P. and Martin, C. J.: Biochem. J. *32,* 844 (1938).
38. Krehl, W. A., Tepley, L. J. and Elvehjem, C. A.: Science *101,* 283, 489 (1945).
39. Chick, H.: The Cause of Pellagra. Nut. Absts. and Rev. *20,* 523–35 (1951).

General Reference

Harris, Seale: Clinical Pellagra, St. Louis, Mo. (1941) pp. 494.

21

Progress in Understanding the Significance of the Inorganic Elements in Nutrition

BEFORE 1842 CHEMISTS and physiologists had only nebulous ideas concerning the origin and significance of the inorganic elements in plant and animal physiology. There had been a controversy over the source of the ash constituents of plants. The earliest investigator of note to conduct experiments on this problem was Theodore de Saussure (1767–1845) (1), an illustrious plant physiologist, and a native of Switzerland. In 1804 he published an account of his investigations on the source and nature of the nutrients of plants. It contained twenty-seven tables of analyses of the content of water-soluble salts, insoluble phosphates, carbonates, silica, alumina, and metallic oxides of wood, bark, leaves, branches and flowers of seven kinds of trees. Other tables gave the same ingredients in the ashes of straw, grains of cereals, and other plants. De Saussure devoted 55 pages to a discussion of the ash constituents of plants, and proved that the nature of the soil had a pronounced influence on their mineral constituents. His studies showed that plants growing on soil containing an abundance of silica or lime were richer in these elements than plants grown on soils deficient in them. His technique broke new ground and influenced greatly the work of plant investigators who followed him.

Thirty-eight years later, Liebig (2) wrote an appraisal of de Saussure's work, expressing his belief that it afforded proof that mineral nutrients were of prime importance to the growth of plants, and that plants secured these essential elements from the soil.

The Origin of Mineral Constituents of Plants

Thales of Miletus (640–546 B.C.) believed that all vegetable and animal substances were derived from water. The earliest investigator to furnish what appeared to be irrefutable proof of the truth of this concept was Van Helmont (1577–1644). In 1652 (3) there was published an account of his classic experiment in which a willow branch weighing 5 pounds was grown to a tree weighing 169.5 lbs. within five years. The branch was planted in an earthen vessel containing 200 lbs. of dried soil and watered with distilled water and rain water. The vessel was covered to exclude dust. The soil, upon redrying, weighed only 2 ounces less than at the beginning. Thus, the conclusion seemed justified that the 164 pounds of wood had been formed from water.

Since Van Helmont did not determine the ash content of the willow tree, his observation had only an indirect bearing on the source of mineral elements which the food was presumed to contain. Later investigations by plant physiologists were to show that the carbon of the wood came from carbon dioxide in the atmosphere, and that rain water contains considerable dust, ammonia, and nitrate, which are washed out of the air. His was a remarkably well-planned experiment for its time. Although he was the discoverer of carbon dioxide, he knew of no technic by which he could have shown that this constituent of the atmosphere, together with water, was the food from which the wood of the willow tree was formed.

Investigations by Shrader and Braconnot on the Origin of Plant Ash Constituents

The state of knowledge of inorganic elements in plant nutrition at the beginning of the nineteenth century is well illustrated by a decision of the Berlin Academy of Sciences in 1800. J. C. Shrader (4), an apothecary, submitted an essay in competition for a prize offered for the best experimental study on the source of earthy matter in plants. He determined the ash in samples of several seeds, and then germinated seeds from the same sources in a soil of flowers of sulfur which he kept moist with distilled water. According to Shrader, the ash content of plants grown in this manner was greater than that which the original seeds had contained. Hence, he said, earthy matter must have been generated during the process of vegetation. He was awarded the prize by the Academy.

In 1806 Braconnot (1781–1855), professor of natural history in the Lyceum at Nancy and Director of the botanical gardens there, investigated the source of inorganic constituents of plants. He used as soil such inert materials as litharge, sublimed sulfur, quartz pebbles, etc. After examining the ash content of seeds and of plants grown under conditions that precluded a supply of earthy matter, he concluded that "the organic force, assisted by sunlight, produces in plants substances regarded as elementary, such as earths, alkalies, metals, sulfur, phosphorus, carbon, and perhaps also nitrogen." (5)

Notwithstanding that some scientists debated the question of the source of mineral constituents of plants, at the time when Shrader submitted his prize essay, there were those who recognized the value of inorganic fertilizers in promoting plant growth. In *Philosophical Magazine* (6), in 1801, the section on agriculture advised that bulbs which were kept indoors should be watered with a solution containing nitre, muriate of soda, and potassium carbonate, plus sugar. In the same journal (7) four years later, there appeared a series of letters in which the writers exchanged their experiences and observations which showed that the ash of peat, or of wood, etc., when used as manures, improved the growth of plants. Benjamin Smith Barton, professor of materia medica, natural history, and botany in the University of Pennsylvania, contributed to this correspondence. He stated that he had observed that dilute solutions of sulfate of iron and copper stimulated the growth of plants, whereas stronger solutions injured them.

Wiegmann and Polstorff's Investigations

In spite of the convincing results of de Saussure's experimental studies, uncertainty on this subject continued among scientists. In 1838 a prize was offered in Germany for the most satisfactory answer to the question whether the ash constituents occur in plants when external sources of them are eliminated, and also whether these mineral constituents are so necessary that the vegetable organisms have need of them for their complete development. The prize was awarded to A. F. Wiegmann, professor in Braunschweig, and L. Polstorff, apothecary in the same city (8).

Wiegmann and Polstorff prepared a synthetic soil composed of clean quartz sand and salts to provide phosphate, calcium, sulfate, manganese, potassium, sodium, chlorine, magnesium, and iron. Plants grown in pots containing the synthetic soil were ashed, and the ash was compared with that of plants grown in pots of soil consisting only of clean sand. The plants used were tobacco, vetch, clover, barley, oats, and buckwheat. The results showed that plants grown in sand and watered with distilled water were undersized and very low in ash content as compared with those which had access through their roots to the salts in the experimental soil. These findings, which confirmed those of de Saussure, were so convincing that chemists and plant physiologists never afterward doubted the importance of inorganic substances in plant nutrition.

The Discovery of the Chemical Nature of Bones

In 1669 Hennig Brand (7) first prepared phosphorus by destructive distillation of the solids remaining after distilling off the water from urine. The reducing substances that formed as the organic constituents were decomposed by heat, abstracted the oxygen from phosphates, and freed elemental phosphorus. This element boiled at 280° C. and the vapors condensed to a waxy solid under the liquid in the receiver. Its property of glowing in the dark aroused great curiosity. In 1748 J. G. Gahn of Sweden discovered that phosphorus was a constituent of bone, and that bones consist largely of calcium phosphate (9). Previously it was thought that bone was a peculiar kind of earth. For some time phosphorus was believed to be present only in animal matter, but it was later found in many kinds of vegetables.

Although the ancients knew of quick-lime, which results from heating calcium carbonate to drive off carbon dioxide, the element calcium was not discovered until 1808, simultaneously by H. Davy and Berzelius. But the "calcareous" nature of bone, egg shell, and shells of molluscs was recognized by the early chemists. Charles Hatchett (10) studied the chemical properties of bones and shells.

In Chapter 7 the experiments by Fordyce and Vauquelin were described. These were the earliest attempts to study the nutritional significance of inorganic elements in animal nutrition. Fordyce proved conclusively that canary hens, to remain in health, must have more "calcareous" substance than is afforded by a diet of seeds. He also thought that his experiments with fish proved that they are independent of a source of bone-forming minerals. Fordyce kept fish in water in contact with the atmosphere. He stated that although they were not given any food over a period of months, they grew rapidly and remained healthy. These experiments, he said, were conducted either by himself personally or by someone whom he designated, and all experiments were under his supervision. It would appear, however, that an attendant secretly fed the fish.

Vauquelin's conclusion that a hen was able to transmute mineral elements to others was accepted by Berzelius (12) as being beyond doubt. Bostock (13) in 1844 discussed the subject in his comprehensive textbook on physiology. He raised the question whether, since various fossal molluscs were abundant in limestone, the creatures had actually created the latter rather than assimilated it from their environment.

Chossat's (14) experiments with birds, reported in (1842–43) advanced knowledge greatly by showing that animals fed wheat alone steadily lost mineral matter, and that this could be prevented by giving a supplement of calcium carbonate. He interpreted his results to signify that phosphorus in the wheat could not be utilized because of deficiency of calcium.

Chossat's further studies (15) had great influence on the experimental work of early agricultural investigators concerned with the animal husbandry type of inquiry on how to feed animals successfully. The numerous feeding studies of this type made during the last half of the 19th century have been discussed by Forbes and Keith (16).

Physical Chemistry Changed the Concepts of Biologists

An event of outstanding significance in the history of physiology was the distinguishing between "crystalloids" and "colloids" by Thomas Graham (1805–1869) (17). His experimental studies of the passage of crystalloids through semipermeable membranes (e.g., bladder, parchment paper) resulted in the establishment of a special branch of chemistry which was of profound importance in the study of certain physiological problems. Graham was professor at Glasgow and in University College, London.

In 1867 M. Traube (18) introduced the so-called precipitation membrane (e.g., copper ferrocyanide), and Pfeffer suggested its deposition in the porous wall of an earthenware vessel to give it great strength. This device made possible quantitative studies on osmotic pressure of diffusible substances, such as solutions of salts and sugars. With this instrument Pfeffer (19) discovered that the osmotic pressure of sugar solutions was proportional to their concentrations, and that it increased with temperature. The deviation from the expected behavior of salts which dissociate in solutions whose osmotic pressures were unexpectedly high, and the correlation of this property with electrical conductivity, were landmarks in the application of chemistry to biological phenomena.

De Vries (20) demonstrated that solutions of analogously constructed substances having the same molecular concentration have the same osmotic pressure. Van't Hoff (21) called attention to the analogy which exists between the laws of osmotic pressure of dissolved substances and of gases, viz., that the osmotic pressure is proportional to the concentration (or inversely proportional to the volume of the solution), and corresponds completely to the Boyle-Mariotte law of the relation between the volume and pressure of gases.

In 1855 Nägeli (22) discovered that certain plant cells, when immersed in sufficiently concentrated solutions of various substances, changed their appearance because of retraction of the cell contents. This phenomenon de Vries called plasmolysis. Nägeli explained the phemonena as caused by semi-permeability of the cell boundary membrane to the plasmolyzing substance and to abstraction of water from the cytoplasm. These phenomena were soon studied intensively by several investigators using many kinds of biological structures. The discoveries are mentioned here because they were important in bringing to light the significance of certain inorganic salts and ions in physiological systems.

Early Views Concerning the Place of Common Salt in Nutrition

There was printed in 1805 a letter from Dr. Samuel L. Mitchell of Columbia University to Dr. Benjamin Mosely (23) of England, concerning the physiological significance of muriate of soda. This presented the most logical discussion of the subject which had appeared up to that time. Mitchell said that of late the idea had been advanced that sea-salt, when taken with the food, was injurious to animal life. "It is pretended that when used as an article of diet it acts merely as a stimulus, without affording nourishment. A fossil and unnatural substance received into the stomach must, it is asserted, be conducive of debility and disease. The employment of it has been ascribed to caprice, and scurvy and scrophula are alleged to be the consequences of an habitual indulgence in it." But Mitchell asserted his belief that common salt is an essential ingredient of the food. He cited the ravenous appetite of grazing animals for salt, dramatically exhibited by the congregation of enormous numbers of deer, elk, and bison at the salt licking places in inland North America. In Kentucky, at Blue-Lick, a marshy area about two miles in diameter where the water contained an uncommon content of salt, these animals, in their eagerness, crowded each other in deep mud, resulting in the miring and death of great numbers. Mitchell concluded that this appetite expressed a constitutional want.

Dr. Mitchell said that the numerous wolves, panthers, and wildcats which prowled about the Blue-Lick did so not because of an appetite for salt, as was the case with the herbivores, but to prey upon the grazing animals. He said that the lack of appetite for muriate of soda by carnivores was to be "explained by their securing a substitute for it in the phosphate of lime, which constitutes the principal part of the bones of the animals they feed upon."

Dr. Mitchell's chemical theory to explain the need for muriate of soda in the human diet is of historical interest. "Salting prevents putrefaction of meat, fish, etc. In putrefaction meat undergoes decomposition with the formation of *septic acid.* With muriate of soda this reacts to form *septate of soda* and free muriatic acid, which latter unites with meat to form *muriate of meat.* . . . Septic acid is a nauseating and unhealthy thing, but when neutralized with soda, is no longer so, and wholesome muriatic acid takes its place."

Boussingault's Experiments with Oxen

Boussingault (24) fed two groups of oxen of three animals each on the same food for one month, one group having salt, the other ingesting no salt other than what was contained in the plants they ate. At the end of one month he observed that the appearance and activity of the animals receiving salt was distinctly superior to those not receiving it. This was especially manifest in the deprived oxen by roughness of coat, matting and falling of hair, their gait, and their exhibition "of a cold temperment." In 1851 Liebig (25) referred to French experiments in which animals were destroyed in more or less brief periods when fed upon substances containing no salts "although otherwise nutritious."

The Earliest Chemical Studies of Saline Constituents in Animal Tissues

Nothing was known concerning the saline constituents of blood until in 1773 and 1776 H. M. Rouelle (26) published his studies. He noted that when blood serum and also dropsical fluid were coagulated by heat, the fluids remaining turned syrup of violets green;

thus, he concluded that they contained a fixed alkali. He added sulfuric acid to the ash of blood, and by crystallizing the resulting sulfates and inspecting the appearance of the crystals, identified the base as soda. He said there were also present crystals of potassium sulfate. Rouelle estimated that about one-tenth of the base content of blood ash was *animal earth,* by which he apparently meant calcium salts.

Heinrich Rose (1795–1864) (27), a professor in Berlin, was the first to study extensively the mineral constituents of animal substances. He discovered columbium, tantalum and antimony pentachloride, devised many laboratory techniques, and was the first to make a study of mass action in chemical reactions. In 1848 and 1850 he published his analytical results, obtained with methods of his own devising, which clearly showed that tissues and secretions differed greatly in their inorganic salt composition. He distinguished three categories of mineral salts: (A) the quantity of salts which could be dissolved by water from 100 parts of ash; (B) the amount which could be dissolved by treating the water-extracted residue with dilute hydrochloric acid; and (C) the fraction which remained after ignition of the residue left from the two extractions.

ROSE'S ANALYTICAL DATA (PER CENT OF TOTAL)

	(A)	(B)	(C)
Ox blood	60.90	6.04	33.06
Horse flesh	42.81	17.48	39.71
Cow's milk	34.17	31.75	34.08
Egg-yolk	40.95	8.05	51.00
Egg-white	82.19	15.52	2.29
Ox bile	90.85	4.93	4.22
Urine	90.87	8.54	0.59
Solid excrement	18.55	62.30	19.15

Prout's Study of Calcium and Phosphate in the Incubating Egg

In 1822 William Prout (28) made the first study of the changes in the calcium and phosphate content of the chick embryo as incubation progressed. He found that the phosphorus content of egg and embryo did not change whereas the calcium content of the embryo increased progressively. He was skeptical about the possibility of calcium being able to pass into the chick from the shell, and was inclined to suspect that this element was formed from other materials.

Liebig's Discovery of the Distribution of Potassium and Sodium Salts in Animal Tissues

In 1847 Liebig wrote a letter to W. A. Hofmann (29) in which he made the prophetic statement, "I see a boundless field before me, and doubt not that for every *quality* of the animal body, something which can be estimated *quantitatively* will also be discovered to which it is indebted for its properties." The principal topic in this letter was a description of Liebig's preparation of creatine from muscle. He then went on to say, "I have found that the fluids without the blood and lymphatic vessels contain only potash, and phosphate of magnesia, whilst the blood and lymph contain merely those of phosphate of soda. If, therefore, the latter is indispensable to the formation of blood and the processes of life, it is evident that an animal on the continent, which finds in plants only potash salts, should have chloride of sodium given to it, by means of which the phosphate of potash is transformed into the chloride of potash, and phosphate of soda. I found further, that the salt-brine which flows from salted meat contained certain alkaline phosphates, and that scurvy is easily explained by the deficiency in salted meat of alkaline phosphates necessary for the formation of blood."

Forster's Experiments with Nearly Ash-Free Diets

After Liebig's discovery of the contrasting distribution of sodium and potassium in blood and lymph as compared with extravascular structures of the animal body, and after the accumulation of quantitative data by H. Rose on the inorganic constituents of different fluids and tissues, the next step in progress of knowledge of the physiological significance of mineral elements was made by J. Forster (30). He restricted dogs to nearly salt-free diets, and observed that the animals experienced disturbances of the functions of the organs, especially of the muscular and nervous systems, and that death occurred in a shorter period than when they were subjected to complete starvation. Forster concluded that certain mineral elements which were constantly found in animal tissues were essential to life, and were, accordingly, indispensable constituents of the diet.

As the source of protein in his experimental diets for dogs, Forster used the residue from the manufacture of Liebig's extract of beef. It was muscle substance from which all water-soluble substances had been extracted. It still contained about 0.8 per cent of ash-forming constituents. To this washed muscle, Forster added fat, sugar and starch. In some experiments with doves he fed only starch and casein.

The Views of Panum and of Hammarsten

The belief persisted in the minds of well-informed men that, with the exception of sodium chloride and those inorganic substances which enter into the composition of bones and teeth, e.g., calcium and phosphate, it was questionable whether mineral salts were important in animal nutrition. This belief rested in great measure on the fact that with the exception of the skeleton, the average content of mineral salts in body structures was only about one per cent. It was believed that salts present in but small amounts were of little importance to the animal.

Panum (31) kept dogs in apparent health from April 19 to July 17 on a diet of barley groats, fat, sodium chloride, and water. Olaf Hammarsten (32), a distinguished physiological chemist, expressed the belief that it was highly probable that a certain amount of alkali phosphate was a necessary constituent of foods, but that the need must be small because Panum's diet provided only small amounts of sodium and potassium salts. In the light of future developments in regard to both inorganic and organic nutrients, the attempt to appraise the significance of body constituents on the basis of the amount present in the tissues represents an interesting illustration of the futility of seeking truth in matters relating to physiology by any path other than carefully planned and controlled experiments.

Von Bunge's Speculations About the Effects of Ash-Free Diets

Von Bunge's reflections on the results obtained by Forster, and his decision to seek the reason for the failure of his animals on ash-poor diets, is an excellent example of the influence a well-planned experimental study may have on the course of future research, even though it may remain in comparative obscurity for many years. Von Bunge reasoned that in metabolism of proteins the sulfur is oxidized to sulfuric acid, and that normally this acid is neutralized by bases taken in the food. Forster's animals, he thought, might have been injured by accumulated acidity because of the lack of basic elements to maintain neutrality in the body tissues. (33) To test this hypothesis von Bunge suggested to his pupil N. Lunin, in the University of Dorpat, that he should feed mice a diet composed of isolated, purified, and recombined protein, carbohydrate, and fat, with and without the addition of bases to neutralize metabolic sulfuric acid. The details of this study are presented elsewhere (p. 203). Lunin's failure to keep mice alive on his "purified" diet, with or without the addition of sodium or potassium carbonate, raised the question why mice could thrive for sixty days on milk alone, but could not survive when given only the principal constituents of milk, casein, lactose, milk fat, and milk ash.

Lunin's experiments were the most illuminating investigations which had ever been made of the number and nature of the essential constituents of an adequate diet. They showed that the inadequacy of his diets was attributable not to inorganic but to organic factors which chemists had hitherto overlooked, and they directed attention to whey constituents as the source of these unidentified substances. Yet neither von Bunge nor Lunin appears to have seen the vista of glorious opportunity which the experiments had brought to view. And neither attempted to study the problem further.

Von Bunge's Explanation of the Craving of Grazing Animals for Salt

In 1847 Liebig (29) had commented on the surprising contrast in the distribution of sodium and potassium salts in the animal body. Like others who were interested in chemistry, von Bunge probably read and reflected on all that this renowned man wrote. Doubtless his interest in the intriguing physiological problem of the reason for the craving of grazing animals for sodium chloride was heightened by what Liebig had written.

The concept of the interaction between two neutral salts originated in the mind of J. B. Richter, chemist in the Berlin Porcelain Works, in 1792 (34). He was the great pioneer in the application of mathematics to chemistry, and in his studies observed that acetate of lime and tartrate of potash were both neutral salts. When brought together in solution, tartrate of lime was precipitated and potassium acetate was formed and remained in solution, and the system maintained its neutrality. It was probably this principle which Liebig had in mind when he wrote the above-quoted letter to Hofmann expressing his views about the interrelation between sodium and potassium in the animal body.

There was nothing new in von Bunge's assertion that animals which subsist on vegetable food ingest much more potassium than sodium salts. In 1845 Boussingault (35) had published analyses of the ashes of plants which brought out this fact. He found clover ash to contain 23.6 to 34.7 per cent of potash, and 0.3 to 2.9 per cent of soda. With the exception of plants grown in salt marsh, as ash analyses accumulated, land plants generally were found to be excessively rich in potash as compared with soda.

But von Bunge in his famous textbook (36) asserted that if there is a lack of sodium as compared with potassium salts in the food, or an excess of potassium compounds other than potassium chloride in the body, there occur chemical reactions which result in loss of sodium. He illustrated this idea by an experiment in which ingestion of vegetable food resulted in an intake of potassium several times that of sodium (37). He said that if sodium chloride were added to an aqueous solution of potassium carbonate, interaction would take place resulting in the formation of sodium carbonate and potassium chloride. This was Richter's principle. Corresponding interactions were believed to occur when potassium phosphate or sulfate were ingested. By this exchange of acid radicals the blood acquired, he said, sodium salts foreign to it, and the kidneys excreted the foreign salts, thus depleting the blood of its sodium. The appetite for salt was a manifestation of the need of the body to restore the sodium thus lost. Von Bunge tested this theory on himself by ingesting all the potassium salts which might occur in foods, such as phosphate and citrate, and proved by analysis of his urine that additional sodium salts were excreted because of the ingestion of the potassium salts. This theory was accepted by physiologists everywhere.

Discoveries by Ringer and Locke on Physiological Antagonism of Inorganic Ions

In 1885 Sidney Ringer of Norwich, England (1835–1910) discovered that various organic structures best retained their functional activity in a solution which contained sodium chloride, potassium chloride, and calcium chloride (38). Soon other investigators studied the most favorable concentrations and ratios of these three salts. Locke (39) found that for perfusion of the surviving mammalian heart, the most favorable concentrations were NaCl 0.9–1.0 per cent, $CaCl_2$ 0.02–0.024 per cent, KCl 0.02–0.04 per cent, and $NaHCO_3$ 0.01–0.03 per cent. He found, as was implied in Ringer's observations, that, individually, the chlorides of sodium, potassium, and calcium had a poisonous action on heart muscle, and that this action was counteracted by the presence of the other two salts. Thus the concept of antagonistic salt action was introduced into physiology.

Loeb's Studies on The Dynamics of Living Matter

The mutually neutralizing action, in the physiological sense, of certain salts was studied in considerable detail by J. Loeb (1859–1924) (40). On testing many different proportions he found that, from the biological standpoint, the most favorable quantitative relations were those between the concentrations of NaCl, KCl, and $CaCl_2$ in which they exist in blood. Loeb's experiments with the minnow, *Fundulus heteroclitus,* illustrate well the significance of certain concentrations of the biologically important inorganic ions for the functioning of living tissues. This minnow can live in distilled water for a considerable time, hence it is to a remarkable degree independent of the osmotic pressure of its surrounding medium. It served admirably for the study of the poisonous action of salts and mixtures of salts in solution.

Pure NaCl or KCl in solution in distilled water, in the concentration in which these exist in sea water, act as poisons to *Fundulus.* However, the fish can live for an indefinite period in a solution of pure calcium chloride in the concentration in which this salt exists in sea water.

It was found that 1 mol of KCl is nearly completely de-toxified by 17 mols of NaCl, or by 8.5 mols of Na_2SO_4. One-half mol of K_2SO_4 was found to be just as poisonous as 1 mol of KCl. The toxicity of potassium salts was dependent on the potassium ion and the de-toxifying effects of sodium salts depended on the sodium ion. $CaCl_2$ de-toxifies a KCl solution even when in concentration of one-thirtieth mol $CaCl_2$ to 1 mol KCl. Strontium chloride showed almost as great de-toxifying action against KCl as did $CaCl_2$. NaCl in the concentration in which it occurs in sea water was only incompletely de-toxified by KCl; only by the further addition of calcium chloride was complete de-toxification brought about.

The physiological disturbance to *Fundulus* caused by the presence of free acids in the water in which it lived could also be arrested by adding certain neutral salts. The minnow could accommodate itself to elevation of temperature, and a rise in temperature could be more easily tolerated when the concentration of the three salts, NaCl, KCl, and $CaCl_2$, in the aqueous medium were increased as the temperature was raised.

Loeb found that the eggs of *Fundulus* developed just as well in salt-free water as in sea water. If fertilized eggs of the minnow were placed in a solution of pure NaCl of the same osmotic pressure as sea water, they soon died but the toxicity of the NaCl solution could be arrested by addition of a small quantity of almost any salt with polyvalent ions. Not only the salts of the alkaline earths but also those of heavy metals (e.g., $ZnSO_4$, Pb-acetate) were found to be effective. Such solutions permitted *Fundulus* eggs to develop, although they soon killed the completed fish.

As an explanation for the mechanism of the antagonistic action of salts in their effects on living creatures or on organic structures, Loeb offered the concept that the mixed salts, in proper proportions, cause a "tanning" of the surface of the cells exposed, whereby the cells become impermeable to certain destructive substances. These included the salts normally found in animal tissues. The cells of fertilized eggs of the fish could, he believed, be "tanned" by NaCl plus a heavy metal, but not the cells of the developed fish.

Loeb's numerous experiments with imbalanced salt solutions, which revealed the antagonistic physiologic action of inorganic ions in living tissues, dramatically illustrated the nutritive significance of the inorganic constituents of the diet as contributors to physiologic well-being. He aptly chose to publish his experiments under the title *The Dynamics of Living Matter*.

The Significance of Calcium in Blood Coagulation

In 1879 Hammarsten (41) discovered that addition of calcium salts facilitated coagulation of blood. However, the fact that calcium ions are indispensable to coagulation was not known until it was demonstrated in 1890 by Arthus and Pages (42). They showed that addition of reagents such as oxalate or citrate, which precipitate calcium, prevented coagulation, and that this property could be restored by addition of calcium ions.

Effects of Uncomplicated Calcium Deficiency

In 1908 MacCallum and Voegtlin (43) showed that administration of calcium salts relieved the symptoms of tetany. Since in 1906 (44) Halsted had successfully treated patients with tetany by administration of beef parathyroids, the role of these glands in regulation of the calcium content of blood was established.

Uncomplicated calcium deficiency was first produced experimentally by G. J. Martin (45), who restricted dogs to a diet containing only 30 ppm. of calcium. He described the occurrence in his animals of widespread hemorrhage, delayed coagulation of the blood, inflammation of the gastrointestinal tract, and great rarefaction of the bones (osteoporosis). The ratio of calcium to phosphate is of great physiological significance, as is related in the chapter on rickets.

The Physiological Significance of Magnesium

This element attracted little attention. Neither Ringer nor Locke included a magnesium salt in their solutions for maintaining functional activity of living tissues during experiments. Denis (46), in 1915, first determined that blood plasma contained 3–4 mg. of magnesium per 100 ml. In 1931 McCollum and Orent (47) restricted young rats to a diet containing only 1.8 ppm. of magnesium. They described the development of a specific syndrome after the animals had been on the diet about 11 or 12 days. This was characterized by dilatation of the cutaneous blood vessels, and extreme hyperirritability, manifested by tetanic seizures when the animals were subjected to sounds like the crackling of paper, the hissing of compressed air, or hand clapping. It was found that the magnesium content of the blood plasma was lowered in this condition. The hyperirritability of the animals could be relieved promptly by the administration of a magnesium salt. These experiments showed that magnesium is an indispensable nutrient.

Phosphorus

In earlier chapters mention was made of the discovery of the element phosphorus in urine, bones, lecithin, and cephalin, and of Mulder's interest in phosphorylated proteins. Before 1840 phosphorus was recognized as a constituent of all natural foods and all body tissues. In 1834 Couerbe (48) advanced the notion that the healthy and morbid conditions of the mental faculties were connected with variations in the amount of phosphorus in cerebral matter. He claimed to have found 1.0 to 1.5 per cent of phosphorus in the brains of idiots, and 3.0 to 4.5 per cent in the brains of insane men, whereas in the brains of sane men he found 2.0 to 2.5 per cent. Lassaigne (49) controverted Couerbe's findings and conclusions, but credulity prevailed over evidence, and the idea became crystallized in the well-known phrase *ohne Phosphor kein Gedank* — without phosphorus, no thought.

In Chapter 14 an account is given of the speculations of several investigators who sought to find the cause of failures when animals were fed diets of isolated and purified substances. They directed their attention to experimenting with phosphorylated proteins, nucleic acid, and lecithin, on the theory that the body could not synthesize organic compounds of phosphorus. In 1909 McCollum (50) proved this concept to be fallacious. He supplied evidence that all organic forms of phosphorus of biological importance could be synthesized in the animal body from orthophosphates in the food.

In 1918 Osborne and Mendel (51) were the first to restrict young rats to a diet adequate in other respects but so deficient in phosphorus as to prevent growth, thus demonstrating anew that this element is an indispensable nutrient. Schneider and Steenbock (52) in 1939 first produced experimentally the pathologic lesions arising from phosphorus-deficiency only. In their experiments both calcium and vitamin D were adequately provided. They observed calcium citrate calculi in the kidneys, ureters, and bladders of their rats. They also noted that in this deficiency state bone, rather than soft tissue, was favored for phosphorus deposition. This was a new and important contribution to knowledge of the action of vitamin D when used in a phosphorous-deficient diet.

The Role of Phosphorus in Nutrition

As with most scientific facts, it took considerable time and numerous studies and discoveries before it was generally accepted that phosphorus, in both inorganic phosphates and organic compounds of several types, is a constituent of bone, brain, nerve, egg yolk, milk protein, and muscle. Among the events which played an important part in establishing this fact were: the discovery of phosphorus in urine by Brand (7) and in bones by Gahn; the discoveries of lecithin by Gobley (1846), of cephalin by Thudichum (1884), and of the phosphorylated protein, casein, by Hammarsten (1874); the careful study of ovovitellin by Osborne and Campbell (53) (1900); and Miescher's description of nucleoproteins and nucleic acids in pus and salmon eggs. However, biological chemistry in its applications to theory concerning nutritional phenomena did not attract much attention until near the end of the nineteenth century.

The most significant investigation before 1900 to shed light on the transformation of organic phosphorus compounds in metabolism was made by A. Kossel (54) (1885). He concluded that during incubation of hens' eggs the phosphoprotein, ovovitellin, changed to nucleoprotein. He based his conclusion on the fact that the fresh yolk substance yielded no purine bases (guanine and hypoxanthin), whereas they were present in the hatched chick.

In 1909 Plimmer and Scott (55) compared the phosphorus distribution in the body of the chick at hatching with that of the fresh egg and the egg at different stages of incubation. Their data yielded a clear picture of the types of transformations of organic phosphorus compounds that occurred in the metabolic processes of embryonic development. These changes they thought were probably duplicated in the metabolism of both growing and adult animals.

That there was no lack of interest in the study of organic phosphorus compounds, their distribution, and properties is shown by the fact that, before 1900, 650 papers were published on these subjects. The increased interest in such studies is apparent by the appearance of 1850 additional papers between 1900 and 1914. Besides dealing with the chemistry of organic phosphorus compounds, the papers were concerned with the nutritional and pathological significance of these compounds. A collection of these studies was compiled and discussed by Forbes and Keith (56) in 1914. At that time opinion was still divided on the question of the indispensability of organic phosphorus compounds — some believed they could not be synthesized, and hence must be provided in the diet; others maintained that all known types of phosphorylated organic substances could be synthesized in the body from inorganic phosphate if the necessary organic precursors were provided in the food. What these precursors were was unknown. Forbes and Keith accepted the available evidence as supporting the indispensability of organic phosphorus compounds as nutrients.

Earliest Experiments on the Nutritive Significance of Organic Phosphorus-Containing Substances in Animal Nutrition

Between 1900 and 1902 Desgrez and Zaky (57) conducted numerous studies with guinea pigs, which they fed bran and cabbage in proportions not stated. They reported the effects produced on the nitrogen and phosphorus excretion of the animals when supplements of egg-yolk lecithin, glycerophosphoric acid, or choline were included in the diet. They interpreted their results to mean that organic phosphorus compounds were of special significance in animal metabolism, and that they should be considered essential constituents of the diet. Since a diet of bran and cabbage will maintain guinea pigs in health over a period of many weeks, it is apparent that the Desgrez-Zaky experiments precluded the discovery of anything of importance relating to their objective.

The Interest of Nutrition Investigators in Phytic Acid

In 1900 Posternak (58), in France, described the isolation and properties of a newly-discovered phosphorus-containing substance which, since it was derived from vegetable sources, he called phytic acid. The calcium-magnesium salt of this acid he called phytin. It was found to be generally present in the seeds of plants, and was especially abundant in the outer layers. Wheat bran was one of the best sources of phytin.

As has been pointed out in Chapter 11, the chemical analysis of foods as a means of assessing their nutritive values steadily lost standing among investigators in nutrition. Baffled agricultural chemists welcomed any new suggestion which offered a tentative explanation for failures to realize expected results in feeding farm animals. Hence, nutrition workers were greatly interested in the possible physiological significance of the new phosphorus-containing compound.

The first extensive study of its importance was made by Jordan, Hart, and Patton (59). They used dairy cows as subjects, and fed them rations low and high in phytin. They interpreted their results to signify that the administration of phytin was beneficial because it regulated bowel function and increased milk secretion. Many years later Mellanby (60) concluded that phytin was poorly absorbed because of its low solubility, and that when cereals formed the greater portion of a diet, the phosphorus and calcium were so poorly absorbed that bone growth was abnormal. This view is further discussed in Chapter 18. In 1909 McCollum (61) studied all available experimental evidence. He concluded that in planning experimental diets derived from known substances, all organic compounds containing phosphorus could be omitted from the formulas, since they could be synthesized from inorganic phosphate and other chemical entities. Eventually this view was accepted by all biochemists. In 1913 Plimmer (62) published an important review of the evidence and concluded that there occur in the alimentary tract enzymes which hydrolyze each class of organic phosphorus-containing compounds here mentioned, and that it is the products of their hydrolytic cleavage which are absorbed.

Phosphorus Deficiency: A Widespread Problem in Animal Production

About 1900–1920 there occurred on farms in South Africa a tragedy which dramatized the injury to grazing animals which may result from soil depletion of the element phosphorus. It was not a new experience, but an old one which was now repeated on a grand scale.

Le Vallant, telling of his travels in Africa in 1785 (63), described how the cattle invaded his camp sites eagerly searching for bones left by his dogs. These they chewed ravenously. When bones were not to be found, the animals chewed one anothers' horns, and even wood and stones. La Vallant said that where the pastures were good, cattle never exhibited this abnormal appetite. He thus attributed bone-chewing to a lack of "calcareous" matter, a conclusion which at that time seemed logical.

The habit of bone-chewing by cattle in South Africa increased in extent during the early years of the twentieth century. Animals manifesting this form of pica became severely malnourished and many died. Theiler and Green (64) discovered that the principal cause of death was infection by the *Bacillus botulinus,* which the cattle sucked from putrid bones. They found that the abnormal craving for bones ceased within a few hours after the administration of any of several sources of the phosphate ion. Hence they concluded that the primary cause of the trouble lay in deficiency of phosphorus in the herbage on which the animals grazed. Analysis of grass from the pastures showed it was extremely low in phosphorus.

After the cause of bone-chewing in cattle was recognized, it was found that this problem occurred among cattle in many parts of the world. The condition resulted from selling animals off grazing lands year after year without restoring to the soil the phosphate thus removed. It had been well known since the time of Liebig that the practice of selling successive crops of cereals and other crops off the land and neglecting to apply fertilizers to restore the mineral elements removed resulted in decreased yields. The disorder arising from phosphorus-deficiency in cattle was the earliest example of failure of the production of satisfactory animals on depleted grasslands.

Phosphorus Compounds in the Metabolic Processes

The phosphate radical assumed a new and highly important interest when, in 1926, the Eggletons announced the discovery in muscle of an organic labile phosphate to which they gave the name *phosphagen* (65). Later this was shown by Fiske and Subbarrow (66) to be phosphocreatin. Within a few years this discovery changed entirely the comprehension by physiologists and biochemists of the chemical processes which underlie muscle contraction. The subject has been discussed from its historical development by Hill (67).

In 1935 Lohmann (68 and 70) isolated adenosine diphosphate from heart muscle and from smooth muscle. From this discovery stemmed the studies which elucidated the physiological role of adenosine triphosphate (ATP) as the source of energy in muscle contraction, owing to the presence in its molecule of an energy-rich phosphate bond.

The role of phosphoric acid in the initiation of gluco- and fructo-polysaccharide synthesis was illuminated by the investigations of C. F. Cori and G. Cori (71) and their associates. Biochemists were long puzzled over how the relatively inert natural hexoses — glucose, fructose, and mannose — in the tissues of animals and of green plants could be activated so as to take part in the metabolic scheme. Modern researches have shown that this activation is brought about by the intervention of adenosine triphosphate and the widely distributed hexokinases. Thus it emerged that phosphoric acid in its various combinations and permutations with organic substances is one of the most versatile of biochemical compounds among all the components of the complex enzyme systems of living matter.

Investigations of the Physiological Significance of Inorganic Elements in 1940

In this chapter an attempt has been made to give an account of the sequence of constructive thought and experiment which brought to light the extent to which physiological functioning of living things depends upon the participation of certain inorganic elements in metabolic processes. The philosophy of Ringer and of Loeb went no further than consideration of physiological antagonism, in the sense of one ion detoxifying another, and the concept of the necessity for "balanced" salt solutions in body fluids. This was a great advance over previous comprehension of essential nutrients merely as structural materials of living matter.

Within two decades after the termination of Loeb's studies on the dynamics of living matter as manifested in the influence of the quantitative relations between the ions of the principal inorganic salts on living tissues, Hart and his associates demonstrated the indispensability of copper for iron utilization by the body. In 1931 Orent and McCollum (72) and Kemmerer, Elvehjem, and Hart (73) demonstrated the necessity of manganese as a nutrient for mammals. These discoveries and others relating to the "trace elements" of physiological importance are considered in Chapter 26. They broadened immensely the outlook of physiologists, biochemists, and pathologists.

By 1930 it was evident to all investigators that for the complete understanding of nutritional needs and physiological processes, it was necessary to induce the specific states of malnutrition which develop when only one of the physiologically important inorganic elements is omitted from a diet which is otherwise satisfactory for the maintenance of health. With this in mind, Orent Keiles and McCollum (74) in 1941 produced the pathological state which results when all nutrients except potassium are provided in the diet. Follis and his associates (75) studied the pathology of this deficiency disease. Orent Keiles and her co-workers (76) also produced the pathological states caused solely by deficiency of sodium and of chlorine. Since these studies did not contribute to the origin of a new concept their further consideration is unnecessary. Follis (77) has written an excellent account of the pathology of deficiency diseases.

REFERENCES

1. De Saussure, N. T.: Recherches chimique sur la Végétation. Paris (1804).
2. Liebig, J.: Ann. der Chemie *42,* 291–297 (1842).
3. Van Helmont, J. B.: Ortus Medicinae (1652).
4. Shrader, J. C.: Zwei Preischriften über die Beschaffenheit und Erzeugung der erdigen Bestandtheile von Getreidearten. Berlin (1800).
5. Braconnot, H.: Annales de Chimie *61,* 187–246 (1807).
6. Philos. Mag. *9,* p. 191 (1801).
7. Philos. Mag. *21,* 53–56, 60 (1805).
8. Wiegmann, A. F. and Polstorff, L.: Ueber die anorganischen Bestandtheile der Pflanzen. Braunschweig (1842).
9. Brand, H.: See Weeks, M. E.: The discovery of the elements (1934).
10. Hatchett, C.: Cited by Thomson, T., Animal Chemistry, p. 250 (1843).
11. Fordyce, G.: A Treatise on Digestion of Food. London (1791).
12. Berzelius, J. J.: Animal Chemistry. London, pp. 73 *et seq.* (1813).
13. Bostock, J.: Physiology. London, p. 511 (1836).
14. Chossat, C.: Compt. Rend. Acad. des Sci. *14,* 451–54 (1842).
15. Chossat, C.: Mem. l'Acad. des Sci. de France 8, (Ser. 2), 438–640 (1843).
16. Forbes, E. B. and Keith, M. H.: Phosphorus Compounds in Animal Metabolism. Tech. Ser. Bull. No. 5, pp. 1–746. Ohio Agric. Exp. Sta. (1914).
17. Graham, T.: Ann. d. chem. u. Pharm. *121,* 1 (1862).
18. Traube, M.: Arch. f. (Anat. u.) Physiol. pp. 87, 129 (1867).
19. Pfeffer, W.: Osmotische Untersuchungen. Leipzig (1877).
20. De Vries, H.: Pflanzenuntersuchungen (1855).
21. van't Hoff, J.: Zeitschr. f. physiol. Chem. *1,* 481 (1887).
22. Nägeli, C. von: Pflanzenphysiologische Untersuchungen (1855).
23. Philos. Mag. *20,* 9–98 (1805).

24. Boussingault, J. B.: Ann. de chim. et de phys. (3rd Ser.) *19,* 117–125 (1847); 22, 116 (1849); Compt. Rend. *25,* 729 (1847).

25. Liebig, J. von: Chemische Briefe. pp. 495–544 (1851); Or Letters on Chemistry, London, pp. 382–440 (1851).

26. Rouelle, H. M.: Journ. de Médecine. 1773 and 1776.

27. Rose, H.: Pogg. Annalen *70,* 449–465 (1848); *76,* 305–404 (1850).

28. Prout, W.: Philos. Trans. p. 365 (1822).

29. Liebig, J. von: Philos. Mag. (3) *30,* 412 (1847).

30. Forster, J.: Zeitschr. f. Biol. *9,* 297–380 (1873).

31. Panum, P. L.: Maly's Jahresbericht d. Thierchemie *4,* 361–365 (1874).

32. Hammarsten, O.: Nordiskt. Medicidskt. Arkiv. *6,* 19 (1874).

33. Bunge, G. von: Lehrbuch der Physiologische Chemie. 4th ed. (1889).

34. Richter, J. B.: Outlines of Stoichimetry, Or the Art of Measuring Chemical Elements. Breslau. (1792).

35. Boussingault, J. B.: Rural Economy in its Relation with Chemistry, Physics and Meteorology; Or Chemistry Applied to Agriculture (1845). Trans. by Geo. Law. Vol. 2, pp. 225–227.

36. Bunge, G. von: Lehrbuch der Physiologische Chemie. Leipzig, pp. 107–110 (1889).

37. Bunge, G. von: Zeitschr. f. Biol. *9,* 104 (1873); *10,* 110, 295 (1874).

38. Ringer, S.: Journ. of Physiol. *6,* 154, 361 (1885); 7, 118 (1886); *16,* 1; *17,* 23 (1895); *18,* 425 (1896).

39. Locke, F.: Journ. of Physiol. London, *18,* 332–333 (1895); Centralbl. f. Physiol. *14,* 672 (1900).

40. Loeb, J.: Biochem. Zeitschr. *31,* 450; *32,* 155, 308; 33, 480, 489 (1911); 39, 167; *43,* 181 (1912).

41. Hammarsten, O.: Nova Acta, reg. Soc. Scient. Upsala (3), *10,* (1879).

42. Arthus, M. and Pages, C.: Arch. de Physiol. (5), 2 (1890).

43. MacCallum, W. G. and Voegtlin, C.: Johns Hopkins Hospital Bull. *19,* 91–92 (1908); J. Exper. Med. *11,* 118–151 (1909).

44. Halsted, W. S.: Amer. J. Med. Sci. *134,* 1–12 (1907); J. Exper. Med. *11,* 175–198 (1909).

45. Martin, G. J.: Growth, *1,* 175 (1937).

46. Denis, W.: J. Biol. Chem. *41*, 363–366 (1920).
47. McCollum, E. V. and Orent, E. R.: J. Biol. Chem. 92, xxx (Sci. Proceedings) (1931).
48. Couerbe, J. P.: Ann. de Chim. et de Phys. (2) *56*, pp. 160–193 (1834).
49. Lassaigne: Journ. de Chim. Med. Tome 1 (2nd Ser.) (1836).
50. McCollum, E. V.: Amer. J. Physiol. *25*, 120 (1909).
51. Osborne, T. B. and Mendel, L. B.: J. Biol. Chem. *34*, 131 (1918).
52. Schneider, H. and Steenbock, H.: J. Biol. Chem. *128*, 159 (1939).
53. Osborne, T. B. and Campbell, G. F.: J. Amer. Chem. Soc. 22, 413–422 (1900).
54. Kossel, A.: Arch. Anat. u. Physiol. pp. 346, 347 (1885).
55. Plimmer, R. H. A. and Scott, F. H.: Journ. of Physiol. (London), *38*, 247–253 (1909).
56. Forbes, E. B. and Keith, M. H.: Phosphorus Compounds in Animal Metabolism. Ohio Agric. Exper. Sta. Tech. Series Bull. No. 5, Wooster, Ohio, pp. 748 (1914).
57. Desgrez, A. and Zaky, A.: Compt. Rend. Soc. de Biol. 58, 794, 795; *54*, 730 (1900).
58. Posternak, S.: Revue gener. de botanique *12*, 5–24, 64–73 (1900).
59. Jordan, W. H., Hart, E. B. and Patton, A. J.: Amer. J. Physiol. *16*, 268 (1906).
60. Mellanby, E.: A Story of Nutritional Research; The Effect of Some Dietary Factors on Bones and the Nervous System. Baltimore, (1950).
61. McCollum, E. V.: Amer. J. Physiol. 25, 120 (1909).
62. Plimmer, R. H. A.: Biochem. J. 7, 34 (1913).
63. La Vallant: Travels Into the Interior of Africa. Trans. by G. G. and J. Robinson, 2nd ed. 1796. Cited by Theiler, A. and Green, H. H.: Nut. Absts. and Rev. *1*, 359 (1952).
64. Green, H. H.: Physiol. Rev. *5*, 336 (1925).
65. Eggleton, P. and Eggleton, G. P.: Biochem. J. *21*, 190 (1927).
66. Fiske, C. H. and Subbarrow, Y.: Science *70*, 381 (1929).
67. Hill, A. V.: Physiol. Rev. *12*, 56 (1932).
68. Lohmann, K.: Angew. Chemie *48*, 165 (1935).
69. Meyerhof, O. and Lohmann, K.: Biochem. Zeitschr. *271*, 89 (1934).

70. Lohmann, K. and Schuster, P.: Biochem. Zeitschr. *294,* 188 (1937).

71. Cori, C. F. and Cori, G.: Biological Symposia *5,* 131 (1941).

72. Orent, E. and McCollum, E. V.: J. Biol. Chem. *92,* 651 (1931).

73. Kemmerer, A. R., Elvehjem, C. A. and Hart, E. B.: J. Biol. Chem. *92,* 623 (1931).

74. Orent Keiles, E. and McCollum, E. V.: J. Biol. Chem. *140,* 337 (1941).

75. Follis, R. H., Jr., Orent Keiles, E. and McCollum, E. V.: Ann. J. Pathol. *18,* 29 (1942).

76. Orent Keiles, E., Robinson, A. and McCollum, E. V.: Amer. J. Physiol. *119,* 651 (1937); J. Biol. Chem. *133,* 75 (1940).

77. Follis, R. H., Jr.: The Pathology of Deficiency Disease. Charles C. Thomas, pp. 24–68 (1948).

22

Progress in the Discovery of the Significance of Iron in Nutrition

THE FIRST CHEMIST to attempt analysis of blood was Robert Boyle, who published in 1684 (1) his observations of the changes brought about when alcohol, various acids, and postassium carbonate were added. He distilled blood destructively, and burned samples to secure the ash. His only important observation was that the ash of blood was of a brick-red color, but he seems not to have suspected that this was due to iron oxide. Boerhaave's *System of Chemistry*, a book first published in 1732, did not add any information about the properties of blood to that already provided by Boyle nearly half a century earlier.

In 1747 Menghini (2) published proof of the presence of iron in blood. There had been a controversy concerning whether blood contained iron. W. B. Johnson (3), writing in 1803, said that J. A. Badia, a professor in the University at Turin, was the first to demonstrate the presence of this element in blood. Johnson said that his view was not accepted by Claude Joseph Goeffroy (1672–1731), an apothecary of Paris who published sixty-four papers, mostly chemical, on his studies of animal tissues in the *Mémoires de Paris*. Goeffroy asserted that the iron found by Badia was formed by the action of fire. But Menghini carefully dried blood, ground it to a fine powder, and lifted out an iron-rich portion by applying a lodestone. This evidence that iron was a normal constituent of blood was accepted by all subsequent investigators.

About the year 1776, Bucquet (4) washed the blood corpuscles from blood clot, and secured the white, fibrous portion and the red matter. In 1797 Wells (5) published his observations on blood in which he explained the reason for the change of color which blood undergoes when exposed to air, and expressed the opinion, contrary to prevailing belief, that the color of blood was not due to iron, but to an organized substance of animal nature.

In 1831 Le Canu (b. 1800) later professor in the École de Pharmacie in Paris, published an elaborate mémoire on blood (6). Six years later he published his thesis for the medical degree which is a valuable historical account of all that had been accomplished in the study of the chemistry of blood to that time.

In 1808 Berzelius (7) devoted sixty pages in his *Animal Chemistry* to the chemistry of blood. He devised the first elaborate method for the analysis of this fluid, in which he distinguished albumen, coloring matter, fibrin, corpuscles, and ash. But it was not until 1838 that he discovered that the red coloring matter was capable of taking up in chemical union a large quantity of oxygen. He concluded that the iron-containing pigment was involved in the respiration of the tissues.

That there was great interest in the clinical study of blood after the appearance of Berzelius' work is apparent from a series of lectures delivered in 1840 by Ancell (8), and by the fact that Simon (9), in his *Animal Chemistry* published in 1845, devoted 250 pages to the chemistry and clinical aspects of blood.

Hematin and Hemoglobin

Hematin was first prepared in crude form by Tiedemann and Gmelin in 1826 (10). Le Canu was the first to prepare hematin in pure form, and may be called its discoverer. He showed that almost all the iron of blood is contained in this pigment. Sanson and Scherer (11) showed that dilute sulfuric acid could remove the iron from a blood clot or from the corpuscles. It thus became evident that the iron in blood was combined with an organic substance. Mulder and Goudoever (12) first prepared "hematin free from iron" (hematoporphyrin) in 1844.

There were two rival theories about the manner in which oxygen was taken up by the blood and conveyed to the tissues of the peripheral system. Liebig maintained that this was accomplished solely by the iron in the corpuscles, while Mulder referred oxygen transport entirely to the oxidation of protein compounds (12). Liebig asserted that the corpuscles of arterial blood contain peroxide of iron;

that in their passage through the capillaries, they lost a portion of their oxygen and combined with carbonic acid, so that in the venous system they no longer contained peroxide of iron. When the corpuscles reached the lungs, an exchange took place between the carbonic acid of the blood and the oxygen of the air.

Iron Deficiency in the Blood in Anemia

The analytical methods devised by Berzelius, and modified by Denis and by Simon, included quantitative estimations of hemoglobin and hematin. The numerous analyses recorded by these investigators brought to light the low iron content of the blood in anemic as compared with normal persons. These findings led to speculations concerning the cause of low red cell counts and low hematin content in the blood in anemias. The diminished iron content pointed to the cause, and suggested the administration of this element as a remedy.

Scientific inquiry by chemical methods of the significance of iron utilization by normal and anemic individuals did not begin until about 1840. However, the treatment of anemias by iron administration, without knowledge of what was actually being done, was practiced from very early times. In Greek mythology it is said that a vulture communicated to Melampus, the earliest Greek physician on record, that rust from a sword would cure Iphiclus of impotency (13).

Frederick Hoffmann (1660–1742) described chlorosis in 1730. Garrison (14) gave credit for the introduction of iron for therapeutic use to Thomas Sydenham (1624–1689), who was famous for the introduction into medicine of tincture of opium, and for the use of Peruvian bark as an antimalarial. Both drugs had long been used as popular remedies. Sydenham recommended "steel tonic," which he prepared by steeping steel filings in cold Rhenish wine. This process resulted in the formation of ferrous potassium tartrate. It will be recalled that Menghini in 1747 settled the controversy concerning whether blood contained iron, so it seems evident that Sydenham had no conclusive proof that he was administering an essential nutrient in his "steel tonic." Nevertheless, since he observed beneficial clinical responses to iron therapy in anemic patients, he deserves credit for having first placed iron in the list of essential nutrients.

In 1845 Simon (9) described the effect of giving metallic iron and tincture of iron to a chlorotic girl whose blood was examined chemically to determine the result. This was the earliest experimental study of its kind. The hematin content of the blood was estimated to be 1.431 grams per 100 ml. Simon stated that the normal value in a healthy person was 6.209 grams. After seven weeks of iron therapy, the hematin of this patient had risen to 4.598 grams. It appears that it was this clinical trial which established by analysis the soundness of iron administration in the treatment of anemia.

In 1876 Hayem (15) discussed the accumulated experience of clinicians in treatment of chlorosis by iron administration, and concluded that the evidence clearly showed that not only was the coloring matter of blood increased by iron, but the number of red cells was also augmented.

Boussingault Recognized Iron as an Essential Nutrient for Animals

In 1867 Boussingault published his experimental data showing the iron content of the bodies of animals (16). He regarded iron as an essential nutrient, and his study was designed to reveal the amount of iron which the rations of farm animals should supply. He found the iron content of a 27-gram mouse to be 0.0030 gram, which was equivalent to 0.00011th part of its body weight. A sheep weighing 32 kilograms contained 3.38 grams of iron, equivalent to 0.00011th of its weight. A fish weighing 182 grams contained only 0.0149 grams of iron, which was equivalent to only 0.000082nd part of its weight. He estimated that a cow weighing 600 kgm. consumed 1.365 grams of iron daily in her ration of hay, and that she gave out in 7.52 kgm. of milk 0.135 gram of this element.

Boussingault then analyzed for iron content thirty-six foods and feeds, and several wines and other beverages, including water from three sources. Using data on the iron content of blood which had been secured by Pelouze, Boussingault calculated the iron content provided daily by rations of French soldiers, English and Irish laborers, and others doing hard labor, and that provided by the rations of horses at reserve in the army. He clearly recognized the provision of an adequate amount of iron as one of the practical problems of both human and animal nutrition. In this he led the way, as in other fundamental studies of normal animal nutrition. His objective was to promote the well-being of animals and secure the maximum production of meat, milk, wool, etc. by the farm animals.

The Influence of Food on the Composition of Blood

In 1871 Subbotin (17) studied the influence of diet on the hemoglobin content of the blood of doves, rabbits, cattle, calves, and dogs. He showed that dogs fed only bread for twenty to thirty-six days became anemic as compared with dogs fed flesh. Suckling puppies were found to have only one-fourth as high a content of hemoglobin in the blood as did well-nourished adult dogs. This was the first recorded observation that anemia occurs in the suckling puppy.

The Discovery That Iron Is Stored in the Fetal Liver

Zaleski (18), in 1886, made the remarkable observation that the liver of new-born animals was much richer in iron than was that of adults. In 100 grams of dried liver of a new-born puppy he found 391 mgm. of iron, but the same weight of liver from two adult dogs contained only 78 and 43 mgm. respectively. Other analyses of the livers of animals of different species showed that the new-born contained five to nine times as much iron as did equal weights of liver from adult animals. This observation was soon followed by a more extended study by G. von Bunge (19) of the role of the fetal liver as a storage organ for iron.

Von Bunge's Observations on the Poverty of Milk in Iron

In 1889 G. von Bunge, professor at the University at Dorpat in Estonia, analyzed the milks of different species of animals. He found them to be very deficient in iron, whereas the other inorganic elements which are conspicuous as component parts of the body were present more nearly in the proportions representing the apparent nutritional needs of the suckling young. Using equal weights of the ash of a new-born puppy and the ash of bitch's milk, von Bunge achieved the following results:

	Ash of a New-born Puppy	*Ash of Bitch's Milk*
K_2O	11.42	14.98
Na_2O	10.64	8.80
CaO	29.52	27.24
MgO	1.82	1.54
Fe_2O_3	.72	0.12
P_2O_5	39.42	34.22
Cl	8.35	16.90

Von Bunge pointed out that his analyses showed that in the case of iron only, among the essential nutrients, the milk of the mother is very inadequate. This deficiency, in the light of Zaleski's discovery, was provided for in the suckling during its dependence on milk by a store of iron which was laid up during prenatal life.

Von Hösslin's Study of Iron Depletion

In 1882 von Hösslin (20) sought to improve the plan of experiment which Subbotin had employed for studying the effects of depriving an animal of iron. Instead of feeding bread, von Hösslin used a diet composed of washed milk curds, bacon, melted pork fat, and HCl-extracted starch. He restricted a dog to this food and observed a steady depletion of its blood in hematin during the first period of the experiment; a marked improvement of the blood resulted when an iron supplement was provided. It was his opinion that a child fed a milk diet would benefit from iron medication, and that the same was to be recommended for persons after hemorrhage.

Von Hösslin's experiment is of interest for reasons other than his demonstration of the usefulness to the body of inorganic iron compounds for blood pigment construction. His diet was so deficient in all inorganic elements and in all vitamins (later to be discovered), that his adult dog would have failed in health dramatically had the experiment been extended a few weeks. Yet inadequate as the diet was, the experiment served admirably to provide an answer to a specific question of whether iron was of physiological value to the animal.

His study illustrates well the promise of achievement in physiological studies by the use of simplified diets. However, it failed to reveal the shortcomings of an experiment carried on for a relatively brief duration with an adult animal of large size, as compared with the advantages of the extended feeding study with a small animal whose periods of growth, reproduction, and survival are much shorter. The latter type of study afforded opportunities which were not comprehended by any physiologist or chemist at that period. Prior to 1910 the use of adult animals for too brief periods of time was a common error among nutrition investigators.

Addison's Study of Anemia

After Sydenham's popularization of "steel-tonic," clinical experience progressively revealed that certain cases of anemias did not respond to iron therapy. Thus in 1849 Thomas Addison (1793–1860) (21) described "pernicious anemia," pernicious, because no remedy could be found for it.

Between 1871 and 1900 there were abstracted in Maly's *Jahresbericht der Thierchemie* 260 papers giving the results of various types of investigations of the physiological significance of iron. These papers dealt mainly with estimations of the iron content of different tissues, absorption of iron from different compounds, rate of loss of iron in the excreta, in milk, etc., the effects of supplements of iron for certain diets, and the results of using various iron preparations in the treatment of anemia. In 1892 Paul Ehrlich introduced the technic of staining blood smears with aniline dyes. This made possible rapid progress in understanding variations of the blood structure in anemias of several origins.

Staining technics and microscopical and chemical methods for blood studies revealed that anemia might result from any one of four causes: blood destruction, as by the malarial plasmodium, which destroys the red cell in which it develops; by persistent hemorrhage, as in hookworm infestation where each site of attachment of the parasite is a bleeding point; by tapeworm infestation, which leads to blood destruction by reason of toxic products formed by the parasite, and by metallic and other poisons (e.g., lead, arsenic, hydrogen sulfide, etc.); and by deficiency of iron in the food.

The Merits of Inorganic and Organic Forms of Iron

The clinical observations which showed that certain individuals in the anemic state did not benefit from the administration of inorganic iron tonics, raised doubts in some minds as to whether organic forms of iron were not superior to inorganic forms in providing for the nutritional needs of the body. The earliest skeptic to attempt to decide this question was von Bunge (22), whose reasoning is still of interest to investigators. He examined egg yolk and egg white and found that practically all the iron in the egg was in the yolk, and that the fresh egg did not contain either inorganic iron salts or hemoglobin. By digestion with artificial gastric juice he prepared from fat-free egg yolk a substance which differed markedly from proteins, and contained both phosphorus and iron. This he called *hematogen.* He believed that this was of great importance in nutrition, and in 1891 his student Socin attempted to compare its value as a source of iron with inorganic compounds of that element. These experiments have been discussed in another chapter (p. 205), and of them it need only be said here that the mice used as experimental animals were kept upon a diet of isolated, purified, and reassembled food substances, free from vitamins. Thus, the animals failed promptly when either source of iron was provided.

In general, two suppositions formed the basis for the views concerning the manner in which inorganic salts of iron might be of benefit nutritionally without supplying iron for the construction of hemoglobin. It was suggested that inorganic iron combined with the hydrogen sulfide, which had long been known to occur among the gases in the intestine, and thus prevented this highly poisonous and blood-destroying substance from being absorbed and injuring the blood corpuscles. Another suggestion was that, although the amount of organically bound iron in the ordinary food taken by man or animal is sufficient for blood-building, the intestinal mucous membrane sometimes became debilitated so as to be unable to absorb iron, and the administration of inorganic iron salts acted as a tonic which toned up the absorbing structures and improved their functional performance.

Pyrrol Derivatives and Iron Utilization

Mention has been made of the preparation of an iron-free derivative of hematin by Sanson and Scherer, and by Mulder and Goudoever in 1841 and 1844 respectively. This derivative came to be known as porphyrin. In 1895 Schunck and Marchlewski (23) prepared pure phylloporphyrin from chlorophyll, and, subsequently, became the first to recognize the great similarity between absorption spectra of hematoporphyrin and phylloporphyrin (24). Then followed the discovery by Nencki and Zaleski (25) in 1901 that both porphyrins yielded on reduction the same pyrrol derivative, which they called hemopyrrol, and which was identified as methylpropylpyrrol.

It soon became obvious from the new knowledge of the chemical nature of hematin, that the synthesis of hematin in blood formation called for organic radicals of the pyrrol type as well as for iron. Accordingly, speculation turned to the question concerning the nutritive needs of the body for a substance or substances of this type, and their distribution in natural foods. The similarity between hematin of blood, chlorophyll of green leaves, and hematogin of egg yolk, the precursor of hematin, aroused great interest among physiological chemists at the turn of the century. Not only was the question of the possible nutritional requirement for pyrrol derivatives for blood pigment formation apparently an important one, but by 1905 it was obvious that an appropriate quota of various amino acids for the synthesis of globin, the protein moiety of hemoglobin, was an important factor in blood formation. Von Bunge's hematogen was never characterized further than to be designated as pseudoneuclein, and it received no further attention by investigators.

The Studies of Whipple and Robscheit-Robbins on Blood Regeneration

No significant advance in knowledge of the relation between food and hemoglobin formation was made until Whipple and Robscheit-Robbins (26) studied the problem between 1925 and 1928. They found that during fasting periods after repeated bleedings, dogs could regenerate considerable amounts of hemoglobin in excess of its daily wastage. The average life of a red cell of human blood is about thirty days, hence 3–5 per cent of the red corpuscles are destroyed daily. Regeneration of blood constituents during fasting must be accomplished by reconstructing them from their degradation products, or from degradation products derived from other tissues of the body. These are increased during fasting when the body is subsisting on its own tissues.

During periods when the dogs were fed only sugar, the formation of hemoglobin was distinctly less than during similar periods of fasting. This was interpreted as a reflection of the reduced tissue degradation owing to the availability of the respiratory food sugar, which exerted a sparing action on the body proteins. When gliadin of wheat was the sole source of protein in the diet, blood regeneration was not improved over the sugar-feeding periods. This was explained on the basis that gliadin, being an incomplete protein, failed to provide essential amino acids or suitable quantitative relations among them for the synthesis of blood proteins.

As early as 1914 studies had been made by several investigators which showed that the stroma, which is the residue of red blood corpuscles after the removal of hemoglobin and bodies soluble in water, consists of lecithin, cholesterol, a nucleoalbumin, and a globulin, together with mineral substances. Formation of blood obviously required, in addition to iron, certain amounts of amino acids, pyrrols, and whatever was necessary for the synthesis of complex lipids and cholesterol. Its formation obviously represented complex nutritional demands for structural units or their precursors, most of which were of unknown nature. Matters stood thus when Whipple and Robscheit-Robbins conducted their experiments designed to show the values of different foods as sources of structural materials for blood formation.

Using dogs which had been prepared by repeated, measured bleedings, Whipple and Robscheit-Robbins distinguished regeneration of plasma proteins, hemoglobin, and stroma. Only their data relating to regeneration of hemoglobin will be considered, as illustrative of their study.

The data secured in these experiments did not reveal the limiting factor in the efficiency of the different foods. Whipple and Robscheit-Robbins attempted to distinguish between stroma-producing and hemoglobin-producing substances in the foods by comparing the rates of red cell and of hemoglobin regeneration in their standardized anemic dogs. Unfortunately, the differences observed were small, and the experimental conditions were so complicated that the significance of their data was doubtful. The merit of these studies lay in the discovery of the great superiority over other foods of liver, kidney, and chicken gizzard for blood formation. This study was so highly rated by scientists that Whipple was honored by sharing the Nobel Award with Minot and Murphy.

HEMOGLOBIN PRODUCTION AS INFLUENCED BY DIET . .

Diet (grams daily)	Hemoglobin production (Two-week feeding period)
Bread 400	3 Grams
Milk 450, bread 400	3 "
Cream 100, bread 400	10 "
Butter 111, bread 350	15 "
Asparagus 200, bread 300	9 "
Spinach 200, bread 300	15 "
Raspberries 200, bread 300	5 "
Raisins 200, bread 300	25 "
Apricots 200, bread 300	48 "
Eggs 150, bread 300	45 "
Whole fish 250, bread 300	13 "
Beef muscle 250, bread 300	17 "
Pig muscle 250, bread 300	30 "
Chicken gizzard 250, bread 300	80 "
Kidney 250, bread 300	70 "
Chicken liver, bread 300	80 "
Beef liver 300, bread 300	80 "
Beef liver 450	95 "

Minot and Murphy's Discovery

The observations of Whipple and Robscheit-Robbins were so striking that Minot and Murphy (28), in 1927, tested the effects of feeding liver to patients with pernicious anemia. Up to that time, this disorder had never responded to medical treatment, although spontaneous remissions had many times been observed by clinicians.

In pernicious anemia the total amount of red cell forming tissue in the bone marrow is increased, as is the case in some other types of anemia. The cells are larger than normal and their nuclei exhibit a peculiar scroll-like arrangement of the chromatin. These megaloblasts differ in appearance from normal immature red cells, and are characteristic of the type of anemia designated as pernicious. It must suffice here to state only that in pernicious anemia the bone marrow is packed with immature red cells which cannot be matured and liberated into the blood stream. Minot and Murphy observed that when patients with this disorder ingested large amounts of liver, a "reticulocyte shower" occurred, which was manifested by the appearance in the blood of a large number of immature red cells. Following this phenomenon, the hematopoietic elements in the marrow were able to resume their normal function of maturing red cells, and the patient experienced remission of the anemia.

The clinical work done by Minot and Murphy dramatically demonstrated that pernicious anemia is a nutritional disease caused by lack of some essential nutrient. Successful efforts were soon made to concentrate the liver-factor effective in the treatment, and a comprehensive program of investigation into the nutritional factors involved in blood formation resulted within a few years in the emergence of a new and very important segment of biochemistry. The most important discovery resulting from this type of study prior to 1940 was that of folic acid.

The great difficulty experienced by pernicious anemia patients in taking the large amount of liver necessary to maintain their improved blood status, led Cohn (29) to prepare a concentrate of liver which was designated fraction G. This contained in high concentration the erythrocyte maturation factor (EMF), and was widely used in clinical work. It was considered to contain the end product of the interaction between something called by Castle (30) extrinsic factor, present in certain foods (e.g., beef muscle), with a substance called intrinsic factor, which is found in the secretions of the gastric mucosa. This liver concentrate was of great service to investigators of the metabolic steps involved in the development and remission of pernicious anemia.

The Utilization of Iron in Hemoglobin Building

An investigation of outstanding importance in the advancement of nutritional science was made in 1925 by Hart, Steenbock, Elvehjem, and Waddell (31). The observation had been made by clinicians that babies on a milk diet often developed anemia during the first year of life. From the observations of von Bunge (19) it had been generally accepted that this was due to iron starvation after the prenatal store of iron in the liver had been used up. Hart and his associates introduced new and surprising concepts of this problem.

They noted that rabbits limited to a diet of milk with addition of sodium citrate developed anemia. Growth continued at approximately the normal rate until the hemoglobin values and red cell counts fell to about 50 per cent of the normal. The addition of ferric salts did not correct the deficiency, but recovery resulted when the diet was supplemented with cabbage, an alcoholic extract of desiccated cabbage, yellow maize meal, or daily dosage of the animals with 25 mg. of purified chlorophyll (free from iron). Anemia did not develop if such supplements were given with a milk and iron diet. They suggested that perhaps vitamin E, identified by Evans and Bishop, might be identical with the substance needed by animals for hemoglobin formation.

Later studies by Hart and his associates (32) on the cause of the anemia produced by an exclusive milk diet were conducted with rats. Milk-diet anemia in this species was not cured by the daily administration of iron as pure chloride, sulfate, citrate, acetate, or phosphate. But the anemia was promptly cured by feeding daily 0.5 mg. of iron in a supplement consisting of the ash of liver, lettuce, yellow maize, or acid extracts of these ashes. These results clearly demonstrated that the failure of animals to assimilate and utilize pure iron compounds for hemoglobin formation was due to deficiency of some inorganic substance, since ashing of a food destroys all organic compounds. They then found that the precipitate formed by passing hydrogen sulfide into a solution of the ash of a natural food, especially of liver, was as effective in preventing or curing milk-diet anemia as was the ash itself. On further inquiry they traced the effect produced by natural foods and ashes in improving iron utilization to their content of copper. Thus it became apparent that milk does not lack any organic substance necessary for iron utilization and for supplying precursors of the pyrrol nucleus of hemoglobin, but that iron cannot be utilized for this purpose except when copper is available.

A controversy lasted several years over the question whether manganese, nickel, germanium, or arsenic could, like copper, make possible utilization of iron under the conditions of the milk-feeding studies. The question was answered by Sheldon and Ramage (33) who examined spectrographically five iron preparations used for therapeutic purposes, and found that copper was present in four of them.

Manganese, they found, was a constant impurity in iron salts available to them.

Later investigations relating to iron as it functions in respiratory pigments had to do with the role of cobalt in metabolism. The role of this element and folic acid in hematopoiesis are discussed elsewhere. But by the time these essential nutrients had come to light investigations of the several types of anemias had progressed so far that it was evident that a number of factors other than the utilization of iron were involved.

REFERENCES

1. Boyle, R.: Memoir for the Natural History of Extravasated Human Blood (1684).
2. Menghini, V.: De Ferreorum Particulerum sede in Sanguis. Commentar. Bononiens (Bologna) ii, p. 475 (1747).
3. Johnson, W. B.: The History and Present Status of Animal Chemistry. London, 1803. 3 vols. vol. *1*, p. 45.
4. Bucquet: Article on blood, in Macquer's Dictionnaire de Chimie. 2nd ed. (1797).
5. Wells: Philos. Trans. (1797) p. 416.

6a. Le Canu, L. R.: Journ. de Pharmacie, *17*, 485, 545 (1831).

6b. Le Canu, L. R.: Études Chimiques sur le Sang Humain, Paris (1837).

7. Berzelius, J.: Animal Chemistry (1808), vol. 2.
8. Ancell, H.: Series of lectures on blood. Lancet (London) (1840).
9. Simon, J. F.: Animal Chemistry. 2 vols. vol. *1*, 100–350 (1845).
10. Tiedemann, F.: Untersuchungen über das Nahrungs-Bedürfniss, den Nahrungs-Trieb und die Nahrungs-Mittel des Menschen. Darmstadt (1836).
11. Sanson and Scherer: Ann. d. Chem. u. Pharm. *40*, 30 (1841).
12. Mulder, G. J. and Goudoever: J. fur prakt. Chem. 32, 185 (1844).
13. The Greek Myths, Robert Graves. Vol. I, p. 234. Penguin Books, Baltimore (1955).
14. Garrison, F. H.: History of Medicine. 3d ed. (1921) p. 319.
15. Hayem, G.: Compt. Rend. 83, 152, 230 (1876).

16. Boussingault, J. B.: Compt. Rend. *64*, 1353 (1867).
17. Subbotin, V.: Zeitschr. f. Biol. *7*, 185–196 (1871).
18. Zaleski, St.: Zeitschr. f. physiol. Chem. *10*, 453 (1886).
19. Bunge, G. von: Zeitschr. f. physiol. Chem. *13*, 399 (1889).
20. Hösslin, H. von: Maly's Jahresbericht *12*, 435 (1882).
21. Addison, T.: London Med. Gazette *43*, 517 (1849).
22. Bunge, G. von: Physiological and Pathological Chemistry, Chapter 25.
23. Schunck, C. A. and Marchlewski, L.: Liebig's Annalen *284*, 81 (1895).
24. Schunck, C. A. and Marchlewski, L.: Liebig's Annalen *290*, 306 (1896).
25. Nencki, M. von and Zaleski, J.: Ber. d. deutschen chem. Ges. *34*, 1, 977 (1901).
26. Whipple, G. H. and Robscheit-Robbins, F. S.: Amer. J. Physiol. *72*, 395 (1925).
27. Robscheit-Robbins, F. S.: Amer. J. Physiol. *83*, 76 (1927); Physiol. Reviews *9*, 666–709 (1929).
28. Minot, G. R. and Murphy, W. P.: Journ. Amer. Med. Assoc. *139*, 759 (1927).
29. Cohn, E. J., Minot, G. R., Alles, G. A. and Salter, W. T.: J. Biol. Chem. *77*, 325 (1928).
30. Castle, W. B. and Minot, G. R.: Pathological Physiology and Clinical Description of Anemias (Ed. by Henry A. Christian). Oxford University Press, New York (1936).
31. Hart, E. B., Steenbock, H., Elvehjem, C. A. and Waddell, J.: J. Biol. Chem. *65*, 67–80 (1925).
32. Hart, E. B., Steenbock, H., Elvehjem, C. A. and Waddell, J.: J. Biol. Chem. *77*, 777–779 (1928).
33. Sheldon, J. H. and Ramage, H.: Biochem. J. *25*, 1608–1627 (1931).

23

The Discovery of Vitamin E (Alpha-Tocopherol)

THE YEAR 1922 marked the emergence of a new concept in nutritional research derived from observations on failure of fetal nutrition in the rat when a certain experimental diet was employed. This failure was obviated by the provision of an unknown substance X contained in various foods but not identifiable with any known nutrient. Many well-planned experiments carried out by Mattill, Evans, Sure, and their associates established the existence of a new member of the vitamin family.

Sterility, premature delivery, fetal death, before or at term, and failure of the parturient mother to deliver her young, had been previously described in nutrition studies on animals fed certain experimental diets. Hart and his associates (1) had in 1911 described fetal death, with premature delivery, and also still-birth at term in cows fed wheat or oat plant products only.

In 1914 Hart and McCollum (2) observed in sows restricted during a period of five months to a ration of maize kernel and a salt mixture, inability to deliver their litters at term. When it was evident that the sows were in a state of exhaustion and were making no progress in parturition, they were killed and the young removed by section. A typical case was a sow from whose uterus eight pigs, alive but hairless, were removed; the pigs did not survive. Although at that time the cause was not understood, this condition was later to be traced to deficiency of iodine.

In 1915 McCollum and Davis (3) made a study of the influence of the composition and amount of the inorganic content of rations on growth and reproduction in the rat. In some of their experimental animals there was sterility; in others gestation was completed but with early death of the young; whereas in still other groups the young were normal and the mortality rate low. They stated that it was apparent that normal growth to maturity is but one of several criteria of satisfactory nutrition.

In 1920 Mattill and Conklin (4) found that rats reared on cows' milk with added iron grew well and appeared to be in good nutritive condition, but were usually sterile. They suggested that milk was deficient in some substance essential for reproduction.

Infertility Traced to Deficiency of a New Vitamin

The outstanding event which stimulated interest and experimental inquiry into reproductive failure of dietary origin was the announcement in 1922 by Evans and Scott (5) that rats raised on certain diets capable of inducing growth were of low fertility in the first generation and wholly sterile in the second. Small supplements of fresh lettuce, wheat germs, or dried alfalfa leaves corrected this defect. Evans and Bishop (6) showed that the "substance X" was not any known nutrient.

In 1923 Sure (7) independently came to the same conclusion, and since the four vitamins then known were called A, B, C, and D, he suggested that the substance X or the "fertility vitamin" be called vitamin E. Sure added velvet bean pod, polished rice, rolled oats, and yellow maize to the list of foods which contained the new substance.

Dietary Fat and Vitamin E Deficiency

Mattill and his associates (8) (1922–24) continued to study sterility in rats on E deficient diets. They described testicular degeneration in E deficient rats. They also found that a high lard content of the diet favored the development of sterility. Evans and Burr (9) (1927) found that vitamin E seemed to be destroyed when mixed with a diet rich in lard, and that the animals remained fertile if an E preparation was given separately.

Resorption of Embryos in E deficient Female Rats

In their study of the effect of diet on the ovulatory rhythm and the various steps in the physiology of reproduction, Evans and Bishop (10) made an illuminating observation which the chemists would have overlooked. They found that on supposedly complete dietaries, which supported normal growth to maturity and apparently normal physiological well-being, rats would exhibit normal estrus cycles and would ovulate, breed, and conceive; however, they were unable to experience normal gestation because of invariable death of the fetuses. As already stated, the cause of this failure of reproduction was traced to a hitherto unsuspected dietary factor, "substance X." The great merit of the study of Evans and Bishop lay in their careful description of the anatomical lesions and physiological manifestations which resulted from lack of a specific nutrient.

They showed that in E deficiency the ovaries are undamaged, the fertilized ova implant, and the weight of the pregnant rat follows the normal curve. The fetus shows the first signs of retarded development at the eighth day of gestation. By the twelfth day defects appear in the blood system which are manifest in abnormality of the fetal liver, and deficiency of blood islands in the yolk sac and of erythroblasts in the heart and blood-vessels. Death of the fetus occurs on the thirteenth day as the result of asphyxiation. The young are not aborted but undergo autolytic dissolution and are resorbed. The dramatic salvaging of the fetuses by giving the mother a suitable dose of vitamin E as late as the fifth day after mating aroused great interest among nutrition investigators.

Evans and his associates (11) also described in detail the anatomical abnormalities which result from deficiency of the antineuritic vitamin and from deficiency of vitamin A, thus showing the syndrome of E deficiency to be unique. They also described the histological changes in the germinal epithelium of male rats in this deficiency state. Their introduction of histological and anatomical technics into the study of E deficiency raised nutrition investigations concerned with other nutrients to a higher level than had been attained by biochemists.

Other Manifestations of E Deficiency

For some years the view was generally accepted that the function of vitamin E was essentially limited to the reproductive mechanism, but this concept proved too narrow. In 1928 Evans and Burr (12) described the occurrence of paralysis in young rats arising from E deficiency. These were the progeny of mothers which were kept on diets deficient in this factor, but given enough of the vitamin to last through one gestation period. Young from these mothers appeared healthy but many suddenly developed paralysis about the twenty-first day. This affliction could be prevented by giving small doses of vitamin E to the young, but only if given before the fifteenth day.

The paralysis in young rats due to vitamin E deficiency was studied in detail by Ringsted (13), who described pigmentation and degeneration of the muscles of the hind limbs. He considered the condition to be identical with that described in 1931 by Goettsch and Pappenheimer (14) in rabbits and guinea pigs kept on a certain experimental diet. The latter investigators had noted that histologically the changes in the muscles were identical with those in muscular dystrophy. They were at first of the opinion that muscle dystrophy in these species was the result of E deficiency, because among the diets which they found to cause the abnormality there was one which had been treated with ferric chloride in ether solution for the purpose of destroying vitamin E. This method had been devised by Waddell and Steenbock (15) and was believed to destroy E completely without deleterious effects on vitamin A. That the untreated diet of Goettsch and Pappenheimer contained vitamin E was shown by the fact that it could cure sterility in E deficient female rats, and could also maintain spermatogenesis in males. But Goettsch and Pappenheimer were misled by finding that administration of a sample of wheat germ oil of proven efficiency as a source of the vitamin for rats failed to prevent muscular dystrophy in rabbits or guinea pigs. They concluded, therefore, that the assumption that deficiency of E was the cause of muscular dystrophy was a fallacy, and that their experimental results had eliminated deficiency of the vitamin as a factor in the production of this disorder. They stated that the lesions "must be referred to some still unknown factor." Their findings may be explained on the assumption that they made a mistake in assessing the E content of some of their rations, or that species varied in susceptibility to muscular dystrophy and requirements for the vitamin.

In further studies Pappenheimer and Goettsch (16) described the transmission of nutritional muscular dystrophy to rabbits *in utero* and stated, "It is not justifiable at the present time to speak of this condition as a deficiency disease. But evidence is accumulating that the addition of vegetable oils (soy bean oil, cottonseed oil) to the experimental diet exercises a protective effect."

In 1936 Morgulis and Spencer (17) expressed the belief that the results of their studies on the cause of muscular dystrophy confirmed the conclusions of Goettsch and Pappenheimer. They wrote that "neither the presence of ferric chloride itself in Diet 13, nor the absence of vitamin E from this diet can be regarded as the principal factor in the production of nutritional muscular dystrophy."

The subject was so intriguing that numerous investigators entered the field. By May, 1941, 1,248 scientific papers had appeared dealing with various aspects of the problem and with different species. The subject became more confused instead of being clarified. Some even denied that certain herbivora require vitamin E. Among these were Thomas and Cannon (18), who reported in 1937 the results of feeding a herd of goats a diet composed of natural foods treated with ferric chloride to destroy vitamin E. The treated diet was tested on male rats and these became sterile after five months. The goats ate the diet for four and a half years and remained in health, as evidenced by the birth of third generation young. Thomas and Cannon were wrong in believing their goats did not secure vitamin E from some source.

Doubt was also cast on the significance of vitamin E as a factor in the etiology of paralysis in young rats by the finding of Evans and Burr. They observed that some young which suckled mothers deficient in E became paralyzed, but when fed a vitamin E deficient diet they recovered spontaneously and remained normal. Yet they found that if wheat germ oil was given within the first six weeks of postnatal life paresis did not develop. If the oil was given from the eighth week paresis began six to eight weeks later. Wheat germ oil did not cure the condition, but prevented its development. The spontaneous recovery of some young must be assumed to have resulted from unsuspected access to vitamin E.

Einarson and Ringsted (19) interpreted their experimental observations to signify that the nervous system was involved in the etiology of experimental muscular dystrophy. Rats kept long on an E deficient diet exhibited ataxia and increasing atrophy of the musculature of the hindquarters. In the earlier stages the muscular changes suggested muscular dystrophy, while in the final stages they distinctly resembled amyotrophic lateral sclerosis. The morbid anatomical picture resembled a combination of two types of systemic degenerations occurring in man, viz., tabes dorsalis and amyotrophic lateral sclerosis. It was suggested, therefore, that E deficiency might play a role in the development of some of the degenerative nervous diseases, especially the muscular dystrophies and amyotrophies.

In 1931 Pappenheimer and Goettsch (20) found that a high fat, E deficient diet caused the development in chicks of nutritional encephalomalacia, but in ducklings on the same dietary regimen muscular dystrophy resulted. Jungherr and Pappenheimer (22) found that in poults subjected to such diets, myopathy of the gizzard occurred. On the same type of diet but low in fat Dam and Glavind (23) found in chicks the development of exudative diathesis, characterized by the accumulation of serum under the skin. Such species differences in response to deficiency are not paralleled in any other deficiency disease.

Mason (24) made notable contributions to knowledge of the manner in which germinal cells are affected in male rats by deficiency of vitamins A and E and by inanition. He found that in E deficiency there are well-defined and characteristic changes in the cell nucleus.

Barrie (25) described in detail the abnormalities in young rats kept on diets deficient in E. He noted abnormally soft skulls, deficient ossification, hypoplastic thyroids, and pathological changes in the cells of the anterior lobe of the pituitary. Gestations were prolonged. He interpreted his observations to lend support to the view that vitamin E is required for the normal functioning of the anterior lobe of the pituitary, and asserted that the symptoms are analogous to those seen after its removal. Verzár (26) had in 1931 suggested such a relationship between vitamin E and the hypophysis. His observations brought the endocrine system into the vitamin E problem.

Experimental Difficulties in the Study of Vitamin E

From the account here presented it will be seen that up to 1939 progress in investigating the nature and function of vitamin E was somewhat erratic, and not so successful as had been the progress made in investigating other vitamins. The technic of investigation was time consuming and expensive, since it involved the use of adult rats or other animals, and their frequent examination throughout the course of long experimental periods. The response of animals deficient in vitamin E was one that is not susceptible of numerical evaluation in respect to weight increase or other criteria involving an arbitrary scale, such as is possible in some other vitamin studies. But a consideration of greatest importance was the inability of chemists to determine the presence or absence of vitamin E qualitatively, or quantitatively, and its susceptibility to destruction in the presence of rancid fats; hence the impossibility of preventing progressive decomposition of E in batches of rations undergoing rancidity during feeding experiments. Furthermore, so long as the experimental inquiries were mostly limited to laboratory animals, those interested in domestic animals were not strongly motivated to undertake studies with economically valuable animals. Such reports as that of Thomas and Cannon, which appeared to show that vitamin E was of no significance in the nutrition of goats, slackened interest in researches with this nutrient.

So long as investigators were employing wheat germ oil, the unsaponifiable fraction from it, or natural foods as sources of vitamin E, there never was certainty in the interpretation of results because of the possible significance of other unidentified substances present. The daily amount ingested could not be estimated. Furthermore, when foods were treated with ferric chloride to destroy vitamin E, there were reasons for believing that other important nutrients, especially vitamin A, were partly destroyed — hence, uncertainty prevailed in interpretation of experimental observations. Isolation and chemical identification of vitamin E was, therefore, of the greatest importance for further progress in the study of its physiological functions. Advances in knowledge bearing on these objectives began with the studies of Olcott and Mattill in 1931.

Isolation and Identification of Vitamin E

Olcott and Mattill (27) fractionated the oil of lettuce, and prepared a fraction having high antioxidant power and high potency as a source of vitamin E. Their discovery that this vitamin has a protective action against development of rancidity pointed to probability that a function of E might be intervention in fat metabolism, especially of unsaturated fats, since its presence in such fats inhibited spontaneous formation of peroxides which is the initial step in rancidity.

In 1936 Evans, H. P. Emerson, and G. A. Emerson (28) prepared from the nonsaponifiable matter of wheat germ oil esters of three alcohols with allophanic acid. One of these was found by biological test to be of high vitamin E potency. This was called alpha-tocopherol, and proved to be the sought-for vitamin E. In 1937 Fernholz (29) subjected alpha-tocopherol to thermal decomposition and to strong oxidation, and identified a number of the simpler chemical substances which were formed. From the nature of these derivatives he was able to suggest a structural formula for the vitamin.

In 1938 Karrer and his associates (30) succeeded in synthesizing alpha-tocopherol, and in proving its biological activity. After 1939 pure vitamin E was available to experimenters both as the natural and the synthetic product. As a result, an advance was possible in formulating experimental diets, and in making certain that the responses of animals fed such diets were the result of deprivation or provision of a single dietary factor.

Old Age Paralysis in E Deficient Rats

In 1940 Mackenzie and his associates (31) restricted rats from weaning age to a diet of highly purified nutrients deficient in vitamin E, and noted that at thirty-two to forty weeks the first signs of paralysis were manifest. Paralysis progressed in severity to such a degree that the hindquarters were dragged along the floor. Attempts to cure the animals through the administration of a vitamin E concentrate over a period of twenty weeks were unsuccessful, but the progress of the neuro-muscular signs was definitely arrested and a growth response was elicited.

Mackenzie and associates (32) also restricted rats to a simplified diet which was rendered almost "fat-free," the total lipid content being only 0.27 per cent; the non-vitamin lipid content including vitamin E concentrate was only 0.156 per cent, and without it only 0.0056 per cent. The other fat-soluble essentials were added in pure form. On this diet rats which developed the early signs of paralysis were restored to normal neuro-muscular function by the administration of vitamin E.

Muscular Dystrophy in the Rabbit

Mackenzie and McCollum were convinced that muscular dystrophy in the rabbit is caused by deficiency of vitamin E and that no other dietary factor was involved. However, they felt that still more conclusive proof was desirable. In order to follow the development of the disease more closely, and to be able to detect the response to potent supplements of vitamin E, they undertook to follow the progress of this disorder in rabbits by noting the food consumption, weight change, and creatine output. In 1932 Goettsch and Brown (34) had shown that in muscular dystrophy in the rabbit on an E deficient diet there is an absolute as well as a relative loss of creatine in the skeletal muscle without any demonstrable loss in either heart or brain. Mackenzie and McCollum felt that such experiments would yield data which would make possible a definite decision concerning the involvement of vitamin E in muscular dystrophy in rabbits. They deemed such a study imperative because of the conclusion of Pappenheimer and of Morgulis, already cited, that the disorder could not be attributed to lack of vitamin E.

Mackenzie and McCollum found that creatinuria in the rabbit developed prior to loss of weight, loss of appetite, or the manifestation of physical impairment. On the basis of these criteria it was possible to predict the onset of the disease with considerable accuracy and to follow its progress to the acute and fatal phase. The creatine output of a healthy rabbit is almost nil, but with the onset of muscular dystrophy it rises, and in thirty to forty days in the case of a rabbit weighing 1 kg. may rise to 80 mg. per day. Severely dystrophic rabbits given daily doses of 5 mg. of natural alpha-tocopherol, resumed eating, and showed a pronounced drop in creatine excretion within two to four days. They increased their food consumption as recovery progressed, gained weight; the physical impairment steadily lessened and disappeared. Therapy was continued through seven months and during this time the animals grew well and became vigorous. No muscle lesions were found at autopsy. The cure was complete and permanent. It seems that the evidence from these experiments prove that the primary lesion in E deficient rabbits is in the skeletal muscles.

Toxicity of Certain Fats and Fatty Acids

In 1923 Hopkins (35) reported that diets containing a high fat content derived from cod liver oil caused injury to rats. He suggested that this was due to imbalance of the fat-soluble vitamins supplied by the oil, as compared with other vitamins in the diet. However, in 1926 Agduhr (36) offered proof that even small amounts of cod liver oil given continuously produced injurious effects, especially on the heart muscle, in mice, rats, rabbits, dogs, calves, cats, pigs, and human infants. In describing the lesions he noted pigment degeneration, fatty degeneration of the heart muscle, replacement of muscle substance by connective tissue, and deposition of calcareous incrustations. Parallel experiments with olive oil, rapeseed oil, or cocoa fat did not produce the lesions caused by cod liver oil. Apparently he did not examine the skeletal muscles of his animals.

This "cod liver oil injury" was studied extensively by Madsen, McCay, Maynard, Woodward, and Davis (37), who confirmed and extended the observations of Agduhr. They, like Agduhr, studied only the heart muscle. It thus appeared that muscular dystrophy involving the heart at least, could be caused by a positive agent inherent in or associated with the highly unsaturated fatty acids in cod liver oil, as well as by deficiency of vitamin E.

The demonstration by Mackenzie and McCollum that muscle dystrophy in rabbits was caused by lack of alpha-tocopherol, and that severely dystrophic animals recovered spectacularly when given tocopherol, afforded an opportunity for investigation of the nature of "cod liver oil injury" in this species. Therefore, they undertook to find answers to two questions: Does vitamin E deficiency, in the absence of animal fat in the food, lead to rapid development of fatal dystrophy? Can alpha-tocopherol prevent dystrophy produced by ingestion of cod liver oil?

Young rabbits were restricted to an experimental diet which contained neither vitamin E nor an appreciable amount of any fats. The animals developed muscular dystrophy as rapidly on the "fat-free diet" as they did on a lard-containing diet of comparable composition. In both instances the muscle lesions were completely prevented by the provision of alpha-tocopherol. From these studies it was apparent that vitamin E deficiency, without any influence of dietary fat, will cause muscular dystrophy in the rabbit.

In another series of experiments the effect was studied of giving cod liver oil and adequate daily doses of alpha-tocopherol to rabbits kept on the "fat-free diet." Half of the rabbits were fed daily 1 ml. of fresh medicinal cod liver oil immediately following the alpha-tocopherol supplement. These animals developed severe muscle lesions. The rabbits of the control group did not receive cod liver oil and remained normal. Obviously, the fatty acids of cod liver oil caused muscle injury.

Cod Liver Oil Injury

The studies of Mattill and his associates revealed that rancid and autoxidizing fats destroy vitamin E. Mackenzie and McCollum suspected that the cod liver oil fed in their experiments destroyed the alpha-tocopherol, even though this was given in separate doses following the administration of the cod liver oil. Because of this, they tried giving the tocopherol and cod liver oil separately twenty-four hours apart to prevent their coming into contact in the alimentary tract. The animals used in this test developed severe muscle lesions. In other experiments in which cod liver oil colored with Sudan III was fed to rabbits, it was found at autopsy four hours later that the stained oil could be seen in the duodenum and small intestine, but that after twenty-four hours no cod liver oil remained unabsorbed. Thus Mackenzie and McCollum concluded that contact of alpha-tocopherol and the fats of cod liver oil within the body after absorption caused destruction of the vitamin. This view was supported by the finding that if the dose of tocopherol was greatly increased, and fed twenty-four hours apart from the oil, the animals were protected. Destruction occurred, but the excessive dose left enough for exerting its function in the tissues.

Since the muscle lesions were the same when dystrophy was caused by giving cod liver oil, or by deprivation of vitamin E and a "fat-free diet," the function of vitamin E as an anti-oxidant *in vitro* as shown by Mattill also holds for it *in vivo.*

Physiological Injury from Ingestion of Rancid Fats

The conclusion drawn by Mackenzie and McCollum was substantiated by the observations made by Whipple (38) in 1932, who described "oxidized fat syndrome" in dogs kept on a diet containing oxidized fat. The manifestations of this disorder were described as loss of hair, skin lesions, anorexia, emaciation, and intestinal hemorrhages. She obtained similar results with rats (39). She did not report examination of muscles for degenerative changes.

Pigment Formation from Oxidized Fats

The studies of Hass (40) in 1938 focussed attention on the polymerization of peroxides of unsaturated fats to form pigments. Martin and Moore (41) were first to note the chocolate-discoloration of the uteri of rats in vitamin E deficiency. Subsequent histological studies by Barrie (42) and by Martin and Moore (43) showed that pigment was deposited in fine granules in cells of the uterine musculature. The most probable source of this pigment appears to be polymerization of peroxides of unsaturated fats. Vitamin E in fats inhibits the formation of peroxides.

Increased Oxygen Uptake of Muscles in Vitamin E Deficiency

In 1934 Victor (44), who was associated with Pappenheimer, found a marked increase in uptake of oxygen by myopathic muscles from E deficient rabbits, *in vitro,* as compared with corresponding normal muscles. The rheobase and chronaxie were also greater than normal. Madsen (45) obtained similar results, and Friedman and Mattill (46) further substantiated the finding by showing that strips of muscle removed from rabbits kept six months on an E deficient diet exhibited oxygen uptake higher than normal. Alpha-tocopherol administration lowered oxygen uptake. The oxygen receptor in the myopathic tissues was not identified.

The experimental evidence available in 1940 seems to demonstrate that the pathological state arising from deficiency of alpha-tocopherol involves abnormal behavior of unsaturated fatty acids in metabolism. Apparently this was referrable to formation of peroxides of these acids and abnormal degradation of these by cleavage in their metabolism, to form peroxides, aldehydes, ketones, and the like, which are injurious to the blood vessels and anatomical elements in the nervous system. It appeared that at least one function of vitamin E is to prevent the formation of peroxides of unsaturated fats in the food before ingestion, and also within the tissues after absorption. It was also certain that the presence in fats of alpha-tocopherol does not arrest but only delays peroxide formation and the subsequent further development of rancidity, and that as rancidity progresses alpha-tocopherol is destroyed.

To extend this account to studies made after 1941 would add little or nothing to the history of thought and experiment which has been here presented. There still remains the possibility that vitamin E may function in some enzyme system in muscles, or in a relation to some endocrine organ.

The use of vitamin E as a therapeutic agent in the treatment of muscular dystrophy in human subjects has without exception met with failure (47). This is in striking contrast to the dramatic cures produced by its administration in the experimentally produced disorder. To the present writer this suggests that alpha-tocopherol is in the normal muscle synthesized into a complex which functions in the respiratory process of that tissue. Human muscular dystrophy may result from loss of the function of synthesizing this complex even when the vitamin is available. In muscular dystrophy in the rabbit, brought about by deprivation of alpha-tocopherol, it appears that the power of utilizing it for synthesis of the hypothetical complex is not lost, hence prompt recovery with muscle regeneration can take place when the missing chemical unit is made available.

REFERENCES

1. Hart, E. B., McCollum, E. V., Steenbock, H. and Humphrey, G. C.: Res. Bull. No. 17, Wisconsin Agric. Exp. Sta. (1911).
2. Hart, E. B. and McCollum, E. V.: J. Biol. Chem. *19,* 373 (1914).
3. McCollum, E. V. and Davis, M.: J. Biol. Chem. *21,* 615 (1915).
4. Mattill, H. A. and Conklin, R. E.: J. Biol. Chem. *44,* 137 (1920). Mattill, H. A. and Carman, J. S.: Proc. Soc. Exp. Biol. and Med. *20,* 420 (1922–23).
5. Evans, H. M. and Scott, K. J.: Science *56,* 650 (1922).
6. Evans, H. M. and Bishop, K. S.: J. Metabolic Res. *1,* 319 (1922).
7. Sure, B.: J. Biol. Chem. *58,* 693 (1924).
8. Mattill, *et al.* Ref. 4.
9. Evans, H. M. and Burr, G. O.: J. Amer. Med. Assoc. *88,* 1462; *89,* 1587 (1927).
10. Evans, H. M. and Bishop, K. S.: J. Metabolic Res. *1,* 319, 335 (1922); Science *56,* 650–51 (1922).
11. Evans, H. M.: J. Amer. Med. Assoc. *99,* 469–75 (1932).
12. Evans, H. M. and Burr, G. O.: Memoirs of Univ. of Calif. *8,* 1–176 (1927).
13. Ringsted, A.: Biochem. J. *29,* 788 (1935).
14. Goettsch, M. and Pappenheimer, A. M.: J. Exp. Med. *64,* 145–65 (1931).
15. Waddell, J. and Steenbock, H.: J. Biol. Chem. *80,* 431–42 (1928).
16. Pappenheimer, A. M. and Goettsch, M.: Proc. Soc. Exp. Biol. and Med. *34,* 522–25 (1936).
17. Morgulis, S. and Spencer, H. C.: J. Nut. *11,* 573–89 (1936).
18. Thomas, B. H. and Cannon, C. Y.: Proc. Amer. Soc. Animal Prod. (1937) p. 59.
19. Einarson, L. and Ringsted, A.: Brit. Med. J. *ii,* 745–46 (1938).
20. Pappenheimer, A. M. and Goettsch, M.: J. Exp. Med. *53,* 11–26 (1931).
21. Pappenheimer, A. M. and Goettsch, M.: J. Exp. Med. *59,* 35–42 (1934).
22. Jungherr, E. and Pappenheimer, A. M.: Proc. Soc. Exp. Biol. and Med. *37,* 520–26 (1937).
23. Dam, H. and Glavind, J.: Skand. Arch. Physiol. *82,* 299 (1939).

24. Mason, K. E.: J. Exp. Zool. *55,* 101–22 (1930).

25. Barrie, M. M. O.: Nature, London *139,* 286 (1937); Lancet *2,* 251–54 (1937); Biochem. J. 32, 1467–73 (1938).

26. Verzár, F.: Arch. f. d. ges. Physiol. *227,* 499–510 (1931); Chem. Absts. *26,* 1013 (1931).

27. Olcott, H. S. and Mattill, H. A.: J. Biol. *93,* 65 (1931).

28. Evans, H. M., Emerson, H. P. and Emerson, G. A.: J. Biol. Chem. *113,* 319–22 (1936).

29. Fernholz, E.: J. Amer. Chem. Soc. *60,* 700–05 (1938).

30. Karrer, P., Fritzsche, H., Ringier, B. H. and Salomon, H.: Helvt. chim. acta *21,* 810–25 (1938).

31. Mackenzie, C. G., Mackenzie, J. B. and McCollum, E. V.: Proc. Soc. Exp. Biol. and Med. *44,* 95–98 (1940).

32. Mackenzie, C. G., Mackenzie, J. B. and McCollum, E. V.: Biochem. J. *33,* 935–42 (1939).

33. Mackenzie, C. G. and McCollum, E. V.: Science *89,* 370–71 (1939); J. Nut. *19,* 345–62 (1940).

34. Goettsch, M. and Brown, E. F.: J. Biol. Chem. *97,* 549–61 (1932).

35. Hopkins, F. G.: Brit. Med. J. *2,* 691 (1923).

36. Agduhr, E.: Acta paediat. *5,* 319 (1926); *6,* 165 (1926); *7,* 289 (1928).

37. Woodward, J. W.; and McCay, C. M.: Proc. Soc. Exp. Biol. and Med. *30,* 241 (1932).
Madsen, L. L., McCay, C. M. and Maynard, L. A.: Cornell Univ. Exp. Sta. Memoir No. 178 (1936).
Davis, G. L., Maynard, L. A. and McCay, C. M.: Cornell Univ. Agr. Exp. Sta. Memoir No. 217 (1938).

38. Whipple, D. V.: Proc. Soc. Exp. Biol. and Med. *30,* 319–21 (1932).

39. Whipple, D. V.: Oil and Soap *10,* 228–29 (1933).

40. Hass, G. M.: Arch. Path. *26,* 1196 (1938); *28,* 177 (1939).

41. Martin, A. J. P. and Moore, T.: Chemistry and Ind. *65,* 236 (1936).

42. Barrie, M. M. O.: Biochem. J. 32, 2134 (1938).

43. Martin, A. J. P. and Moore, T.: J. Hyg. *39,* 643 (1939).

44. Victor, J.: Amer. J. Physiol. *108,* 229 (1934).

45. Madsen, L. L.: J. Nut. *11,* 471 (1936).

46. Friedman, I. and Mattill, H. A.: Amer. J. Physiol. *131,* 595 (1941).

24

The Discovery of the Necessity for Certain Fatty Acids in the Diet

FOR SEVERAL DECADES nutrition investigators believed that no important physiological problem existed with which fat was concerned except the manner of the degradation of fatty acids in the course of their oxidation. There were two reasons for the general acceptance of this view: the early proof that fats could be synthesized in the body from carbohydrates, and the evidence produced by Rubner that fat and carbohydrate in metabolism are interchangeable in isocaloric values. However, this point was not actually proven, and in 1920 Osborne and Mendel (1) sought an answer to the question. They used young rats as experimental subjects. To these they fed a diet of starch 72, protein (washed meat residue, thoroughly extracted with water) 23, and salt mixture 5. In addition, each rat received daily 0.4 gm. of brewer's yeast and 0.2 gm. of dried alfalfa leaves. An experimental group was fed the same mixture and supplements, but the washed muscle was extracted five times with ether containing a little alcohol. This procedure removed all but traces of fat. Young rats grew as rapidly on both these diets as on diets with the usual fat content. The conclusion seemed warranted that if fats are essential in the diet during growth, the amount necessary must be exceedingly small. The experiment was not crucial since both the yeast and alfalfa leaf supplied small amounts of fats.

In 1921 Drummond and Coward (2) reported that rats could grow from weaning to maturity on diets freed as far as possible of neutral fats. At that time these observations seemed conclusive, but they later proved to be in error.

The indispensability of certain fatty acids in mammalian nutrition was demonstrated in 1929 by an admirable series of experiments by Burr and Burr (3) of the University of Minnesota. They used a diet composed of purified casein, sugar, yeast, and a salt mixture. The yeast was defatted by ether extraction. It supplied sufficient amounts of water-soluble vitamins, several of which were still unrecognized. The fat-soluble vitamins were provided by the inclusion of a concentrate of the non-saponifiable fraction of cod liver oil. The diet was complete except for a source of fat.

Within three months on this diet young rats developed a syndrome hitherto undescribed. First there appeared a generalized scaliness of the skin, progressive scaling, ridging, and necrosis of the tail, denudation and swelling of the feet, loss of hair, and hyperkeratosis of the skin. Degenerative changes in the kidneys accompanied by passage of blood into the urine were the terminal symptoms.

Burr and Burr (4), testing a number of fats from different sources, soon found that only unsaturated fats possessed preventive or curative properties. Two years later, with Miller (5), they identified the essential factor as linoleic acid. When given this fatty acid as a supplement to the experimental fat-free diet, rats nearing the moribund condition recovered from their lesions and appeared normal.

In later studies by several investigators it was found that either linolenic acid or arachidonic acid could replace linoleic acid in the diet. Turpeinen (6) found that arachidonic acid was three times as potent as linoleic acid in promoting recovery of rats exhibiting the fatty acid deficiency syndrome.

These three acids stand in the following relations to each other: linoleic and linolenic acid are both C_{18} acids, the former containing two and the latter three pairs of double bonds. Arachidonic acid contains in its molecule twenty carbon atoms and four pairs of double bonds. It appears that although the body of a mammal is capable of synthesizing from carbohydrate all the saturated fatty acids found in ordinary fats, and also the singly unsaturated oleic acid, it cannot produce synthetically the more highly unsaturated members of the series. It is logical to interpret the findings of Turpeinen to mean that arachidonic acid is the actual essential fatty acid and that it can be synthesized from either linoleic or linolenic acids.

The discovery of the indispensability in mammalian nutrition of the unsaturated fatty acids named, was of great importance to progress in the discovery of still unknown nutrients. These discoveries depended on studies of the effects of diets which were chemically characterized as far as possible. Thenceforth all investigators of nutrition problems included a source of the essential fatty acids in their simplified experimental diets.

REFERENCES

1. Osborne, T. B. and Mendel, L. B.: J. Biol. Chem. *45*, 145 (1920–21).
2. Drummond, J. C. and Coward, K.: Lancet ii, p. 608 (1921).
3. Burr, G. O. and Burr, M. M.: J. Biol. Chem. *82*, 345 (1929).
4. Burr, G. O. and Burr, M. M.: J. Biol. Chem. *86*, 587 (1930).
5. Burr, G. O., Burr, M. M. and Miller, E. S.: J. Biol. Chem. *97*, 1 (1932).
6. Turpeinen, O.: J. Nut. *15*, 351 (1938).

25

The Discovery of Vitamin K

The discovery and extensive investigation of the antihemorrhagic nutrient, or rather a group of related chemical substances which play the specific role of enabling the animal body to synthesize prothrombin, represents one of the best illustrations in the science of nutrition of the formula for success in the detection and identification of a new nutrient. This formula included these successive steps:

1. The chance observation by an investigator using an experimental diet which causes malnutrition in an animal, and the accurate description of the chief features of the pathological changes involved.
2. The testing of different classes of natural foods which, when given as supplements, prevent the appearance of the lesion.
3. The investigation of the effects of extractives from the protective foods, prepared by applying solvents of strongly contrasting properties to them.
4. The intensive study of methods for further separation of the curative extracts or concentrates into their several constituents, and testing by suitable feeding experiments the values of these fractions for preventing the appearance of the lesions, and the eventual success in identifying the species of molecule to which the protective foods owe their value.
5. The determination of the distribution of the new dietary factor in natural or derived foods by feeding studies.
6. The synthesis of the biologically important chemical by organic chemists.

The Discovery of the Existence of a Blood Clotting Nutrient

In 1930 Horvath (1) first mentioned an effect of some unknown dietary factor on blood clotting. He observed that the coagulation of the blood of chickens was accelerated by diets containing sprouted soy beans.

In 1931 McFarlane and his associates (2) were conducting experiments to determine the need of chickens for fat-soluble vitamins. With this purpose in mind, they employed an experimental diet consisting of 70 per cent polished rice and 15 per cent marmite (a yeast autolysate preparation), together with protein sources such as fish meal and casein. They experienced heavy losses of birds from hemorrhage when the diet contained ether-extracted fish meal, but no hemorrhage occurred when unextracted meal was fed. They further noted that when the blood of hemorrhagic chickens was kept in the laboratory overnight it failed to clot. McFarlane and his associates were the first to definitely relate blood-clotting time with an ether-soluble substance in fish meal.

Dam's Discovery of a Nutrient Essential for Blood Clotting

About 1929 Henrik Dam (3), while a student at the University of Copenhagen, conducted experiments to determine whether hens could synthesize cholesterol. His experimental diet consisted of casein, starch, marmite, salts, and paper (to supply indigestible matter). Using several modifications of this type of diet, he observed that chickens developed subcutaneous and intramuscular hemorrhages resembling those of scurvy. These were not prevented by the administration of lemon juice, indicating that the lesions were not of scorbutic nature. The hemorrhagic condition was not prevented by substituting yeast or wheat germ for marmite, the specific purpose of which was to supply water-soluble vitamins. Neither was it prevented by modifications of the salt mixture, by feeding pure cholesterol, cod liver oil, linseed oil, or by irradiation of the birds with ultraviolet light. These oils and irradiation were used because of their value in the prevention of rickets. Thus Dam had discovered a hitherto unsuspected pathological condition which was clearly due to some dietary deficiency.

In 1934 Dam described the disease in detail (4) and included gizzard erosions as a characteristic feature. However, the cause of this was later found to be unrelated to the blood clotting factor. Dam and Schönheyder (5) noted anemia and retardation of growth in birds fed hemorrhage-inducing diets. Extending his studies, Dam (6) showed that the antihemorrhagic substance was fat-soluble, as McFarlane had noted, and was not identifiable with vitamins A, D, or E. Since it was essential for the normal clotting of blood he suggested the name vitamin K, the initial letter of the German word "Koagulation."

He found the new nutrient to be present in large amounts in hog liver fat. It remained in the easily soluble non-sterol fraction of the non-saponifiable part of the fat, and could be extracted from the petroleum ether solution of the non-saponifiable concentrate by 90 per cent methanol. It was stable to heat at water-bath temperature for twelve hours in a layer 1 to 2 mm. deep. Dam also showed that a large number of cereals, seeds, vegetables, fruits, animal organs, and fats contain vitamin K.

In 1935 Dam and his associates (7) described experiments which greatly extended knowledge of the nature of hemorrhagic disease. They found that the amount of prothrombin was below normal in the blood of birds fed diets deficient in vitamin K. The blood of chickens became depleted of prothrombin in about three weeks on K deficient diets. Three days after feeding vitamin K rich preparations the prothrombin returned to normal as did clotting time.

Species Variation in Requirements for Vitamin K

When fed the same diets which caused hemorrhages in chickens, rats and guinea pigs did not develop hemorrhages nor decreased clotting time. Vitamin K concentrates were not effective in the treatment of hemophilia. These observations led to the belief that this vitamin was not essential for certain species of animals.

In 1935 Hawkins and Whipple (8) observed the bleeding tendency in dogs with biliary fistulas of long standing. The condition could be partially relieved by feeding bile. Further progress was made in 1938 by Smith, Warner, Brinkhous and Seegers (9). They restricted dogs with biliary fistulas to a diet very low in vitamin K and noted that while the feeding of bile slowly benefited the animals, there was a rapid return of the normal prothrombin content of the blood when vitamin K concentrates were fed along with bile. They thus demonstrated that vitamin K is essential for the dog.

Clinically, Brinkhous and associates (10) found low values for prothrombin in twenty-seven cases of obstructive jaundice and one case of biliary fistula. In cases where the prothrombin level was 35 per cent of normal or less, there was an increased bleeding tendency. By administering vitamin K concentrates made from alfalfa, emulsified with bile salts, a rapid restoration of prothrombin occurred. This was evidence that man, too, requires vitamin K.

Demonstration of the Bacterial Synthesis of Vitamin K

In 1935 Almquist and Stockstad (11) found that an increase in the anti-hemorrhagic factor could be produced in fish meal or in rice bran by moistening these and allowing them to stand in the moist state for a considerable time. They also discovered that vitamin K was present in the feces of chickens (12) restricted to a diet which was devoid of the vitamin and on which they developed hemorrhagic disease. Chicken feces which were allowed to stand twenty-four hours showed an increase in content of the vitamin resulting from synthesis by fecal microorganisms. Conditions which favored bacterial growth were conducive to the formation of the vitamin. Almquist and Stockstad pointed out that this explained the failure of some investigators to produce the disease when employing diets that others had used successfully.

Studies on the Chemical Nature, Preparation of Concentrates, and Purification of the Vitamin

Almquist and Stockstad also carried out chemical studies which showed that vitamin K was neither an acid nor a base, and that it was not associated with chlorophylls, sterols, carotenes, or xanthophyll.

In 1936 Almquist (13) secured vitamin K from alfalfa meal by extracting it with hexane. Since it was found to be alkali-labile, saponification for removal of fats was impracticable. He removed from the crude material the green pigments by adsorption upon activated magnesium oxide, and the red and orange pigments by adsorption on charcoal. The fats were removed mechanically after hardening by chilling. The vitamin was then extracted from the hexane into methyl alcohol. By this technic he obtained a reddish oil which was effective as a preventive of hemorrhagic disease in an amount of 2 mg. per kg. of food. The vitamin was in the unsaponifiable fraction of the oil. It was found to be soluble in polar and non-polar organic solvents, but not in water nor 50 per cent alcohol. It was relatively stable to heat and light and to contact with air. Almquist and Stockstad (14) further proved that the antihemorrhagic factor, vitamin K, was not the nutrient concerned with the gizzard erosion in chickens, which was first described by Dam. This lesion, they found, could be prevented or cured by some substance present in the saponifiable fraction of the oily material extracted from alfalfa.

Almquist (15) achieved further purification of vitamin K by distillation under high vacuum. By this procedure he secured a yellow oil which was effective in preventing the hemorrhagic disease when fed at a level of 0.5 mg. per kg. of food.

Thayer and his associates (16) extracted alfalfa with a light petroleum ether and obtained an oil which contained crystals in suspension. These crystals were recrystallized from a mixture of benzene and absolute alcohol, and then from absolute alcohol, acetone, and absolute alcohol, in turn. They thus obtained colorless crystals the biological activity of which did not increase on further recrystallization. The crystals melted at 69° C. and proved to be pure vitamin K.

In the same year Dam and associates (17) succeeded in isolating the vitamin in pure form by using a combination of molecular distillation and chromatography.

The Discovery of the Chemical Nature of Vitamin K

Advances in knowledge of the chemical composition of vitamin K were rapidly achieved in 1939. Four groups of investigators made notable contributions. These groups were lead by Almquist, of the University of California, Doisy, of Washington University, Fieser, of Harvard University, and Karrer, of the University of Zurich. Karrer worked in collaboration with Dam, of Copenhagen.

Almquist and Klose (18) made the important discovery that pure synthetic phthiocol, which is 2-methyl-3-hydroxy1:4-naphthoquinone, possessed antihemorrhagic potency. When given to chicks in an amount of 20 mg. per kg. of vitamin K-free diet, it maintained the average blood-clotting time at 2.1 minutes in one test and at 1.6 minutes in a second. With a dosage of 10 mg. per kg. of food, the clotting time was maintained on an average at 1.8 minutes. Chicks fed the unsupplemented basal diet had prolonged clotting times.

Almquist and Klose suggested that phthiocol was probably the simplest member of a homologous series of antihemorrhagic substances.

Simultaneously and independently, Doisy's group (19) observed that a red pigment was formed when vitamin K preparations were treated with sodium methylate. They suggested that the vitamin might be a 1:4-quinone; on testing 1:4-naphthoquinone, they found it to possess antihemorrhagic properties.

Careful study of the products obtained when naturally occurring vitamin K was treated with ozone, and when oxidized with chromic acid, led them to identify the phytyl radical and phthalic acid, and a second acid which they tentatively identified as 2-ethyl-1:4-naphthoquinone-3-acetic acid. On the basis of these observations they suggested that vitamin K_1 was probably 2-ethyl-3-phytyl-1:4-naphthoquinone. The same group of workers tested various synthetic quinones and found that some possessed vitamin K activity while others did not.

Fieser and his associates (20) also tested many synthetic quinones and found some active and some inactive. They concluded that there was a close resemblance between the natural vitamin K_1 and K_2 and the 2:3 dialkyl-1:4-naphthoquinones.

The terms vitamin K_1 and K_2 had their origin in the isolation by Dam and his associates (17) of a light yellow oil which showed absorption spectra of four maxima at 248, 261, 270, and 328 mu. This was identified as 2-methyl-3-phytyl-1:4-naphthoquinone and was called vitamin K. In the same year the Doisy group isolated a form of vitamin K which contained the farnesyl radical in place of phytyl-group. This became known as vitamin K_2.

The Discovery of the Therapeutic Usefulness of Vitamin K

Shortly after nutrition investigators and chemists demonstrated the existence of a hitherto unsuspected nutrient, whose function was to participate in the formation of prothrombin and hence regulate the coagulability of the blood, clinicians began to study its usefulness for the control of hemorrhagic tendency in man. In March, 1939, Butt and others (21) discussed the results of the earliest clinical trials in cases of various types of obstructive jaundice with reference to the level of prothrombin during the preoperative and postoperative course. A rough inverse relation between prothrombin and coagulation time could be demonstrated. The experience of several distinguished clinicians who discussed the paper of Butt and his associates, clearly showed that oral administration of vitamin K concentrates which were effective in preventing hemorrhages in chicks, were useful in the management of human subjects with this disorder.

Burch and Meade (22) were the first to employ vitamin K preparations in the successful treatment of hemorrhagic retinitis. Helmholz (23) and Waddell and his associates (24) demonstrated its value in preventing hemorrhage in newborn infants.

Thus within a single decade, by following the well-established formula for success in vitamin discovery and identification, the outstanding pioneers in the study of the antihemorrhagic vitamins solved every important problem concerning its existence, physiological function, nature, distribution, and synthesis, as well as its usefulness in clinical medicine and in animal husbandry.

REFERENCES

1. Horvath, A. A.: Amer. J. Physiol. *94,* 65–68 (1930).
2. McFarlane, W. D., Graham, W. R. and Richardson, P.: Biochem. J. *25,* 358 (1931).
3. Dam, H.: Studies on the Biological Significance of Sterols (Dissertation). Inst. Biochem. Copenhagen; Inst. of Pathol. University of Freiburg i. Br. (1933), 162 pp.
4. Dam, H.: Nature *133,* 909–10 (1934).
5. Dam, H. and Schönheyder, F.: Biochem. J. *28,* 1355–59 (1934).
6. Dam, H.: Nature *135,* 652 (1935).
7. Dam, H. and Schönheyder, F.: Biochem. J. *30,* 1075 (1936).
8. Hawkins, W. B. and Whipple, G. H.: J. Exp. Med. *62,* 599 (1935).
9. Smith, H. F., Warner, E. D., Brinkhous, E. M. and Seegers, W. H.: J. Exp. Med. *67,* 911 (1938).
10. Brinkhous, K. M., Smith, H. F. and Warner, E. D.: Amer. J. Med. Sci. *50,* 196 (1938).
11. Almquist, H. J. and Stockstad, E. L. R.: J. Biol. Chem. *111,* 105–13 (1935).
12. Almquist, H. J. and Stockstad, E. L. R.: J. Nut. *12,* 329–35 (1936).
13. Almquist, H. J.: J. Biol. Chem. *114,* 241–45 (1936).

14. Almquist, H. J. and Stockstad, E. L. R.: Nature *137,* 581–82 (1936).

15. Almquist, H. J.: J. Biol. Chem. *115,* 589–91 (1936).

16. Thayer, S. A., MacCorquodale, D. W., Binkley, S. B. and Doisy, E. A.: Science 88, 243 (1938).

17. Dam, H., Geiger, A., Glavind, J., Karrer, P., Karrer, W., Rothschild, E. and Salomon, H.: Helvet. chim. Acta. 22, 310–13 (1939).

18. Almquist, H. J. and Klose, A. A.: J. Amer. Chem. Soc. *61,* 1611 (1939).

19. MacCorquodale, D. W., Binkley, S. B., Thayer, S. A. and Doisy, E. A.: J. Amer. Chem. Soc. *61,* 1928–29, 1932 (1939).

20. Fieser, L. F., Bowen, D. M., Campbell, W. F., Fieser, M., Fry, E. M., Jones, R. N., Riegel, B., Schweitzer, C. E. and Smith, P. G.: J. Amer. Chem. Soc. *61,* 1925–26, 1926–27 (1939).

21. Butt, H. R., Snell, A. M. and Osterberg, A. E.: J. Amer. Med. Assoc. *112,* 879 (1939).

22. Burch, E. P. and Meade, J. R.: Minnesota Med. 22, 32–33 (1939).

23. Helmholz, H. F.: J. Indiana Med. Assoc. 32, 71–74 (1939).

24. Waddell, W. W., Jr., Guerry, DuP., Bray, W. E. and Kelley, O. R.: Proc. Soc. Exp. Biol. and Med. *40,* 432–34 (1930).

26

Trace Elements in the Nutrition of Plants and Animals: Zinc, Copper, Iodine, Manganese, Flourine, and Cobalt

In Chapter 21 an account is given of the pioneering studies of chemists who established the indispensability for plant and animal nutrition of the inorganic elements which are prominent constituents of the ashes of vegetable and animal tissues. It is pointed out that as late as 1874 so distinguished a chemist as Hammarsten questioned the importance in animal physiology of sodium and potassium, on the strength of Panum's experiment which had kept dogs in apparent health for two months on a diet low in these elements. Hence it is not to be wondered at that chemists and physiologists were slow in realizing the metabolic significance of certain elements present in plants and animals in exceedingly small amounts, and which were often overlooked by analytical chemists, even after delicate tests for them were devised. Progress in thought and experiment in this field can best be described by first giving an account of the outstanding events in the discovery of the roles played by trace elements in plant nutrition.

"Water Culture" Method for Study of Essential Nutrients for Plants

After Wiegmann and Polstroff (p. 321), in 1842, established by experiments the necessity of providing in the soil certain inorganic salts for the nutrition of plants, the next great advance was made by the Prince of Salm-Horstmar (1) in 1849. Wiegmann and Polstorff had used various inert materials as artificial soils, but from these traces of various mineral elements could be dissolved out by the water supplied to the seeds and plants. The Prince of Salm-Horstmar employed as an artificial soil carbon which he prepared by charring crystalline sugar, an essentially ash-free substance. With this soil he attempted to determine indispensable and dispensable plant nutrients. Analytical chemistry had not at that period advanced far enough to enable him to realize his objective of refined experimental inquiry. He concluded that plants required silica, alumina, and manganese, and that they could thrive without a source of magnesium. It is obvious that one or more of his nutrient salts contained magnesium, since this is a constituent of chlorophyll. But he rendered great service to plant physiologists by introducing an experimental technic far superior to those of earlier investigators. He demonstrated that normal plants could be grown on an inert soil when the nutrient solution provided only inorganic salts of the right kinds. Thenceforth progress was limited only by the purity of the salts used in nutrient solutions, and the employment of porcelain or platinum vessels from which nothing could be dissolved.

The outstanding investigators in plant nutrition during the second half of the nineteenth century were Raulin, Sachs, Pfeffer, and Knop. These men sought to determine which of the inorganic elements were essential for plant growth. They were all followers of Pasteur, who was the great innovator in the study of the nutritive requirements of yeast.

In 1857 Pasteur (2) described an experiment in which he placed yeast cells in a sugar solution without mineral substances. The yeast did not induce fermentation of the sugar, but on the addition of some ash of yeast to the solution, alcoholic fermentation set in. A year later, Pasteur (3) concluded that acetic acid-forming microorganisms which he studied required only potassium, magnesium, calcium, and phosphate, and that they could dispense with sulfur.

Nutrient solutions used by plant physiologists as late as 1897 differed greatly in composition. Sachs (4) included sodium chloride in his solution, although most plant physiologists at that time believed that neither sodium nor chloride was necessary for the growth of plants. Pfeffer (5) used a solution which contained neither sodium nor magnesium. The confusion in the minds of plant physiologists concerning the mineral nutrients which were essential for the health of plants was due to the fact that even the purest inorganic salts available contained traces of essential nutrients. The experimenters always added more to their solutions than they realized, and, accordingly, drew unwarranted conclusions from their observations.

The metabolic significance of a trace of a mineral substance was illustrated dramatically in 1890 by Ville (6). He found that if phosphate was omitted from the nutrient solution of yeast cells they were unable to ferment sugar. The addition of only 0.0005 gram of phosphate ions per liter brought about the initiation of alcoholic fermentation.

The Discovery of the Biological Significance of Zinc

In 1854 Braun (7) detected the presence of zinc in the ashes of vegetables. He stated that this was the eighteenth inorganic element found to occur in vegetable substances.

In 1869 Raulin (8) performed experiments with *Aspergillus niger* which introduced a new era into the study of plant physiology. He used a medium with the following composition:

Water	1500.	Potassium carbonate	0.6
Sugar candy	70.	Ammon. sulfate	0.25
Tartaric acid	4.	Zinc sulfate	0.07
Ammon. nitrate	4.	Iron sulfate	0.07
Ammon. phosphate	0.6	Potassium silicate	0.07
Mg. carbonate	0.4		

With this medium, which contained no added calcium salt, Raulin observed that the yield of the mold was considerably reduced by the omission of the zinc sulfate. This was the earliest demonstration of the physiological significance of a trace of a metallic element hitherto unrecognized as important in the metabolic functioning of plants.

Plant physiologists were slow in recognizing the importance of Raulin's observation. It was eventually proven that in many parts of North America and elsewhere, soils contain an insufficient amount of available zinc to meet the needs of fruit trees and various farm crops. The pathologic effects of zinc deficiency in plants were described in 1935 by Reed and Dufrenoy (9).

Zinc, an Indispensable Nutrient for Animals

Zinc occurs in practically all animal tissues, but it is most abundant in the liver and pancreas. Its concentration in blood seems to be variable. Colostrum contains about three times as much zinc as does milk.

The earliest attempt to determine whether zinc is essential in animal nutrition was made by Bertrand and Berzon (10) in 1922. Although their diet was deficient in essentials other than zinc, the observation that their animals receiving a supplement of zinc survived 25 to 50 per cent longer than the controls afforded evidence that this element plays a role in metabolic processes. In 1927, Hubbell and Mendel (11) found that rats on an experimental diet to which zinc was added were in better condition than the negative controls. In 1934 Todd, Elvehjem, and Hart (12) prepared a zinc-low diet for rats. It contained 1.6 mg. zinc per kg. On this ration the animals became unthrifty and lost their hair. The addition of a supplement of zinc improved the growth of the animals and prevented alopecia.

The Biological Functions of Zinc

In 1939 Keilin and Mann (13) found highly purified carbonic anhydrase to contain about 0.3 per cent zinc. This enzyme occurs in red blood cells and other tissues. Its function is to catalyze the decomposition of carbonic acid into carbon dioxide and water.

Zinc also occurs in association with the enzyme uricase, which catalyzes the conversion of uric acid into allantoin. This was shown by Holmberg in 1939 (14). In 1940 Hove, Elvehjem, and Hart (15) showed that in the presence of amino acids, phosphatase of the intestine is activated by the zinc ion.

In 1940 Day and McCollum (16) devised an adequate control diet which provided approximately 0.15 microgram of zinc per day per rat. After two to three weeks young rats restricted to the zinc-deficient regimen ceased to grow and suffered extensive hair loss. The denuded areas were rough and scaly. Follis, Day, and McCollum (16a) described the pathologic lesion in the dorsal skin as hyperkeratinization, with marked changes in the striatum mucosum, and atrophy of hair follicles. Extensive keratinization of the epithelial lining of the esophagus was also observed. Skin from the tail, ears, and paws showed no deviation from the normal structure.

Discovery of the Biological Significance of Copper

In 1840 Devergie (17) reported that he had detected the presence of copper in the healthy body. Its presence in various tissues was confirmed by a number of investigators. The first to describe its presence in the blood and the liver of *cephalopoda, ascidiae,* and *mollusca* was Harless (18) in 1847. A year later, Bert (19) became the first to recognize the role of the blue copper pigment in the blood of these species in oxygen transport during respiration. But since small amounts of copper were found in the ashes of both plant and animal substances, this occurrence was generally regarded as accidental, and of no biological significance except as a respiratory pigment in the blood of some lower organisms.

The improvement of the health of plants by application of copper was first clearly demonstrated in 1917 by Floyd (20), who reported beneficial results from treating citrus fruit trees exhibiting the disease exanthoma, or die-back. The first indisputable evidence that copper is an essential nutrient for the higher plants was furnished by the experimental studies of Sommer (21). But it was not until 1933 that copper was widely accepted as an essential constituent of productive soils. In that year Sjollema (22) proved that "reclamation disease," or yellow-tip, could be prevented by application of copper to the soil. This disease affected oats and other cereals, beets, peas, beans, and other crops grown on soils reclaimed from heath and moorland in Denmark, Holland, and some other places. In the same year, Brandenburg (23) demonstrated by water culture technic that oats grown in a medium which contained less than 0.5 mg. of copper per liter showed deficiency symptoms.

The Discovery That Copper is an Essential Nutrient for Animals

In 1925 Hart and his associates (24) made a study designed to show the relative availability of several salts of iron for restoration of the blood of anemic individuals to the normal hemoglobin content. With this objective, they restricted young rats three to six weeks of age to a diet of milk only, a food which is almost iron-free. The rats grew well for four to six weeks, but at the end of this time their weights became stationary, and rapid decline set in. Blood examinations showed greatly reduced red cell and hemoglobin content. When any one of several pure salts of iron was given with the milk, the condition of the blood was not improved. This result was astonishing in view of the long and favorable experience of clinicians in the use of iron preparations for the treatment of anemias of certain types. Hart and his associates first tested the effect of giving the animals a small supplement of maize, lettuce, or beef liver along with the milk-iron diet. Each of these natural foods caused rapid improvement of the blood of the anemic rats.

They next found that feeding the ash of maize, lettuce, or liver with the iron-milk diet was as effective as were the foods themselves. A systematic fractionation of the ashes of these substances, and feeding tests with the fractions, revealed that their value in promoting iron utilization for hemoglobin formation was due to their copper content. The manner in which copper functions in this connection has not been discovered, but several facts emerged before 1940 which indicate that this element acts as a catalyst in certain biological oxidation mechanisms. The earliest example of such action was discovered by Hess and Unger (25) who, in 1921, observed the destruction of the antiscorbutic vitamin in milk by the catalytic action of minute amounts of copper. Barron (26) studied the mechanism of this process.

In 1938 Bull, Marston, Murnane, and Lines (27) proved that copper deficiency was the cause of ataxia in lambs grazed on certain pastures in Australia. As a result of the several studies referred to it became evident that copper is an essential nutrient.

Early Observations on the Use of Iodine in Simple Goiter

In his *Geographical and Historical Pathology* (1885), Hirsch gave an extended account of clinical observations and conclusions concerning the cause of goiter and of cretinism. The facts established by centuries of observation were that the disease was restricted to certain localities, and that the iron, calcium, or magnesium content of drinking water might cause hypertrophy of the thyroid gland.

The element iodine was discovered by Courtois in 1811. In 1820 Coindet (28), a physician in Geneva, Switzerland, where goiter was prevalent, suggested that the newly-discovered iodine was the curative agent in burnt sponge, which had long been believed to be an effective remedy for goiter. Harington (29) stated that the earliest reference to the use of burnt sponge in the treatment of goiter was in the writings of Arnoldus de Villa Nova (A.D. 1280).

McCay (30) called attention to the assertion by Boussingault, in 1825, that iodine was the only specific known for goiter. He had reached this conclusion while engaged in mining enterprises in South America. There he observed that Indians who obtained salt from one source suffered from goiter, whereas others who used salt from another source were free from the disease. The latter salt was found to contain iodine as a prominent impurity, whereas this was absent in the former.

Coindet was successful to a degree in the treatment of even large goiters with iodine. But the injudicious administration of excessive amounts of this element worked harm to patients and brought the remedy into disrepute. The unfortunate results of the misuse of iodine turned medical opinion against it and caused abandonment of its use in the treatment of goiter.

The Discovery of Iodine in the Thyroid Gland

The subject remained controversial until 1896, when Baumann (31) discovered that in comparison with other tissues the thyroid gland was rich in iodine. Once again there was a revival of interest in iodine deficiency as the cause of goiter. The renewal of prophylactic and therapeutic use of iodine was now based on more careful control of dosage. The result was the firm establishment of goiter prevention. Iodine soon became recognized as an essential nutrient for man and animals.

Soon after Baumann's discovery, Marine and his associates began the study of the histological changes in the thyroid gland in relation to its iodine content. Marine and Williams (32) found that a fall in the iodine store preceded any cellular changes. Pups born of a mother three-fourths of whose thyroid gland had been removed, and which had been kept on a diet low in iodine, had enlarged thyroids with the histological changes characteristic of goiter. The same mother when fed iodine during a subsequent gestation, delivered young whose thyroids were normal in all respects.

Marine led the way by his histological studies of the normal thyroid and of the gland in hyperplasia and hyperfunction (33). He concluded that "hyperplasia indicates hyperactivity but not necessarily hyperfunction. Myxedema and cretinoid states may occur in individuals and animals with typical hyperplasia. It is more accurate to consider all functional hyperplasia as indicating relative or absolute iodine deficiencies, and colloid goiter as the recovered, resting, and physiologically normal stage."

The normal gland is composed of many closed alveoli filled with the jelly-like material known as colloid, and lined with a single layer of cuboidal epithelium. In 1901 Oswald discovered that the iodine of the gland was contained in the colloid. He named the substance thyreoglobulin. Notkin (34) had previously (1895) shown that the physiologically active principle of the thyroid gland resided in a protein substance which he called thyreoproteid.

Marine and Lenhart (35) proved that the store of iodine in the gland varied inversely with the degree of active hyperplasia, and that in extreme degrees of thyroid hyperplasia the iodine store was almost completely exhausted. They demonstrated that enlargement of the thyroid does not occur if the diet contains adequate amounts of iodine, but in iodine deficiency it begins to increase in size as soon as its iodine content falls below 0.1 per cent of the dried gland tissue.

During the first quarter of the twentieth century the relation between simple (endemic, or colloid) goiter, cretinism, myxedema, and Graves disease (exopthalmic goiter) became clear, and their relation to iodine deficiency was fully established both clinically and experimentally.

In 1896 Drechsel (36) isolated from a coral (*Gorgonia cavolini*) an organic iodine-containing compound which he called iodogorgonic acid. This substance was synthesized by Wheeler and Jamieson (37) by the action of iodine on tyrosine in faintly alkaline solution. It proved to be 3,5, diiodo-tyrosine. It was later isolated from thyreoglobulin of the thyroid gland by Harington and Randall (38). Thyroxine, the iodine-containing amino acid which is yielded on hydrolysis by thyreoglobulin, is the substance to which the thyroid gland owes its physiological function. It was first isolated in 1915 by Kendall, and was synthesized by Harington and Barger (39).

Iodine in Animal Nutrition

The disfavor which iodine therapy incurred because of the administration of excessive dosages disappeared as the new discoveries just mentioned accumulated. Recognition of its value was greatly hastened by several observations of the widespread occurrence of goiter in animals, an affliction which caused great losses in animal industries in certain areas.

The early settlers of Michigan were unsuccessful with farm animals. The principal cause of their failure was the prevalence of goiter. About 1870 this disease disappeared on many farms. No explanation for this relief came to light until 1909, when Marine and Lenhart (35) described the relation of iodine to the structure of the thyroid gland in sheep, dog, ox, and hog. The disappearance of goiter in domestic animals in Michigan was the result of the development of mining and refining salt in that state.

When crude rock salt was recrystallized, large quantities of mother-liquor, rich in iodine, accumulated. The best disposition of this was to evaporate the water and sell the crude residue to farmers for stock feeding. Its high iodine content protected the animals against goiter.

Salmon and trout reared under hatchery conditions near Buffalo, New York suffered greatly from goiter. Marine and Lenhart (35) demonstrated that addition of potassium iodide to the water in the ponds caused regression of the enlarged thyroid glands of the fish, and return to their normal histological structure.

For years there were losses in the Yellowstone River Valley of large numbers of pigs, lambs, calves, and colts, as the result of thyroid disease. Many pigs were born in a hairless condition, with great enlargement of the thyroid glands. Others were still-born, or died within a day or two. In 1916 G. Ennis Smith (40) correctly interpreted the situation, and showed that for the prevention of the disease it was only necessary to administer sodium or potassium iodide to pregnant animals. Hart and Steenbock extended observations in this field (41).

McCarrison (42) supported the view that although goiter may result from iodine deficiency, it occurs more commonly from other causes, even when there is present in the food a sufficiency of this element. He based his view on observations that animals kept in cages develop goiter spontaneously because of unsanitary environment.

McClendon (43) made an extensive survey of the relation between the iodine content of water and incidence of goiter, and provided convincing evidence that lack of this element is conspicuous where the incidence of the disease is high.

Marine and Kimball (44) and others demonstrated that in goitrous areas the disease can be prevented or cured by the administration of iodide. Their work was confirmed, and this resulted in medical approval of the domestic use of iodized salt for the prevention of goiter. The endocrine function of iodine has been fully discussed by Salter (45).

Goitrogenic Substances in Foods

In 1928 Chesney, Clawson, and Webster (46) discovered that rabbits develop large goiters when restricted solely to a diet of cabbage. The thyroid hyperplasia thus produced is associated with lowered metabolic rate. Marine and his associates confirmed this observation. Certain toxic substances (e.g., acetonitrile) cause hyperthyroidism. Marine could not induce the development of goiters by administration of mustard oil (allylisothiocyanate). The goitrogenic substance in certain vegetables (e.g., turnip) has not been identified. Salter (45) gives an extensive account of all experimental studies bearing on this subject.

Manganese in Animal Nutrition

Although there was evidence that manganese played a role in animal metabolism, the premise was not put to conclusive test until 1931. In that year Orent and McCollum (47) tested a basal diet extremely low in manganese, and the same diet with a supplement of 0.005 per cent manganese. They also employed a diet of milk plus copper and iron salts, and one with milk with copper, iron, and manganese supplements. Groups of female rats were restricted to these rations soon after weaning. From the age of about 67 days, for a period of 150 days, the estrual rhythm was studied by taking vaginal smears daily. In all cases the cycles were normal. There was no difference between the growth curves of rats on the manganese-free diet and those on the same diet with added manganese. The animals on the milk diets showed somewhat inferior growth. When mated with normal males fertility of female rats on the manganese-deficient diet was approximately normal, but there was complete failure to suckle the young. These, it was found, could not be reared by foster-mothers on stock diet. Addition of 0.005 per cent of manganese to the basal diet prevented this abnormality. In male rats testicular degeneration was well marked by the one hundredth day on the diet, and complete sterility resulted. The testicular damage was not reparable by administration of manganese. It was suggested that the symptoms observed might be the result of failure of some hypophyseal hormone.

Coincident with the appearance of the account just given, Kemmerer, Elvehjem, and Hart (48) described their observations on the effects of feeding mice solely on whole milk, which is extremely low in manganese, and on the same milk supplemented with iron and copper, without the addition of manganese. Growth was improved by the addition of manganese (0.01 mg. Mn. per mouse daily). Mice on the manganese-low diet failed to ovulate normally, but those receiving manganese had normal estrual cycles.

Daniels and Everson (49) fed rats mineralized milk deficient in manganese, and confirmed that the females produced non-viable young. However, they found that their deficient females suckled normal foster young. Waddell, Steenbock, and Hart (50) attributed the subnormal weight gains in animals restricted to a mineralized milk diet to deficiency in calorie intake.

There was never a satisfactory explanation of the observations made by these investigators of the differences in the behavior of manganese-deficient female rats as respects maternal instinct and lactation. The rations of the different laboratories were not the same. It is not unlikely that they inadvertently provided different fractions of the minimum manganese requirements.

Manganese in the Nutrition of Birds

The function of manganese in the nutrition of birds assumed practical importance in 1937 when Wilgus, Norris, and Heuser (51) discovered that a bone abnormality which was called perosis, also known as "slipped tendon," was caused by a deficiency of manganese in the food. The condition was described in 1930 by Hunter and Funk (52) and by Payne (53). The lameness caused by abnormality of bone structure, characterized by enlargement of the tibial-metatarsal joint, twisting or bending of the distal end of the tibia and proximal end of the metatarsus, and slipping of the gastrocnemius tendon from its condyle had long been believed to be caused by errors in feeding.

At the Cornell Agricultural College farm Wilgus and Norris had recommended to farmers a ration which had for some years kept the station flock free from the disorder. Then a high incidence of slipped tendon again appeared. Investigation showed that this was coincident with securing limestone grits from a new source without any other change in the feeding system. Chemical analyses were made of samples of the old and the new grits to determine the impurities in them. It was found that the old grits contained appreciable manganese, whereas the new source grits were almost free from it. With this clue, Wilgus and Norris tested the effect of adding a supplement of manganese salt to the ration and found that this prevented the disorder. They demonstrated that for the protection of young chickens against slipped tendon the ration must contain 40–45 ppm. of manganese.

Lyons and Insko (54), at the Kentucky Agricultural Experiment Station, discovered that low hatchability of eggs in that area was caused by deficiency of manganese. They fed hens a locally grown manganese-deficient diet, and observed that less than 10 per cent of their eggs hatched. Those embryos which were sufficiently developed for observation but which had died in the shell had very short legs. Another lot of eggs was obtained from hens on the same ration with a supplement of forty parts per million of manganese as sulfate. These had high hatchability and the chicks had normal bones. They then tested the effect of the injection of 0.03 mg. of manganese sulfate directly into the albumen of eggs from hens fed the low manganese diet. This treatment resulted in great increase in hatchability and in normal chicks.

Fluorine in Nutrition

The nutritional significance of the element fluorine in determining perfection of tooth structure and resistance to dental caries is a recent discovery. As was the case with a considerable number of other inorganic elements, the early analytical chemists revealed its presence in teeth, shells, and bone. In 1805 Gay-Lussac wrote a letter (55) in which he stated that an Italian chemist, Morichini, had observed that when teeth of a fossil elephant were powdered and treated with sulfuric acid, "fluoric" acid (hydrofluoric) was evolved, as shown by the etching of glass by the fumes. Berzelius made many tests and always found fluoride present in teeth of recent origin as well as those of fossil remains. Later chemists never failed to find it present in bones and teeth. Ehrhardt (56), in 1874, recommended administration of potassium fluoride to pregnant women and to children during the period of tooth development. His views as to the importance of providing fluoride in the interest of sound teeth did not rest on experimental evidence.

In 1892 Sir James Crichton-Browne (57), in a lecture before British dentists, expressed the belief that the high incidence of tooth decay in England was due to deficiency of fluoride in the diet. He ascribed this deficiency to the recent increase of refined cereal foods in human dietaries. He attributed perfection of enamel structure, which he referred to as "hardness," to calcium fluoride as a structural component. He recommended restoration of fluoride to the diet as a constituent of foods, but did not mention water as a source of this substance.

The role of fluoride in dental health came to light through a series of events. Dentists in the area of Colorado Springs were puzzled over certain peculiarities in the teeth of many of their patients. A survey of the public school pupils revealed that the abnormality, known as mottled enamel, was limited to children who were born and reared there, or who had come there to live during the period when their teeth were in process of development. Children whose teeth were developed before coming to that area did not exhibit the lesion. Teeth having mottled enamel were poorly formed, exhibited white, chalky-appearing areas, and were often discolored. It had been noted that such teeth were not as susceptible to dental caries as were normal teeth. At a meeting of Colorado Springs dentists in 1908 a movement was started to investigate the cause of the abnormality.

In 1925 McCollum, Simmonds, Becker, and Bunting (58), in the course of investigations on the physiological significance of certain inorganic elements, conducted an experiment in which 0.01 per cent of sodium fluoride was added to the diet of rats. The skulls of these animals were whiter and more porous than those of control animals, and lacked the luster of normal bone. The rami of the mandibles were thinner and less prominent than those of animals which had received no fluoride supplement.

There was osteoporosis of the alveolar process, the ridge of the jawbone containing the tooth sockets. In normal rats the anterior surfaces of the incisor teeth have a bright orange color, whereas the incisors of fluoride-fed rats were bleached. These incisors were so brittle that the lower ones broke off at the gum line. The upper incisors were then without opposing teeth and so overgrew into almost complete circles, sometimes penetrating the roof of the mouth. Dr. Bunting, a dentist distinguished for his investigations of dental caries, described these abnormal teeth and interpreted the effect as a retrograde disturbance in tooth development. The incisor teeth of rats, like those of other rodents, grow continuously throughout the life of the animal and only these teeth were severely affected. The molars were well developed but exhibited abnormal whiteness and lack of the pearly luster of normal teeth. The abnormalities described were not at that time identified with mottled enamel.

Finely ground natural rock phosphate had been used extensively as a supplement to the rations of farm animals. This may contain three to four per cent of fluorine. Interest was greatly aroused by the publication of the paper by McCollum and his associates (58) which contained illustrations showing the nature of the abnormalities in teeth resulting from feeding fluoride. Tolle and Maynard (59) at Cornell University, and Reed and Huffman (60) at the Michigan Agricultural College, demonstrated that feeding rock phosphate caused loss of the reddish-yellow color which is normal in the teeth of cattle, and thickening and roughening of the mandibular bones. They also failed to associate the dental abnormalities with mottled enamel.

In 1916 Black (61) described the histological changes in mottled human teeth. He found the cementing matrix between the enamel rods was lacking, and that in severe cases the enamel rods were not well calcified.

Mottled teeth are characterized by the presence of dull chalky-white or paper-white patches distributed irregularly over the tooth surface. These lusterless teeth are frequently pitted and corroded, are structurally weak, and do not hold fillings well. The staining, which is yellow to dark brown or black, is secondary since some teeth remain white.

McKay's Studies of Mottled Enamel Distribution

McKay (62) was the outstanding pioneer in the study of the epidemiologic occurrence of mottled enamel. It was he who interested Black in the histological study of teeth manifesting this abnormality. In 1931 Churchill (63) reported to him the presence of a high fluorine content of water samples obtained at Bauxite, Arkansas, where mottling of the teeth was severe among children who grew up there. This led McKay to suspect fluorine as the cause of the disorder. Through his efforts, several new areas were discovered where mottling of enamel occurred. He pursued his investigations and demonstrated that the causative agent was in the water supply, and was, presumably, fluorine. Conclusive evidence that excessive fluoride ingestion caused mottled enamel was secured by Margaret Cammack Smith.

The Studies of Margaret Cammack Smith on Dental Fluorosis

In 1930 McKay (62) published results based on many years of study concerning the geographic distribution and cause of mottled enamel; he gave a complete list of references to publications bearing on the subject. This was a very important contribution, since it created widespread interest in the problem and provided convincing evidence that the disorder was associated with something present in drinking water in certain localities.

Margaret Cammack Smith and her associates (64) tested on rats the effect of giving them water from St. David, Arizona, where mottled enamel afflicted every person reared in that area. No mottling of the enamel resulted. However, when the experiment was repeated with water from the same locality but which had been rendered by evaporation ten times as concentrated as the naturally occurring product, the rats developed lesions of the teeth like those of the residents of St. David. Thus, mottled enamel was definitely related to the drinking water though the specific factor involved remained unknown.

At this stage of their investigations Smith and her associates studied the paper of McCollum et al., published in 1925 (58), describing the effects of feeding fluorine to rats. They noted that the teeth of the rats given concentrated St. David water were like those described by the Johns Hopkins University investigators. This clue led the Arizona group to repeat the experiments of McCollum et al. and confirm their results. Smith and her co-workers then analyzed the water of St. David and found it to contain from 3.8 to 7.15 mg. of fluorine per liter, while the water from neighboring localities which were free from mottled enamel contained little or no fluorine. Afer the publication of Smith's convincing studies, few doubted that excessive fluoride ingestion caused the hypoplasia characteristic of mottled teeth.

Fluorine in Drinking Water Reduces Caries-Susceptibility in Teeth

In 1938 Dean and his associates (65) reported that the incidence of dental caries was significantly lower in communities where the water contained fluorine above certain concentrations, than in communities nearby where water contained little or no fluorine. Thus

Galesburg and Quincy, Illinois, where climate and living conditions are identical, afford a striking example. Galesburg water was found to contain 1.9 parts of fluorine per million, whereas Quincy water contained but 0.1 to 0.2 parts per million. Dean et al. examined 273 children 12 to 14 years old in Galesburg, and 330 of the same age group in Quincy. The total number of filled, untreated carious, extracted and missing teeth in the Galesburg group was 236, and in the Quincy group 706. These investigators found a similarly contrasting incidence of dental disease in thirteen cities where there were wide differences in the fluorine content of drinking water. There were no inconsistencies in the findings in the different localities.

There is no unanimity of opinion as to the mechanism of the caries-preventing action of drinking water containing 1 part per million or more of fluorine. Nevertheless, surveys conducted by reputable investigators provide convincing evidence that the use of fluorine-containing drinking water during the period of tooth development reduced the incidence of carious lesions by about 50 per cent.

Fluoride is a structural component of normal enamel. In its absence the composition of the enamel is abnormal. Even in areas where the drinking water contains as much as 14 parts of fluorine per million, and the teeth of persons whose infancy and childhood were spent there are severely affected, clinical experience indicates no adverse influence on the general health of the people who spend their lives there.

The subject of fluoride in relation to dental caries has been discussed by The Research Commission of the American Dental Association (66).

Cobalt in Animal Nutrition

About 1925 biochemists interested in animal nutrition began to consider the possible physiological significance of the trace elements which had been found to exercise beneficial effects on the growth of plants. Bertrand (67), in 1926, reported the presence of 0.09 to 0.022 mg. per kg. of nickel in liver and brain respectively. Cobalt was also found in most samples examined. McHargue (68) found traces of cobalt in all animal tissues examined. Stare and Elvehjem (69) stated that if this element occurs in animal and plant products it is in extremely small amounts. They found less than 0.01 mg. of cobalt in 100 gm. of milk and a like amount in the body of a rat.

In 1933, therefore, the evidence available supported the view that cobalt occurred in extremely small amounts in the animal body and that it was probably of no physiological significance. The fallacy of this idea was soon revealed.

In areas of New Zealand, Australia, Scotland, Florida, and many other places, a disorder occurred in ruminants which, according to the locality, was called *pining, coast disease, bush sickness, enzootic marasmus, nakuruitis,* and other names.

The syndrome in sheep exhibits progressive emaciation, loss of appetite, and the development of severe anemia and lethargy. The anemia suggested iron deficiency. Analyses of herbage from pastures on which sheep developed coast disease, as the disorder was called in Australia, showed that this element was generally deficient in quantity. In 1934 Underwood (70) discovered that the livers and spleens of affected animals contained excessive amounts of iron. This disposed of the concept that deficiency of iron could be responsible for the disease. Underwood concluded that the trouble lay in inability of affected sheep and cattle to utilize iron in their nutrition.

In the same year, Filmer and Underwood (71) reported that they had prepared from limonite (an iron ore consisting of ferric hydroxide) an iron-free preparation which was effective in curing their anemic sheep. This iron-free mixture of mineral substances they separated into several fractions by the usual analytical procedures and tested each fraction on sick sheep. In this way they traced the curative substance to the fraction consisting of cobalt, nickel, and zinc. A trial of pure cobalt chloride showed that cobalt was the element which could prevent or cure the disease.

In 1935 Marston (72), almost simultaneously with Underwood and Filmer, found that cobalt was the curative agent in coast disease and enzootic marasmus. Lines and Marston had been led to try administering cobalt to sheep as a result of the report in 1929 by Waltner and Waltner (73) that administration of cobalt or its salts induced polycythemia in animals.

In 1938 Underwood and Elvehjem (74) reported on their attempts to produce cobalt deficiency in laboratory animals. They fed a diet believed to contain only 6 micrograms of cobalt per kilo but failed to produce anemia in rats. Frost, Spitzer, Elvehjem, and Hart (75) observed that when dogs were kept on a similar ration and were rendered anemic by bleeding, the administration of cobalt seemed to stimulate hematopoiesis in some animals.

By 1941 symptoms of cobalt deficiency had been observed only in the ruminants, sheep and cattle. Further researches on the physiological significance of cobalt were to bring to light astonishing facts which were to place this element, in the form of an organic complex to which the name vitamin B_{12} was given, among the most important and versatile of the essential nutrients. By 1954 more than 1200 papers had been published in which were described experimental and clinical studies on the biological role of this extraordinary substance. Chronologically these researches are beyond the scope of this history.

REFERENCES

1. Fürst zu Salm-Horstmar. Journ. f. prakt. Chem. *46,* 193 (1849); Ann. de chim. et de phys. (3rd Ser.) 32, 461 (1851); Versuche und Resultate über die Nahrung d. Pflanzen. Braunschweig (1856).
2. Pasteur, L.: Ann. de chim. et de phys. (3rd Ser.) *58,* 388 (1857).
3. Pasteur, L.: Études sur le vinaigre (1868).
4. Sachs, J.: Bot. Zeitschr. *18,* 113 (1860).
5. Pfeffer, W.: Pflanzenphysiologie. 2nd ed., Leipzig (1897). Vol. I pp. 139 *et seq.*
6. Ville, C.: Compt. rend. *111,* 158 (1890).
7. Braun, A.: Philos. Mag. (4th Ser.) 8, 156 (1854).
8. Raulin, J.: Ann. sci. nat. (5th Ser.) 2, 224 (1869).
9. Reed, H. S. and Dufrenoy, J.: Hilgardia *9,* 37–113 (1935).
10. Bertrand, G. and Berzon, B.: Compt. rend. *175* (1922).
11. Hubbell, R. B. and Mendel, L. B.: J. Biol. Chem. *75,* 567 (1927).
12. Todd, W. R., Elvehjem, C. A. and Hart, E. B.: Amer. J. Physiol. *107,* 146–56 (1934).
13. Keilin, D. and Mann, T.: Nature *144,* 442 (1939).
14. Holmberg, C. G.: Biochem. J. 33, 1901 (1939).
15. Hove, E., Elvehjem, C. A. and Hart, E. B.: J. Biol. Chem. *134,* 425 (1940).

16. Day, H. G. and McCollum, E. V.: Proc. Soc. Exper. Biol. and Med. *45,* 282 (1940).

16a. Follis, R. H., Day, H. G. and McCollum, E. V.: J. Nut. *22,* 223 (1941).

17. Devergie: Ann. d'Hygiène (July, 1840) p. 180.

18. Harless, E.: Muller's Arch. (1847) pp. 148–57.

19. Bert, P.: La pression barométrique. Paris (1878).

20. Floyd, B. F.: Florida Agric. Exp. Sta. Bull. No. 140 (1917), 31 pp.

21. Sommer, Anna L.: Plant Physiology *6,* 339–45 (1931).

22. Sjollema, B.: Biochem. Zeitschr. *267,* 151–56 (1933).

23. Brandenburg, E.: Tijdschr. Plziekt. *39,* 189–92 (1933).

24. Hart, E. B., Steenbock, H., Waddell, J. and Elvehjem, C. A.: J. Biol. Chem. *65,* 67 (1925); *77,* 797 (1928).

25. Hess, A. F. and Unger, L. J.: Proc. Soc. Exp. Biol. and Med. *19,* 119 (1921).

26. Barron, E. S. G., Barron, A. G. and Klemperer, F.: J. Biol. Chem. *116,* 563 (1936).

27. Bull, L. B., Marston, H. R., Murnane, D. and Lines, E. W. L.: Commonwealth of Australia Council Scient. and Indust. Research, Bull. 113, 23 (1938).

28. Coindet, J. R.: Ann. de chim. et de phys. *15,* 49 (1820).

29. Harington, C. R.: Lancet, London, *i,* 1199 (1935).

30. McCay, C. M.: Science *82,* 350 (1935).

31. Baumann, E.: Zeitschr. f. physiol. Chem. *21,* 319 (1896); Munchen. med Wochnschr. *43,* 398 (1896).

32. Marine, D. and Williams, W. W.: Arch. Intern. Med. *1,* 349 (1908).

33. Marine, D.: J. Amer. Med. Assoc. *104,* 2334 (1935).

34. Notkin, J. A.: Virchow's Arch. f. pathol. Anat. etc., 144, Suppl. Bd. 224 (1896).

35. Marine, D. and Lenhart, C. H.: Arch. Intern. Med. *3,* 66 (1909).

36. Drechsel, E.: Zeitschr. f. Biol. *33,* 85 (1896).

37. Wheeler, H. L. and Jamieson, G. S.: Amer. Chem. Journ. *33,* 365 (1905).

38. Harington, C. R. and Randall, S. S.: Biochem. J. *23,* 373 (1929).

39. Harington, C. R. and Barger, G.: Biochem. J. *21,* 169 (1927).

40. Smith, G. E.: J. Biol. Chem. *29,* 215 (1917).
41. Hart, E. B. and Steenbock, H.: J. Biol. Chem. 33, 313 (1918).
42. McCarrison, R.: J. Amer. Med. Assoc. *78,* 1 (1922); Brit. Med. J. *i,* 178, 636 (1922).
43. McClendon, J. F.: Iodine and the Incidence of Goiter. Univ. of Minn. Press (1939).
44. Marine, D. and Kimball, O. P.: J. Lab. and Clin. Med. 3, 40 (1917).
45. Salter, W. T.: The Endocrine Function of Iodine, Harvard Univ. Press (1940).
46. Chesney, A. M., Clawson, E. A. and Webster, B.: Bull. Johns Hopkins Hosp. No. 43, 261 (1928).
47. Orent, E. R. and McCollum, E. V.: J. Biol. Chem. *92,* 651 (1931); Science 73, 507–08 (1931).
48. Kemmerer, A. R., Elvehjem, C. A. and Hart, E. B.: J. Biol. Chem. *92,* 623–30 (1931).
49. Daniels, A. L. and Everson, G. J.: J. Nut. *9,* 191–203 (1935).
50. Waddell, J., Steenbock, H. and Hart, E. B.: J. Nut. *4,* 53 (1931).
51. Wilgus, H. S., Norris, L. C. and Heuser, G. F.: J. Nut. *14,* 155 (1937).
52. Hunter, J. E. and Funk: Proc. 22nd Ann. Meeting of Poultry Science Assoc. at MacDonald College, Quebec (1930) p. 45.
53. Payne, L. F.: Science *71,* 664 (1930).
54. Lyons, M. and Insko, W. M.: Science *86,* 328 (1917); Ky. Agric. Exp. Sta. Bull. No. 371, pp. 63–75 (1937).
55. Gay-Lussac, J. L.: Ann. de Chem. *55,* (1) 258 (1805).
56. Ehrhardt, J.: Monatsheft für Rationelle Aerzte *19,* 359 (1874) (Heilbronn).
57. Crichton-Browne, J.: Lancet, London 2, 6 (1892).
58. McCollum, E. V., Simmonds, N., Becker, J. E. and Bunting, R. W.: J. Biol. Chem. *63,* 553–62 (1925).
59. Tolle, C. D. and Maynard, L. A.: Amer. Soc. Animal Production. Proceedings (1928) p. 15.
60. Reed, O. E. and Huffman, C. F.: Mich. Agr. Exp. Sta. Quart. Bull. No. 10, p. 152 (1928).
61. Black, G. V.: Dental Cosmos *58,* 132 (1916).
62. McKay, F. E.: J. Dent. Res. *10,* 561–68 (1930); J. Amer. Dent. Assoc. *20,* 1137–49 (1933).

63. Churchill, H. V.: Ind. Eng. Chem. 23, 996 (1931).

64. Smith, M. C., Lantz, E. M. and Smith, H. V.: Univ. of Arizona, Coll. of Agr. Bull. 32, 253–282 (1931).

65. Dean, H. T., Arnold, F. A., Jr. and Elvove, E.: U.S. Public Health Rep. 57, 1115 (1942).

66. Dental Caries. Findings and Conclusions of its Causes and Control. Compiled by the Research Commission of the American Dental Association, 2nd ed. (1941). New York.

67. Bertrand, G.: Science *64,* 629–30 (1926).

68. McHargue, J. S.: Amer. J. Physiol. 72, 583 (1925).

69. Stare, F. J. and Elvehjem, C. A.: J. Biol. Chem. 99, 473 (1932–33).

70. Underwood, E. J.: Austral. Vet. J. *10,* 87–92 (1934).

71. Underwood, E. J. and Filmer, J. F.: Austral. Vet. J. *11,* 84–92 (1935).

72. Marston, H. R.: J. Council Scientific and Indust. Res. 8, 111 (1935).

73. Waltner, Klara and Waltner, K.: Klin. Wochenschr. 8, 313 (1929).

74. Underwood, E. J. and Elvehjem, C. A.: J. Biol. Chem. *124,* 419 (1938).

75. Frost, D. V., Spitzer, E. H., Elvehjem, C. A. and Hart, E. B.: Amer. J. Physiol. *134,* 746–54 (1941).

27

Discoveries Arising from Fractionating the B-Complex

WITH FEW EXCEPTIONS, this history of nutrition research includes only investigations completed before 1941. Therefore, there still remain for consideration the discovery of biotin, pyridoxin, pantothenic acid, para-aminobenzoic acid, and inositol, as essential nutrients and constituents of the B-complex of vitamins. Their separation from natural foods, characterization as chemical compounds, synthesis, and the initial steps in describing the pathological states which supervene when any one of them is lacking in the diet of an animal, represent great triumphs of nutritional investigations.

By the year 1930 it was well known that an adequate diet must provide essential amino acids and inorganic elements, a source of glucose, an unsaturated fatty acid, the fat-soluble vitamins A, D, E, and K, and the water-soluble (B-complex) factors thiamin, riboflavin, and the still uncharacterized pellagra-preventing vitamin generally called P-P factor. It was also known that when a diet containing all of the known nutrients in a purified state was fed to young animals (rat, chick), growth soon ceased, skin and nerve lesions developed, and speedy decline and death of the animals followed. However, when crude aqueous extracts of various natural foods, such as yeast or liver, were given as supplements to the purified food mixtures, animals in severe states of malnutrition could recover their health and resume growth. When extracts of certain other foods were given, or when a supplement of any one of several natural foods was provided in addition to the purified mixtures, the symptoms of nutritional failure produced were strongly contrasting in details. Such observations left no room for doubt that several essential nutrients remained to be discovered.

In 1937 the Committee on Vitamin Nomenclature of the American Society of Biological Chemists, and the American Institute of Nutrition, defined as components of the B-complex only the three above-named vitamins. The Committee was, however, well aware of the existence of unidentified nutrients. The status of the B-complex about 1935 may be illustrated by the following glossary of terms commonly met with in scientific journals at that time:

Vitamin B_3: A growth factor for the pigeon. The same term was used to designate a factor which cured specific paralytic symptoms in rats and chicks, and was later called B_4.

Vitamin B_4: A factor associated with specific paralytic symptoms in rats and chicks.

Vitamin B_5: A weight maintenance factor for the pigeon.

Vitamin B_6: 1. An antidermatitis factor for rats (György).
2. Other names for what seemed to be the same, or nutrients similar to B_6, were vitamin H, Factor Y, and Factor I. These terms all designated a factor or factors associated with nutritional dermatitis.

Vitamin H.: A substance protective against injury caused by feeding raw egg white. It was often termed the antidermatitis factor.

Vitamin W: A supposed "growth factor" for the rat.

Factor I: That part of the B-complex other than B_1 and riboflavin which was adsorbed on fuller's earth under specified conditions. Factor I was believed to contain B_6.

Filtrate factor: A factor which prevented nutritional dermatosis in chicks.

Antiacrodynia factor: Same as B_6.

Antialopecia factor: Anti-gray hair factor. Also called anticanitic factor.

During the decade preceding 1940 about four hundred investigators contributed reports of experimental work directed toward the characterization of the dietary factors enumerated above, and to identification of the specific pathological changes which were caused by selective starvation of an animal for a single one of them. This aspect of their studies was beset by great difficulties.

Confusion of Pathological Changes in Deficiency Diseases

As experimental studies multiplied, alopecia, or loss of hair, was reported to result from deficiency in the diet of riboflavin, tryptophan, zinc, biotin, pantothenic acid, and inositol respectively. The pattern of hair loss in these specific deficiency states differed considerably, but it was not possible in the earlier years of the investigations to distinguish these diseases on this basis.

Graying of hair (achromotricia) was found to occur in animals deprived of either copper, pantothenic acid, or p-aminobenzoic acid. This symptom was not specific enough and was, therefore, not very useful in distinguishing the unknown nutrients.

Animals fed purified diets containing all of the then known vitamins and other nutrients developed skin lesions from which recovery could be brought about by the provision of crude extracts of natural foods. György (1) stated that at least three scaly dermatoses could be produced in the rat and that these could be prevented or cured by nutritional means. One of these, the so-called rat acrodynia, was of special importance for advancement of knowledge. Careful study of this disease afforded the principal clue to the discovery of biotin and its relation to egg white injury.

In 1939 Oleson, Bird, Elvehjem, and Hart (2) described a study in which they distinguished four distinct deficiency states arising from diets containing all the known nutrients but supplemented in different ways by fractions of extracts of natural foods. Their observations and those of György well illustrate the complexity of the problem of finding the number and nature of the nutrients unidentified at that time.

They restricted young rats to a diet consisting of sucrose 76–78 per cent, casein 18 per cent, a salt mixture 4 per cent, together with thiamin, riboflavin, nicotinic acid (which had then recently been found to be the anti-pellagra vitamin), the four fat-soluble vitamins, and choline. The significance of choline had recently been shown by Best and co-workers (3) to prevent the deposition of fat in the livers of rats fed high fat diets, and was suspected of being an essential nutrient for that species.

After four to six weeks, symptoms of the rat acrodynia described by György developed. In animals which survived beyond this period Best et al. observed an erosion around the eyes causing a spectacled-eye appearance. There were subcutaneous hemorrhages of the paws and bleeding from the nose. Reduction of the hemoglobin content of the blood, paralysis, spastic gait, loss of equilibrium, and difficulty in locomotion were also often noted.

Oleson and his associates investigated the curative values of a number of fractions of the water-soluble substances of liver. The preparations used and the result obtained were as follows:

1. They treated water extract of liver with fuller's earth. The filtrate from the earth cured the spectacled-eye condition, but material which was eluted from the fuller's earth did not do so.
2. The eluate from the fuller's earth prevented both hemorrhage and paralysis. The nutrients which prevented these symptoms were (along with the factor curative for rat acrodynia) adsorbed on the earth, and were present in the eluate.
3. A combination of the fuller's earth filtrate and eluate prevented the development of specific symptoms, but had not the growth-promoting properties for rats possessed by the unfractionated liver extract. This suggested that an essential nutrient had been lost during fractionation. This they designated factor W. In 1940 factor W was identified by György and his associates (4) as biotin.
4. Oleson and associates found that supplementing their basal diet with maize oil or linoleic acid increased the growth rate and retarded the development of dermatitis and the other symptoms.

Early Investigations of Biotin

In 1913 Osborne and Mendel had reported that 18 per cent of egg white, when fed as the sole source of protein, supported normal growth in young rats. In 1916 Bateman (5) reported that raw egg white caused diarrhea when fed in amounts corresponding to the protein content of normal dietaries. He found that it was rendered innocuous by heat coagulation and by treatment with alcohol. He suggested that egg albumin was indigestible due to its anti-trypsin. The detrimental effects of feeding raw egg white aroused great interest among nutrition investigators after Boas (6), in 1927, described in rats given this substance "eczematous dermatitis, alopecia blepharitis, spasticity, and in some instances skin hemorrhages, and edema of the feet."

Parsons and Kelly (7) found that the toxicity of egg white for rats followed the protein fraction when the latter was precipitated by saturating its solution with ammonium sulfate; and that egg white denatured by contact with strong ethyl alcohol and leached in running water during fifty hours was as toxic as before.

Parsons and Lease (8) found that dried yeast, dried egg yolk, wheat germs, and dried milk cured the dermatitis caused by the raw egg white only if they were given in amounts one to three times that of egg white in the diet. In marked contrast, the inclusion of one-fourth as much cooked liver and kidney as of the egg white fed protected the animals against injury. Cooked kidney was nearly twice as potent as cooked beef liver, and the potency of both was increased by cooking. Of particular interest was the finding that heating liver or kidney at 100° C. for six days destroyed their protective value. Cures of severe dermatitis were observed in rats by giving single large doses of kidney after a day's fast.

Parsons and Lease (9) demonstrated that the dermatitis caused by feeding raw egg white differed from that caused by riboflavin deficiency. They also demonstrated that ordinary solvents did not extract from raw liver or kidney the substance which prevented egg white injury, but that after digestion of extracted liver residue with papain, a considerable portion of the active substance could be extracted with water or 25–60 per cent alcohol. Methanol also extracted the protective factor from digested kidney or liver. The investigations of Parsons and her associates strongly indicated that a specific dietary essential was necessary for the prevention or cure of egg white injury.

Isolation and Identification of Biotin

György (10) led the way to isolation and identification of the nutrient which prevents or cures the pathological condition brought about by feeding raw egg white to rats and chicks. In 1937 (11) he found that treatment with nitrous acid, ketene, formaldehyde, or benzoyl chloride, inactivated the substance, which he named vitamin H. On this evidence he concluded that the vitamin appeared to be an ampholyte, and particularly an amino acid.

Birch and György (12), by means of electrodyalysis, found the pH of the anti-egg white vitamin to lie between 3 and 3.5. They employed the acid property of the substance as a means for separating it. The sodium salt was found to be soluble in absolute alcohol, whereas the calcium and barium salts were insoluble in that solvent. These properties were useful in its isolation. The substance (vitamin H) which they secured in pure form proved to be the nutrient, a deficiency of which caused egg white injury.

The "Bios" Problem — Discovery of Biotin

While investigators of the nutritive needs of rats and chicks were attempting to learn the nature of the factors involved in egg white injury, there was great activity by others engaged in inquiry into the minimum nutritive requirement of yeast cells and of bacteria. The latter type of studies yielded information of great value in clarifying the problem of the vitamin needs of mammals and birds.

In 1871 Pasteur (13), in commenting on some results obtained by Liebig, recorded his observation that certain yeasts were unable to proliferate when small seedings were made in a solution containing only the necessary inorganic salts and sugar, and that others were able to respond with multiplication at rates much slower than when complex organic substances were present in the medium. The subject of the nutritive requirements of yeasts did not arouse interest until 1901 when Wildiers (14) brought it to the attention of biologists. He expressed the belief that yeast required for its nutrition an organic substance which he called "bios."

Eighteen years later Williams (15) proposed to use as a test organism for assaying for the antineuritic vitamin (B_1) a single cell or very small seedings of yeast in a culture medium composed of the necessary inorganic salts and sugar. Very small additions of food extracts to the basal medium caused rapid proliferation of yeast cells in hanging drop cultures observed under the microscope. A modification of the method was devised in which the yield was determined by weighing. This test was soon found by several investigators to be unreliable since extracts in which the antineuritic factor had been destroyed also stimulated growth of yeasts.

As a result of Williams' publications, bacteriologists began to investigate simplified nutrient media with a wide variety of supplements. They observed their effect on the growth and biological functioning of many kinds of bacteria. Such studies brought to light a number of organisms which were suitable for microbiological assay of nutrients essential for birds and mammals. Because of their searches for information concerning the minimum nutrient requirements of microorganisms, bacteriologists became concerned with the problem of determining the number and nature of the nutrients in crude extracts of natural foods. As pointed out above, such extracts had been found to provide factors indispensable for rats or chicks fed basal diets consisting of the nutrients then known.

Miller Demonstrated Existence of Bios I and II

In 1931 Miller (16) found that an extract of "malt combings" (rootlets), when precipitated with alcoholic barium hydroxide solution, was separated into two components. Removal of barium from the precipitate left a component which he called Bios I; Bios II remained in the filtrate. Neither of these preparations alone stimulated yeast proliferation, but a combination of them was effective. Bios I was associated with i-inositol, which had been discovered in muscle by Schearer in 1850, and called muscle sugar. Bios II remained unidentified.

Williams and Saunders (17) made a critical study of different strains of yeast, and concluded that in relation to the "bios" problem no single substance was wholly responsible for yeast growth stimulation. They concluded that inositol, vitamin B_1 (thiamin), and pantothenic acid (then recently discovered) played the important roles in this effect, and that pantothenic acid was especially important. From that time forward it was realized that, for assay purposes in vitamin investigations, careful choice of yeast strain or other organism was necessary. This view rested on the evidence that the synthetic powers of different strains of microorganisms differed markedly. The selection of microorganisms useful for biological assay of vitamins was rapidly developed by a number of investigators.

Kögl's Isolation of Bios II from Egg Yolk

In 1936 Kögl and Tönnis (18) studied the problem of isolating Bios II. From boiled yolks of duck eggs they extracted a substance in crystalline form which, when tested for stimulation of "Heferasse M" (yeast-strain M), was so potent that they could detect it in dilution of 1 to 400,000 of the basal nutrient medium, which they called "biotin." They believed this to be identical with Bios II. In their studies they found that their strain of yeast was not stimulated to proliferate by addition to the basal medium of vitamin B_1, vitamin C (ascorbic acid), or amino acids.

In 1933 Allison, Hoover, and Burk (19) gave the name coenzyme R to an indispensable nutrient for *Rhizobia,* one of the nitrogen-fixing soil bacteria.

Further Studies by György of the Anti-Egg-White Factor

In 1940 György and associates (20) obtained conclusive experimental evidence that vitamin H, biotin, and coenzyme R were the same substance. It became evident that the nutrient, a deficiency of which caused egg white injury in birds and mammals, was also essential for the nutrition of yeasts and certain bacteria.

Du Vigneaud and his associates (21) suggested the correct structural formula for biotin on the basis of study of its degradation products. The vitamin was synthesized by Harris and his coworkers (22) in 1943.

The Discovery of Avidin, Its Relation to Biotin

It has been pointed out that Parsons and her associates showed that the substance which prevented egg white injury was bound to protein of egg white. Eakin, Snell, and Williams (23) isolated from raw egg white a protein, which they called *avidin.* This protein forms a firm union with biotin and prevents its absorption from the intestinal tract. Dosing animals with biotin in excess of the binding power of avidin for the vitamin prevented or cured the lesions of egg white injury. Coagulation of egg white destroys the power of avidin to combine with biotin; hence biotin deficiency does not occur if heated egg white is used.

The Discovery of Pyridoxin

The complexity of the problem of distinguishing symptoms arising from deficiency of any one of the uncharacterized essential nutrients in the crude extracts prepared from natural foods, and their prevention or cure by fractions prepared from such extracts, has been emphasized in earlier pages of this chapter. The investigations which represent the most constructive thought in tracing the way to isolation and identification of pyridoxin, were directed toward the study of the specific nutrient, a deficiency of which was the cause of the so-called "rat-pellagra."

After having critically examined the chemical properties of each of the unidentified nutrient factors mentioned in the glossary on p. 406, and the effects of such preparations on the prevention or cure of "rat pellagra," György (24) concluded in 1934 that it might be the alkali-stable factor Y, which had been described by Chick, Copping, and Roscoe (25). In order to designate the substance more specifically associated with the prevention of the skin lesions in rats, believed to be a pellagra-like dermatitis, György proposed the name vitamin B_6.

Birch, György, and Harris (26) made a thorough study of the problem and proved that Goldberger's P-P factor, riboflavin, and B_6 were different substances, and that the last-named factor was not curative of pellagra in human beings. This necessitated the decision that what had been called "rat pellagra" was not the analog of human pellagra, nor of "blacktongue" in dogs, but was a distinct pathological syndrome.

György called this syndrome "rat acrodynia," and identified vitamin B_6 as the rat anti-acrodynia factor. In a later paper Birch and György (27) described the distribution of B_6 in natural foods, and its chemical properties. They noted that B_6 was adsorbed on fuller's earth from acid solution; precipitated by phosphotungstic acid, and migrated towards the cathode on electrodialysis; inactivated by benzoylation but not by treatment with nitrous acid; and soluble in ethyl alcohol but not in acetone, amyl alcohol, or ether. These facts warranted the conclusion that the vitamin did not contain a primary amino-group, but that it was a basic substance, and might contain a hydroxyl group.

Lepkovsky's Contributions to the Isolation of Pyridoxin

In 1936 Lepkovsky, Jukes, and Krause (28) were successful in distinguishing Factor I and Factor II from aqueous extracts of natural foods. They showed that Factor I was identical with György's vitamin B_6 and Chick's Factor Y. Factor II was found necessary for the maintenance of health and growth in rats, but did not cure rat dermatitis (rat acrodynia). It did, however, cure dermatitis of dietary origin in chicks. Factor II was later to be identified with pantothenic acid.

In 1938 it had become certain that the B-complex, or the water-soluble vitamins other than the antisorbutic factor, consisted of no less than five components. Nicotinic acid, which had recently been shown to cure blacktongue in dogs and human pellagra, was found not to cure "rat acrodynia." It was well known that thiamin and riboflavin had no relation to the syndrome of "rat acrodynia." Biotin, too, had become available in crystalline form. Hence, it was evident, from the proof that "rat acrodynia" was a nutritional deficiency state distinct from all others known at that time which could be prevented or cured by crude aqueous extracts of certain natural foods, that the B-complex consisted of at least five components. The problem of isolation of the new nutrient was now sufficiently simplified so that its isolation and identification was soon to be expected.

The Isolation and Synthesis of Pyridoxin

Investigators in 1936 were generally in agreement that Factor I, Factor Y, and vitamin B_6 were identical. Lepkovsky (29) described a method for the isolation of crystalline Factor I. Almost simultaneously, Keresztesy and Stevens (30) and György (31) reported the crystallization of vitamin B_6. Animal tests soon established the identity of the three preparations. Also in 1938, Kuhn and Wendt (32) in Germany, and Ichiba and Michi (33) in Japan independently isolated the new vitamin. Lepkovsky (34) expressed his belief that in 1931 Ohdake, in Japan, had isolated pyridoxin, but had not known how to prepare experimental animals to determine its significance as an essential nutrient.

In 1939 Stiller, Harris, Folkers, Keresztesy, and Stevens (35), of the Merck and Co. laboratories, discovered the structure of the molecule of pyridoxin (B_6). Harris and Folkers (36) announced that they had synthesized the vitamin. Its molecular structure is designated as 2-methyl-3-hydroxyl-4,5-di(hydroxymethyl)-pyridine. The significance of this nutrient in human and animal nutrition was revealed through investigations which were of later date than 1940, and are, therefore, not described here.

The Discovery of Pantothenic Acid, Its Nutritive Significance

The existence of pantothenic acid and its nutritive significance for the proliferation and fermentative activity of yeast cells first emerged from the studies of R. J. Williams. He began in 1919 to study the nutritive requirements of yeast, and appears to have believed that what Wildiers had called "bios" was the antineuritic vitamin, then called vitamin B. It later became evident that the "bios" essential for the strain of yeast which he employed was not the antineuritic vitamin, since extracts made from various sources which were free from the antineuritic factor exerted great stimulating effect on yeast proliferation.

Williams and his co-workers (37) studied the properties of the new substance, using a specific strain of yeast as a test organism. They employed with success fractional electrical transport, by means of which they were able to separate pantothenic acid from other components of extracts of natural foods. Williams and Saunders (38) secured a concentrated preparation of the acid which, with their yeast strain, was effective in doses of 0.0008 gamma per milliliter of nutrient medium.

By 1935, Williams (39), without first having obtained the substance in a state of purity, had found its approximate molecular weight and ionization constant, and that it contained more than one hydroxyl group, and a nitrogen atom with barely detectable basic properties. He found, further, that it did not contain in its molecule aldehyde, ketone, sulfhydryl, basic nitrogen, aromatic, or sugar groups. Four years later, he and his associates isolated the pure acid in the form of its calcium salt (40).

It was pointed out in the account of the discovery of pyridoxin that two kinds of dermatitis could be produced experimentally in chicks. One was due to egg white injury, the other resulted from feeding chicks a heated diet of natural foods supplemented with casein. Through the study of the latter form of dermatitis in chicks, evidence was obtained which indicated that Williams' pantothenic acid, hitherto tested only as a yeast nutrient, was essential for birds. Chick dermatitis was prevented or cured by the inclusion of pantothenic acid in the diet. This fact was discovered simultaneously by Jukes (41) and by Woolley and associates (42). The latter investigators described the chemical properties and affected a partial synthesis of the new vitamin.

In 1940 György and Poling (43) found that graying of hair in rats was caused by deficiency of pantothenic acid. In the same year Daft and Sebrell (44) pointed out that development of hemorrhagic adrenal necrosis in the rat resulted from pantothenic acid deficiency. In 1940 Salmon and Engel (45) also studied the lesions of the adrenal glands in pantothenic acid deficiency. Thus, pantothenic acid found a place in the B-complex of vitamins.

Discovery of the Biological Significance of p-Aminobenzoic Acid

The aminobenzoic acids were familiar to chemists for many years previous to the discovery that one of them, para-aminobenzoic acid, was of nutritive significance. For a half century it had been used as an intermediate in the manufacture of the azo-dyes. In 1940 Nielson and associates (46) reported the concentration and fractionation of a substance which prevented graying of the hair of piebald rats. This substance was isolated and identified as p-aminobenzoic acid. Martin and Ansbacher (47) found that on a certain experimental diet young mice suffered a loss of hair color, and that the graying could be prevented by feeding either a crude extract of rice polishings, or small doses of p-aminobenzoic acid. Rubbo and Gillespie (48) showed that this substance was an essential factor for bacterial growth. Para-aminobenzoic acid was soon found to be widely distributed in plant and animal tissues. Its solubility in water placed it among the B-complex vitamins.

The Discovery that Inositol is Essential in Mammalian Nutrition

The identification of Bios with inositol has been already mentioned in connection with the studies on yeast nutrition. In 1940 Woolley (49) found that young mice became hairless when maintained on a diet of purified food substances containing all known nutrients. He suggested that this species required a still unidentified factor which he called "mouse anti-alopecia factor." His experiments demonstrated that pantothenic acid, biotin, and p-aminobenzoic acid would not prevent alopecia in this species. However, since a supplement of phytin (inositol hexaphosphoric acid ester), or inositol prepared from liver, prevented the loss of hair, he concluded that inositol was an essential nutrient for the mouse.

Gavin and McHenry (50) demonstrated that inositol is essential in the diet of the rat since in its absence fatty livers developed in this species.

REFERENCES

1. György, P., Sullivan, M. and Karsner, H. T.: Proc. Soc. Exper. Biol. and Med. *37,* 313–15 (1937).
2. Oleson, J. J., Bird, H. R., Elvehjem, C. A. and Hart, E. B.: J. Biol. Chem. *127,* 23–42 (1939).
3. Best, C. H., Hershey, J. M. and Huntsman, M. E.: Amer. J. Physiol. *101,* 7 (1932); J. Physiol. *75,* 56 (1932).
4. György, P., Melville, D. B., Burk, D. and du Vigneaud, V.: Science *91,* 243 (1940).
5. Bateman, W. G.: J. Biol. Chem. *26,* 263–91 (1916).
6. Boas, M. A.: Biochem. J. *21,* 712–24 (1927).
7. Parsons, H. T. and Kelly, E.: J. Biol. Chem. *100,* 645–52 (1933).
8. Parsons, H. T. and Lease, J. G.: J. Nut. *8,* 57 (1934).
9. Parsons, H. T. and Lease, J. G.: Biochem. J. *28,* 2109–15 (1934). Lease, J. G. and Parsons, H. T.: J. Biol. Chem. *105,* 1–11 (1934).
10. György, P.: Zeitschr. arztl. Fortbildung *28,* 417 (1931).
11. György, P.: J. Biol. Chem. *119,* xliii-xliv (Proc.), (1937).
12. Birch, T. W. and György, P.: J. Biol. Chem. *131,* 761–66 (1939).
13. Pasteur, L.: Compt. rend. Acad. 1871, p. 1419.
14. Wildiers, E.: Le Cellule *18,* 313 (1901).
15. Williams, R. J.: J. Biol. Chem. *38,* 465 (1919); *42,* 259 (1920).
16. Miller, W. L.: Canad. Chem. and Metall. *15,* 134–36 (1931).
17. Williams, R. J. and Saunders, D. H.: J. Biol. Chem. *105* (Proc.) xcix–c (1934).
18. Kögl, F. and Tönnis, B.: Zeitschr. f. physiol. Chem. *242,* 43–73, 74–80 (1936).
19. Allison, F. E., Hoover, S. R. and Burk, D.: Science *78,* 217 (1933).
20. György, P., Melville, D. B., Burk, D. and du Vigneaud, V.: Science *91,* 243–45 (1940).
21. du Vigneaud, V., Hofmann, K. and Melville, D. B.: J. Amer. Chem. Soc. *64,* 188–89 (1942).
22. Harris, S. A., Wolf, D. E., Mozingo, R. and Folkers, K.: Science *97,* 447–48 (1943).
23. Eakin, R. E., Snell, E. E. and Williams, R. J.: J. Biol. Chem. *136,* 801 (1940); *140,* 535 (1941).

24. György, P.: Nature *133,* 498–99 (1934).

25. Chick, H., Copping, A. M. and Roscoe, M. H.: Biochem. J. *24,* 1748 (1930).

26. Birch, T. W., György, P. and Harris, L. J.: Biochem. J. *29,* 2830 (1935).

27. Birch, T. W. and György, P.: Biochem. J. *30,* 304–15 (1936).

28. Lepkovsky, S., Jukes, T. H. and Krause, M. E.: J. Biol. Chem. *115,* 557 (1936).

29. Lepkovsky, S.: Science *87,* 169 (1938).

30. Keresztesy, J. C. and Stevens, J. R.: Proc. Soc. Exper. Biol. and Med. *38,* 64 (1938).

31. György, P.: J. Amer. Chem. Soc. *60,* 983 (1938).

32. Kuhn, R. and Wendt, G.: Ber. d. deutsch. chem. Gessellschaft, *71,* 1118 (1938).

33. Ichiba, A. and Michi, K.: Sci. Papers Inst. Phys. Chem. Res. (Tokyo) *34,* 1014 (1938).

34. Lepkovsky, S.: Pyridoxine, in The Biological Action of the Vitamins. Ed. by E. A. Evans. Univ. of Chicago Press, 1942.

35. Stiller, E. T., Keresztesy, J. C. and Stevens, J. R.: J. Amer. Chem. Soc. *61,* 1237 (1939); Harris, S. A., Stiller, E. T. and Folkers, K.: *Ibid. 61,* 1242 (1939).

36. Harris, S. A. and Folkers, K.: Science *89,* 347 (1939).

37. Williams, R. J., Lyman, C. M., Goodyear, G. H., Truesdail, J. H. and Holiday, D.: J. Amer. Chem. Soc. *55,* 2912 (1933).

38. Williams, R. J. and Saunders, D. H.: Biochem. J. *28,* 1887–93 (1934).

39. Williams, R. J.: J. Biol. Chem. *110,* 589 (1935).

40. Williams, R. J., Weinstock, H. H., Jr., Rohrmann, E., Truesdail, J. H., Mitchell, H. K. and Meyer, C. B.: J. Amer. Chem. Soc. *61,* 454–57 (1939).

41. Jukes, T. H.: J. Amer. Chem. Soc. *61,* 975 (1939).

42. Woolley, D. W., Waismann, H. A. and Elvehjem, C. A.: J. Amer. Chem. Soc. *61,* 977 (1939).

43. György, P. and Poling, C. E.: Science *93,* 202 (1940).

44. Daft, F. S. and Sebrell, W. H.: Pub. Health. Rep. *54,* 2247 (1939); With Babcock, S. H., Jr. and Jukes, T. H.: *Ibid.* 1333 (1940).

45. Salmon, W. D. and Engel, R. W.: Proc. Soc. Exper. Biol. and Med. *45,* 621 (1940).

46. Nielson, E., Oleson, J. J. and Elvehjem, C. A.: J. Biol. Chem. *133,* 637 (1940).

47. Martin, G. J. and Ansbacher, S.: J. Biol. Chem. *138,* 441 (1941).

48. Rubbo, S. D. and Gillespie, J. M.: Nature *146,* 838 (1940).

49. Woolley, D. W.: J. Biol. Chem. *136,* 113 (1940); Science *92,* 384 (1940); J. Biol. Chem. *139,* 29 (1941).

50. Gavin, G. and McHenry, E. W.: J. Biol. Chem. *139,* 485 (1941).

28

The End of an Era: New Horizons

ASIDE FROM the difficulty of bringing into proper perspective the nutrition investigations of the past fifteen years, it seems logical to close this history of ideas with the year 1940. Essentially that year marks the achievement of the primary objectives set by pioneers in this field of study. They sought to discover what, in terms of chemical substances, constituted an adequate diet for man and domestic animals, and that purpose was realized.

Beccari (1745) concluded that man, except for the spiritual portion of his being, was composed of wheat gluten. At the same period Haller, the best informed physiologist of his generation, said, *"Dimidium corporis humani gluten est."* Which when translated is, "Half of the human body consists of gelatin," later chemists modified this to mean that half the body substance is converted into gelatin when treated with super-heated steam in Papin's pot. According to Prout (1827) the essential nutrients in foods could be comprehended within the albuminous, saccharine, and oleaginous principles. But in 1832 William Beaumont contested the opinion of others that there were various kinds of nutrient substances was in error; there was, he said, but one kind of food, or *aliment,* present in all foods.

More than a hundred years of further experimental inquiry was required to reveal that an adequate diet must provide in appropriate amounts forty or more specific chemical substances identified as amino acids, vitamins, fatty acids, carbohydrates, and inorganic elements. With the exception of folic acid and vitamin B_{12}, by 1940 these had been identified, isolated, and characterized chemically. Their occurrence in nature had been investigated, and the first steps had been taken in describing the pathological changes in animals which result from a deficiency of each of them. The type of experiment essential for the discovery of unidentified nutrients was widely understood, as illustrated in the succession of vitamin discoveries described in the preceding chapter. The end of an era had been reached. From that time on, new objectives motivated nutrition investigators. The writer has deemed it inadvisable to attempt to discuss progress beyond that point.

Much more had been achieved than investigators of the last century ever dreamed of. In 1900 we were almost blind to the relation of foods to health. From the generally accepted belief that only protein, carbohydrate, fats, and an ill-defined supply of inorganic salts were all that needed consideration in assessing quality in a diet, knowledge had advanced in forty years to the triumph of understanding that such great human scourges as beriberi, scurvy, pellagra, rickets, goiter, and several types of anemia, were caused by specific defects in the food supply. These defects were identified, and the knowledge gained made practicable the prevention of the diseases.

Before the emergence of the science of nutrition many millions of people in every generation, from ignorance, led lives blighted by malnutrition. Inferiority and suffering of domestic animals, with consequent economic loss, was even more widespread throughout the world. The new knowledge brought about improvement of health and its attendant elevation of the status of human life above the sordid, to a degree scarcely equalled by any other agency concerned with the prevention or cure of disease. Implicit in physiological well-being is the prospect for betterment of courage, ideals, purposes, and achievement. Viewed from this standpoint, the rise of the science of nutrition is one of the greatest events in human history.

Horizons of biologists widened rapidly as successive vitamins were discovered, and the physiological roles of these and of individual amino acids, fatty acids, and inorganic nutrients emerged from animal experiments. Nutrition investigators scarcely realized the importance to every department of biology of the discovery of the hitherto unsuspected nutrients. Among the millions of compounds in organic and inorganic nature, they were seeking the forty-odd chemical entities uniquely fashioned for combining and interacting to form the many kinds of macromolecules so associated in the organization of the cells of plants and animals as to catalyze the succession of chemical changes which result in the physiological functioning of living things. These are the elect among the many compounds synthesized by green plants from inorganic nutrients. They must be derived from plants by all of the higher animals, but given them, animal tissues are capable of a great number of synthetic processes in their metabolic activity. The observation that many fungi and bacteria require in their media the same nutrients as animals, gave these a general rather than a particular interest in biology.

In every department of their science biochemists were handicapped in proportion to the number of unidentified components of the systems which they attempted to study. The discovery of the vitamins and of the metabolic functions of the trace elements as components of enzyme systems, placed them in a highly favorable position for rapidly advancing knowledge in many segments of the science. It opened the way to detailed study of the chemical action in macromolecular histological units.

After the discoveries of cell structure by Schleiden and Schwann, most biologists sought to learn the secrets of living matter by the study of histological details which could be made visible by staining and magnification. Such methods advanced the understanding of biological phenomena to a great degree. But chemists could make little progress in the study of physiological problems until they had identified the chemical compounds which function as nutrients, and from which the macromolecular structures are synthesized. These all-important substances came to light through nutrition studies, and almost all of them through experiments on mammals and birds.

As this narrative of the sequence of constructive thought is brought to a close the prospect for achievement in elucidating the secrets of cellular activity appears bright. Conventional optical cytology, which prevailed until after 1920, has been replaced by molecular cytology based on the structure of macromolecules, and the manner in which they are organized to carry on the enzyme-catalyzed reactions which are the basis of physiology. Present day studies are making clear the manner of reshuffling of functional groups and structures and their conversion into others in the processes of metabolism.

New and powerful tools such as isotopes, ultraviolet and infrared absorption, Raman spectra, electron microscopy, and the momentous synthetic technics of organic chemistry, afford new opportunity for biochemists to discover structural groups of elements and their arrangement and bonding within complex molecules.

Physiology, botany, zoology, bacteriology, embryology, genetics, immunology, and virology all started as separate fields of inquiry. However, as biochemistry and organic chemistry advanced to the stage of identifying the primary chemical units which are the indispensable nutrients for animals, it became clear that all these divisions of knowledge embraced in separate courses of study are chemical in nature, and each tend progressively to become divisions of biochemistry. The essential nutrients are the most important units with which biochemists in every segment of the science deal in extending knowledge of the phenomena of life.

And finally, the emergence of the concept that in the utilization of the essential nutrients there is not absolute specificity in their fabrication into macromolecules, resulted in illuminating the theoretical basis of pharmacology. This new concept concerns the action of anti-metabolites, substances so closely related chemically to the essential nutrients that they may be incorporated in macromolecules of cellular structures in their stead. However, they do not function in metabolism as do the natural chemical units which they replace, and so they block metabolic processes. The therapeutic application of this new guide to the synthetic chemists gives great promise for the fashioning of new drugs for specific purposes in therapy.

INDEX OF NAMES

INDEX OF SUBJECTS